ISBN: 978-0-

To Ken and Maureen

Thank you for your visit
to our little place in France
I hope you will take pleasant
memories of your visit here.

Best wishes

Chris Hyman

Other books by Chris Higginson

Reluctant Assassin 1

Reluctant Assassin 2

1st Provocative Verse

Rhodesian Memories

Provocative Verse E-book

Rhodesian Memories E-book

French Bread E-book

FRENCH BREAD

A Burgundy story

by

Chris Higginson

A lonely baker lady with murder in her heart
Prepares a magic mixture in bread in bun and tart
Patisseries that poison all unsuspecting folk
Is '*Pain*' she feeds to people 'til the frogs no longer croak

An English speaking family move to France, then buy a house in a small village. They learn to adapt to rural French life with the backdrop of Burgundy. Time reveals an undercurrent of intrigue and murderous intent.

ISBN: 978-0-9805083-0-7

Author's note: This book is a work of fiction however some of the historical events took place as described. All of the non-family characters are imaginary but some of the light-hearted anecdotes are real but pertain to other places and people and have no connection in any way to the fictional "village" described herein.

My initial concern, which brought about this story, was that significant numbers of people are dying here in France, at about retirement age. I pondered the reasons and developed this book as an explanation.

Please take the final solution "with a pinch of salt".

I have left it to you to distinguish between the fictional storyline and the anecdotal descriptions of life in France, from the perspective of visitors to this country and from the French peoples' observations about themselves.

FRENCH BREAD

A Burgundy Story

by

Chris Higginson

PUBLISHED BY ZANJ PRESS
IN ASSOCIATION WITH
LIGHTNING SOURCE UNITED KINGDOM
LSUK

SALES ENQUIRIES TO:

www.lightningsource.com

Or

bread.french@gmail.com

For the latest information on how to obtain
this book, and others written by this author
in your global zone.

Main personalities in approximate order of appearance:

Monsieur Seguin, estate agent from Seurre
Jacques, on chômage from Thompson Industries
'Fawlty', station master
M. Le Duc, He who walks by Himself
M. Fabien Lafarge, schoolmaster of the fifties, retired
Marie Peron, (nee Rufin) present day Baker's Wife.
M. and Mme Rufin, village bakers of the fifties
'PP' Pierre Peron, married to Marie (Rufin)
Roger du Bois, taxi company owner of the fifties
M. Claude Monet, Mayoral contestant
Augustin Février on chômage from ceramic factory
Father Dedicus, village priest
Sandrine, widow, 85
Madame Beringer the present day Mayoress
M. Corbier, retired gendarme
Michel Bonnadot, the Post Master and husband of Michelle
M. and Mme Vincent retired
Dr. Melun, G.P.
M. de Gouvier, post WW2 château owner
Monsieur André Thomassin, The Ratman
Monsieur Tichet, the Tax Man
Pierre and Francine, animal lovers

Contents

Illustrations of buildings in this book are examples of these wooden and brick structures, which have been preserved for posterity. The style is typical of the Bourgogne, and some of these structures may be seen at the "Ecco Museum" in Seurre.

Dedicated
to all those people
who have discovered the pleasure
that can be derived from
the judicious imbibing
of good wine
food
and
cheese
…with friends…

The House

Well <u>here</u> '**It**' is at last, or is it?

At last I have found '**It**', or have I?

I've been looking for long enough... months? No longer... years perhaps?

Perhaps I should explain.

I have been asking my Guardian Angel to find me a house.

Not any old house: "***I would like a house on a navigable river, with trees and no neighbours. It can be a house that needs some renovation perhaps, but also one that I can buy for a bargain price.***"

My Guardian Angel?

You know: the one that we all think we have, or secretly hope we have, who will come and bail us out of difficulty, or who will 'show us the way', or find those winning lottery numbers? That ethereal spirit who is always slightly beyond our reach?

Well my 'Guardian Angel' has been having a tough time with me recently and has had to work above and beyond the call of normal duty. This is because I have been asking rather a lot of it (her?) recently. I am slightly concerned that at any moment he, or she, might decide to resign and go and find an easier human to lead through the labyrinth of life.

After all, it can't be easy for her to look after someone who doesn't stick to one thing for long enough for an angel to take a bit of time off. Do angels need to meet up with other angels occasionally? Do they rest when their human charges are behaving themselves and obeying the fundamental laws of Nature? Those laws which include settling down in one place and raising a family? Those laws which mean providing for the children in a way that they, in turn, will go forth into the world and continue the Cycle of Life.

If ***I*** was ***my*** angel, I would have resigned a long time ago.

Why?

Because the Guardian Angels of people who are controlled by wandering stars have their work cut out and pasted onto that clipboard in the sky that declares that:

"Your toil will never be easy or mundane; your human will never settle and be satisfied; he will always disrupt everything, just after you have granted his wish; all you will get, if you're lucky, is an occasional 'thanks!' "

And so it is with my life up to this point.

No sooner have I settled into a pattern of life that seems organised and preordained, than I flap away from my perch to find another branch on which to settle.

And it is happening again.

Here I am, standing on the edge of the Saône River in the middle of France, looking at a house that is up for sale from a deceased estate. It is a three story building constructed with hand-made red bricks in a French Bourgogne style, which is to say: "not very interesting!" It has a rectangular floor plan, regular windows with regular wooden shutters and a roof that looks like an afterthought on a Doll's House.

The 'house' is exerting ***no*** magnetic pull on my soul.

I have bought houses in the past which, when I arrived and looked at them, I knew instinctively that ***this*** was the one that I had been looking for, and that '***It***' was where I wanted to live. That is until my 'wandering star' came to take me by the scruff of my neck and to urge me off to yet another horizon and another destination.

This house is not attracting me in that compelling way and yet, it is exactly what I have been asking for. It is a house 'on the banks of a navigable river with trees and a garden and not hemmed in by humanity'.

True, it is on the edge of a village, but it a small village and the average age of the residents of the village is somewhere in the region of sixty eight. The consequence of this is that the village is apparently so quiet that it seems moribund, and that, for me, is not such a bad thing.

I have been searching for a retreat far away from the hustle of modern living.

In fact, as the Estate Agent drove me through the village on my way to have a look at this house for the first time, I had the impression that there was nobody living here at all. There were no parked cars in the single potholed road that leads down to the river, no pedestrians and no dogs.

It was rather like driving though one of those French towns that are depicted in Hollywood 'War Movies', where the buildings are decrepit with shattered shutters and garden walls of broken stone. I half expected to hear the sound of a German World War 2 Tiger Tank starting up; then with squeals of tracks in motion, to come around the corner with its turret turning to fix me in its sights.

In this place it is easy to imagine a time warp backwards of some sixty years.

The houses in this village seem to have been neglected from some time before the Second World War. There appears to have been little enthusiasm for renovation and improvement since then.

"The reason for this," the Estate Agent had explained to me last Friday, "is because the valuation of houses and consequent community tax is judged by the external appearance of each residence. What is the point to make it ***'propre'*** just so that the Mayor can examine it and declare a higher tax must be paid? Or worse still, have your neighbours report to the authorities that you are living above your station?"

He had accompanied these observations about French life with a 'Number 73' in the dictionary of 'Gaelic Shrugs'. Number 73 includes the gestures of 'hands open, thumbs outwards, head slightly to one side, corners of the mouth turned down and one eyebrow raised'.

I have been in France long enough to know that the closest translation of this shrug would be something in the regions of: "Yes we know it is a crazy system, but that is the way that it is, and so what can we mere mortals do about it? Hein?"

Any feeling of warmth or attraction that I might have developed for this house in front of me is being reduced by the weather. It is a drizzling November day with low grey clouds that are being herded over the arthritic bare branches of trees above me, by the South-westerly breeze. The tapering limbs of these trees seem to scratch at the bellies of these sullen pregnant shapes as they glide past. I feel as though I have lost my sense of colour because the scene resembles an old blurred photograph. Shades of grey and shadow smudge the watercolour outlines of trees and buildings. There is nothing to look at because there is nothing of interest. If I wore glasses, I would be polishing the lenses to try and defog them, to see what I was missing.

The house has been empty for years and during this time the branches have grown towards the building, so that now they are picking apart the tiles of the roof. It seems that, under the influence of the wind, the trees are poking sticks at the house. The sticks are shaped like the wizened hands of witches with long misshapened nails. One swaying branch has created a gaping hole through which I can see the battens below, which are now rotten from exposure to the weather. Where the tiles are still intact, they are covered by a layer of moss that has thrived from inattention. The annual deposits of leaves from the trees have combined to form a coating of compost on the roof, in which a zoo of insects is now living.

This means I will have to remove and replace the entire roof if I buy this place. I am sure that I will find all sorts of other problems inside.

I know that I will have to replace the complete plumbing system with copper tubing, because all the old lead pipes have burst in several places due to winter freezing.

The electrical junction box has got a bird's nest in it, which is not occupied at the moment, but I suspect that the rightful residents will be back to stake their claim to it in the Spring. The several birds that have built their nests in the house will probably demand access though several broken windows, no doubt claiming some sort of ancient French 'right of way'.

The kitchen is cavernous with a simple rusty wood-burning stove and a single sink. The bathroom has a huge stained metal bath and, of course, that essential piece of French plumbing, a bidet.

Anything of interest in the house has been stolen. Even the skirting boards have been prised away from the walls. This is because, I imagine, the thieves had been searching for valuables that may have been secreted there and forgotten.

The electrical wiring consists of aluminium wire covered with decayed rubber and cloth, which should induce an interesting firework display of sparks, if anyone should bother to restore electrical power to the circuit.

The rotten wood panelling inside the house should burn well, in spite of the damp that has risen through the walls and ancient tile floor. The basic structure of the house is still sound and there is a fine old oak staircase that spirals up to the attic. The oak framed windows seem to have survived neglect.

This house has little appeal in its present state, except perhaps for somebody with a desire to communicate with ghosts. The Realtor has already told me that people thought the house was haunted by the previous occupant, who had died several years ago.

"Old Madame Trolly lived here with her seventeen cats," explained Monsieur Seguin, the Estate Agent, "until she became bedridden. That's when the social services stepped in to take her to a residential nursing home. She had no known living relatives, so after her death the house had to be held for five years, in case somebody should lay a claim to the estate. After that, the State can put the house on the market, in order to recoup the expenses it incurred."

Shrug 43: 'chin drooped, mouth pursed, both eyebrows raised, with apologetic look'.

"The village council has to advertise the house in the press before they can take it over and find a use for it. The Mayor wants to buy it for herself, but she knows that the villagers will accuse her of insider dealing, so she is effectively out of the running! I have placed advertisements to appear in the Monday edition of the 'Bien Public'."

Today is Sunday afternoon, so if I am going to make a move to buy this house I will have to initiate the purchase first thing on Monday morning, before anybody else knows that it is on the market. I had only spotted a small picture of the house in the Estate Agent's display window, before he placed the advertisement in the regional newspaper. This picture showed a wall of 'colombage', which is a term used to describe the pattern of beams of a wooden structured building. Each part of France has its own unique design and pattern of colombage.

I've got the impression from Monsieur Seguin that a Swiss person has put in an offer on the house, 15% below the asking price. The village council, who are in charge of the sale, are divided as to whether to accept. The Swiss are known to have more money than the locals, and there have been several occasions in the region when they have bought old barns and converted them, with local labour, into desirable residences.

"Yes, we like the Swiss and the Germans who come here to buy properties," the agent had said. "They create work for the artisans, and because they are away living in Switzerland and Germany making money while the renovation work is done for them, they are not here to supervise the reconstructions. This means that the work can proceed at 'our' pace. This is something that they have to learn to understand if they want to live in France with us. They 'live to work' and so we have to educate them that here in France, Life is for eating, drinking and making love. They need to learn this before they come to settle here, otherwise they will never be happy!"

I already knew about this rural French 'pace of life', which is why I do my own renovations!

I learned the hard way how long it takes to order, and get delivery of, a non standard size window. I had made this error once, when I placed an order shortly before the 'French National Holiday' month of August.

The window took three months to arrive.

July, August and September are three months reserved for anticipation for, enjoyment of, and recovery from, the annual holiday.

July is for planning the holiday, August is for tanning in the sun and September is for scanning the 'Jobs available' columns, in order to pay for the summer break.

It is better to fit in with this scheme of things than to try and resist it.

As I explained to my wife, Marlene, "I have been trained by the rural French, so why shouldn't other foreigners be trained as well?"

I know that one of the problems for the village council, regarding the sale of this house, is that winter is not the best time to market a house in France. Most of the moves and transactions take place during the summer school holidays. Normally people start searching for houses after the New Year.

Monsieur Seguin has explained to me, "The Mayor of the village is keen to have this sale consummated quickly, because she has a project for the village. This project, what ever it is, will be made possible by the money from the sale. She wants to get her development started so that she will have something to show, when the next Mayoral elections are held. She wants to bolster her re-election campaign."

He gave me all this background information when he brought me here, from the nearby village of Seurre. Whether I had extracted it, or whether he had primed me with it, only time will tell. He doesn't know what the Mayor's project is, or else if he does, he isn't going to tell me. Perhaps he thinks that there might be a commission in it somewhere, for him, and the less he says to me, the better.

I am intrigued to think that, in this apparently abandoned village, there are political aspirations at work.

"The Mayor is due to retire from her full time job as a supervisor at an enterprise in Dijon," continued Monsieur Seguin, "and she is keen to be elected for another term of office as Mayor. It seems that she is planning her retirement occupation. It is not a bad job, being Mayor! She is building a new house here in this village, and she intends to stay."

As he said this, he tapped the side of his nose with a forefinger.

This universal gesture is not listed in the book "Gaelic Shrugs", but I understand it to mean that there is 'money' to be made, being a Mayor. I hope that he only means that the salary, added to a pension, is good. This all seems a little strange to me, because I know that in some of these rural villages the residents have difficulty finding somebody, or anybody, who is prepared to be Mayor. Some of the villages have the same Mayor, who conveniently does nothing, term after term.

"Why change anything, for the sake of change?" was a question put to me soon after I arrived in France.

Anyway, ***if*** I want to buy this house, I need to make a decision before the advertisements appear in the newspaper, because after that there will be more competition.

But in reality this house requires too much work.

The garden is a mess and, although I know that my wife will rise to the occasion and tackle it, it will be unfair of me to ask. The half dead apple trees have fallen over. A walnut tree is leaning over the back of the house at an inebriated angle. There are volunteer thorny acacias everywhere, which seem to have sprung from an underground root system. Every fruit tree is smothered with ivy. And my wife has only just got our present garden looking good, after three years of hacking, pruning and planting.

Our main problem is that I am only halfway through renovating our present house, which I had bought three years ago. It has been an undertaking of enormous proportions. There is so much more to do on it than either of us anticipated.

And ***that*** house is only now becoming acceptable, after three years of living in a shambles of half finished projects.

When we bought our present house, the plumbing system had consisted of only one tap in the kitchen and the outside toilet had to be flushed with a bucket of water from the well. The family that used to live there had raised five children in these conditions. There was no bath or shower in the house, only a cold water shower in a shed behind the house. The electrical system consisted of a network of loose wires attached to light bulbs in strange places. The kitchen had only one electrical plug.

That place had also been in a mess when I bought it.

The 'trigger' that had made me buy it was that I had fallen in love with the beams in the attic.

They had been covered with cobwebs and racks for drying beans at the time, but their stout and artistic construction had wooed me. They had been erected by the men who used to build the wooden barges which had been used on the canal and waterway systems of France. When steel replaced wood in the nineteenth century, as the method of construction for barges, these artisans had turned their skills to building beams and supports for roofs of houses.

These arrangements of beams are works of art as they replicate the system of ribs and bulkhead supports inside the barges. Of course the structure for the roofs have been built inverted, like an upside down ship.

When I first saw this attic of beams I knew what a wonderful room it could be. I knew I could make a lounge that would make the most of these beams, which had been fashioned by the wood craftsmen of yesteryear.

I had a feeling that it would be like living inside the masterpiece of an ancient 'ébéniste'.

I have a weakness for old wood. I love the character and the warmth of it. I like to feel the grain and the knots that show its scars in the battle for survival. How better can I show respect for these skeletons of ancient forests than to live within their protection.

And on that daft sentiment I had bought the house, only then to be confronted by the reality of bringing the rest of the building up to modern safety standards. I am trying to keep the traditional feel of the house, but with modern facilities. I am installing lamps that look like old paraffin or gas ones, but with special electric bulbs that give the impression of bygone lighting. I am hiding the switches and the electrical plugs in order to try to keep the appearance of yesteryear. I am hoping that the end result will give a warm and mature feel to the place.

I get a sort of satisfaction when I work on the family home that seems to be an almost primeval pleasure, perhaps the sort of feeling that a caveman enjoyed as he prepared his cave for his family. It is an emotion that gives me more pleasure than buying a finished article, into which I have not put any effort. For example, I prefer to rebuild a vehicle before I use it, although it takes longer and maybe more expensive. It makes it mine.

So it is with all the houses I have owned.

And, slowly, my present house is coming right.

Our three children now have their own bedrooms, each with their individual showers. I have installed a central heating system as well as two toilets and a bathroom, and the garden is becoming a place where we can invite guests, and be proud of the flowers and lawn.

It is a different life for our children after living on our boat, which we have done, off and on for several years, since we set sail from Southern Africa. That is not to say that living in a house is better than living in a boat, but it does allow them to fit in with the other children at school. If they want to be individuals who live on boats and sail around the planet, which is what I would like to do, then that is something they can do later in life, if they wish. Right now I want to give them the option to live like normal human beings, in a house, so that they can fit in with their peers at school.

But our house, which we are living in and renovating at the moment, still isn't finished.

I have to spend another couple of years of work on it in order to develop it into the vision that I had when I bought it.

And I still have to renovate my trusty ocean-going yacht, which carried us all from the southern tip of Africa.

She is moored in the river awaiting my attentions. She is the reason that I have been searching for a house on the banks of a navigable river. I want to live somewhere with the possibility of anchoring our trusty old (yes wooden *again*!) boat in front of the house.

I have also just started a new job, which means that I have to be away from home, for anything up to two weeks at a time.

This is not the time that I should be considering buying another house.

This house in front of me requires too much work. They say it is haunted, but there isn't any 'feel' to the place. It is as though there is a vacuum here into which all vibrant life will be sucked and will disappear. It is also built with bricks, handmade bricks I grant you, but bricks, which I consider a chilly material with which to build a home.

I can feel no positive energy from this place;

And yet the old Forge has got a charm of some sort.

This is a building to one side of the main house. It faces the river. I estimate that it is about four hundred years old, built with an oak beam skeleton. The beams have been pirated from other even older buildings. I have found markings and holes in the beams that indicate that they have been used before.

Half of the roof is missing and part of the building has been used for coal storage and another part of it to house animals. There is a row of outbuildings attached to the Forge which look as though they will fall down with the blast of a good sneeze.

One of them, curiously, houses a twin 'side by side' toilet. Two holes have been carved into what looks like a sturdy wooden box. These holes are slightly different in size and shape. It looks as though they have been specially carved for 'his and hers' individual comfort.

When I saw the twin toilet for the first time, I had a fleeting imaginary glimpse of a French peasant couple sitting together, holding hands and discussing the events of their day. Perhaps they talked about the growth of the grapevines that they have strung on supports along the edge of the river, or maybe they discussed the condition of their flock of sheep that graze on the nearby common land.

It seems a rather friendly idea, for them to have shared this one time of the day when they could sit together and plan their lives.

The Estate Agent pulled an expression of disapproval when he saw the toilets.

It was not really a shrug this time; it is a French expression that I have named "Rotation du Nez", or 'Rotation of the Nose'.

This involves a slightly pursed mouth, and a nodding of the head that rotates the end of the nose in a small clockwise circle.

This expression has multiple meanings, which suit many circumstances, and is an essential part of the French vocabulary. You will not find it listed in any phrasebook. Be careful though, because it can be quite powerful in terms of expressing disapproval. It would smack of insubordination if used to an employer, but children use it to parents with impunity, these days.

My daughter is an expert at it.

Particularly when we ask her to do something of which she disapproves, which is just about everything these days, as she has just had her fourteenth birthday.

It is an expression that is not as offensive as the one used by young actresses on American Television, where they look sideways, giving a shocked expression with a jaw drop, that translates as "you must be really *stupid* to think that I think *that*!"

The 'Rotation du Nez' is much more diplomatic.

It has more élan.

It can mean almost anything that you want to '*say*', but don't want to actually verbalise.

However, I can see that these twin toilets have not been used for a long time, because the main house has an indoor toilet. This indoor toilet is one of those ancient contraptions with a header tank near the ceiling, and with a chain that hangs down to one side. When you pull the chain, you hear a series of intestinal clanks from the plumbing, then a series of groans, after which it vomits a bucket of water into the bowl. The clatter of the mechanism, the groaning and whoosh of the water would wake any household at night.

No wonder the villagers think the place is haunted.

"That toilet," Monsieur Seguin explained, "was the first toilet in the village to be installed inside a house! Madame Trolly considered herself to be almost Bourgeoisie, with her restaurant in Dijon and her other properties, which she had back then. All the other houses in the village had their toilets in the garden. Some of the houses here still have no indoor plumbing!"

I can not help feeling that there is something peaceful and relaxed about wandering off in the morning to a small outhouse, to contemplate Nature and to commune with it at the same time. On second thoughts, a garden loo could be a little chilly in winter.

With regard to the Forge, outbuildings and twin toilet, Monsieur Seguin advised me, "The best thing to do with them is to get a Bulldozer and raze it all to the ground. I have a friend who can help you, for a fee!"

He doesn't express a shrug this time, just a creasing around the eyes with a lift to his moustache.

They are amazing things, these French Moustaches.

They seem to lift and droop with the moods of the owner, quite unlike 'Middle Eastern Moustaches', which are large immobile 'statements of fact' on the face.

A French Moustache has character.

They are looked after with great care. They may express virility or disapproval; depression or happiness. Monsieur Seguin seems to enjoy stroking his, as though it is a personal furry pet.

I don't have a moustache, so this means that there are a whole range of French expressions that are denied to me. I have the possibility to learn how to speak in French, to shrug in French, but as I don't have a moustache I know that I will never master this language.

A moustache adds an exclamation mark to the end of a body language statement.

A moustache transmits a mood.

It is so much more effective than the spoken word which, once expressed, is lost in the passage of time. A moustache is a continuous declaration of the disposition of its owner.

I tried growing a moustache when I was at sea with the family, but my wife objected to it and, because she was always on the prickly end of a kiss, she won. She also objected to the fact that it grew with three different colours, red, black and grey, which didn't even match our Red Ensign on the boat. I shaved it off, but the consequence is that my communication with French people is now partially compromised.

In spite of Monsieur Seguin's opinion that the Forge should be destroyed, it is the attraction of this building alone that is bringing me back again and again, to look at this unfriendly haunted house on the river.

He showed it to me for the first time last Friday afternoon. I returned with Marlene and our children on Saturday morning and they all condemned it.

"It's a dump!" was their consensus of opinion.

I came back on Saturday afternoon with only Marlene, who again pointed out the pitfalls and logical reasons why it was not a good idea to get involved with yet another project.

"You just don't have the time. Think about it! Every time you start a new job you get lost in it for a year, while you get acclimatised. You have so much more commuting to do now. And… you haven't started renovating our attic yet!"

On Sunday morning, under the guise of buying a morning newspaper, again I visited the house by myself, and again the overwhelming sense of my wife's reasoning was obvious.

But here I am again, on Sunday afternoon, standing and looking at this bleak place, trying to see into the future, trying to see what it could be like in five, or maybe ten years from now.

I am looking for a sign, or a feeling, or anything to combat the logic that already I have too much on my plate. I know that if I should buy this house, it will be an unwise move. It will be illogical, expensive and I don't have enough hours in the day to start another renovation project.

The drizzle is still bleeding from the sombre sky. The wind is wafting and buffeting about. It is not steady enough to be a good sailing breeze. It is more like those annoying small gusts that toss your umbrella to one side and then dribble rain down your neck, to soak your collar. I am used to the discomfort of wind and rain together, after sailing across a couple of oceans but this weather here seems to have a depressive feel about it.

There is a carpet of fallen autumnal leaves under the trees which is damp and turning into compost for next year's growth. I judge that, by the girth of these trees in this mini forest next to the Forge, they have been repeating this cycle for more than a hundred years.

The place is deserted.

The birds have migrated.

No squirrels.

Not even any crows.

The soil hasn't been turned for so long that there isn't even a hopeful Robin perched on the broken garden wall.

Nothing.

And then I hear a rhythmic fluting on the wind.

There is music in the air.

A piper?

No several pipers are playing a single note symphony. They are in tune, with a steady cadence that seems to beat in the air around me. 'Life' suddenly has a sound that has been so noticeably absent up until now.

The resonance is behind me and the source of it is approaching up the river.

I turn towards the cause and there I see four swans in flight.

They are holding a tight Vic formation, flying low over the water.

I see their hazed mirrored reflections in the drizzle blurred surface.

As I gaze enraptured, they flare their wings.

The fluting stops and all sound is held in suspension.

They slow in flight, and as they approach their stalling speed they extend their webbed feet and ski across the surface, still maintaining their precise formation. It is as though they are reaching down to touch their inverted reflections, with their feet. They settle into the water and then start to retract their pristine white wings. It takes a while for them to settle all their feathers.

After a serene check that all their flight equipment is properly stowed away, with a final waggle of their tails, they start to paddle.

I hear them making soft noises to each other.

It seems that they are congratulating one another with little purring sounds.

In the half-light of this wintry afternoon they gleam with an angelic white sheen. They look as though they are glowing with an internal neon light. They glide with a grace that can only be copied but never captured, even by a ballerina on ice. Their elegance brings the river to life.

Before they arrived the river was a swirling, swollen, monotonous mass of sullen water on its way to the sea. Now that has all changed.

There is a focal point.

A candle has flicked to life and lent a 'raison d'être' for this sombre scene, like the canvas painting of an old master artist, where a glimmer of light expels the shadows out of the frame.

Their presence is like a twinkle of light in the eye of an old man, whose face now radiates pleasure. A sparkle has spread like hope.

I am spellbound.

I know that this is my sign.

There is no possible way that I can not come and live here in order to watch these spectacular creatures. I have to be able to see them as they fly and float and love and live. I will watch them as a caterpillar might watch a butterfly, enviously wishing I could fly, but knowing I will never pass the chrysalis stage. My career is flying and my passion is sailing, but I know that I will always be enacting an artificial copy of the real thing, because I can only do what these birds do, with mechanical aids.

Perhaps by being close to them I might understand and feel something of their life, of their beauty, their serenity and their competition to survive in this harsh climate.

In order to do this I must live here, even if it means that I have to do years of work on the house.

It will be worth it just to be able to pause and watch these birds that represent the pinnacle of airborne grace, as I paint and scrape at my earthbound lodgings. It won't be the same if I visit the river in order to watch them; I need to live here among them. I want to try and understand what it is that I find so fascinating about these large birds. I have always been attracted to birds in nature, and this fascination is one of the things that I miss most from my young days in Africa, with its spectacular range of avian life.

And so my decision is made.

The next morning I arrive at Monsieur Seguin's office to sign the documents that declare that I will buy the house for the full asking price. No offers and no conditions.

He seems delighted. It must be one of the easiest sales he has ever conducted. Some houses in these small villages take ages to sell. Our present house had been on the market for seven years before we bought it. In the first week we owned it, we started to pull it apart in order to discover all the hidden problems that we suspected lay beneath the surface. While we were staring at the first pile of plaster and ripped wallpaper that we had torn from the walls, there was a timid tap at the door.

I opened it, wondering who it could be.

"Bonjour, Monsieur," said an elderly lady. She was standing outside the front door which opened onto the street. She was holding the handlebars of her bicycle.

"Is it true," she asked, "that you have bought this house?"

"Yes," I replied, "we signed at the beginning of the week to buy it, we have paid the whole amount to the Notaire, and the owners have let us have immediate possession."

"Ah," she said, "my husband and I have been thinking of buying this place. You see, we live three kilometres away in Chamblanc, and everyday I have to come to collect our bread on my bicycle. I am seventy five years old now, and my husband said that maybe we should move closer to the baker. It is getting hard for me to cycle in winter, when the snow and the wind are here. So we went to the Notaire today, to say that we want to buy, and zut! He said that the house is sold!"

"Yes. I am sorry Madame. But the Agent said that it was on the market for something like seven years!"

"Ah yes," she said. "But in France we like to take our time to make a decision of this magnitude."

"Perhaps your husband could collect the bread for you, Madame?" I ventured.

"Oh no," she answered, "He could not do that. He is retired, you know. We have lived all our lives in Chamblanc. This would have been our first big move. And now we are too late."

I felt that somehow it was my fault. Here was this fit old lady who had got a genuine reason to buy this house, and I had bought it because of a whim to renovate the attic.

"Come inside, Madame." I invited her. "Let me show you what it is really like."

She came in and walked around the pile of rubbish on the floor, where we had stripped it from the walls. She looked at the mess.

"And this Madame is just the beginning. We have to remove these internal walls, and I have to lay pipes under the floor. We have to rip everything up and rebuild it. I think that, maybe Madame, there is a bit too much work to do on this place for you to *really* want to buy it. Don't you think?"

"But yes, Monsieur," she sighed, "perhaps you are right. My husband will not want to do work like this at his age. Perhaps we must continue to live where we are and I will continue to collect the bread, as I have always done. That is life."

We did see her occasionally after that, cycling with her baguette sticking up out of her handlebar basket.

"Bon courage," we shout to each other.

The lesson I learned from this transaction was that once a deal is signed in France concerning property, that is that.

No Gazumping.

The transaction is complete.

Now I have done it again. I have bought a house knowing precious little about the village around it. There is only three kilometres between my two houses, but that in France is a long way, because distance is still judged by the time traditionally taken on foot, or on horseback. The modern concept of car travel is still rather too new a concept, for some of these people in these rural areas.

So now I have to find out more about this small village into which I have committed myself for reasons that any sensible Frenchman, and my wife, regard as being completely illogical.

And they are right.

Who else but a crazy foreigner would buy a haunted house with a broken down Forge? And then declare it wasn't the house he wanted, but that he was intrigued by the four hundred year old wreck that teeters under the trees?

"No… foreigners to France are definitely crazy."

My wife Marlene will confirm that.

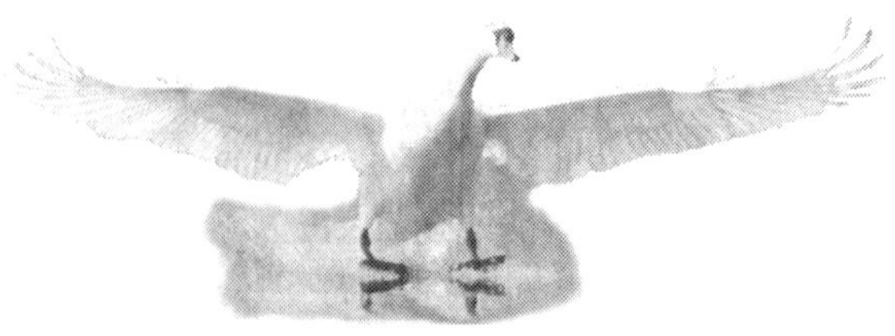

The transaction for the sale of the house is scheduled to take place in the offices of the Notaire in Seurre, Monsieur Fontaine. He is an elderly man who has been in practice here for many decades. He has an air about him that seems to me to be from a Dickinsonian period. A quill and an inkpot would not be out of place on his desk. There are no spider webs on the leather bound books which sag on the shelves of his office, but I feel that spiders would not be out of place here. We first met him when he officiated at the purchase of our first house in Seurre.

Monsieur Fontaine conducts the meeting with Marlene, myself and Madame Beringer who is the Mayor of the village where the river house is located. She is neat, suited and gives me the impression that we must be slightly in awe of her, as she is 'The Mayor'. She evaluates us with a glance that seems more of an assessment of our potential as new members of the village, rather than whether we are worth knowing as individuals. We will represent two votes when we move, and when our children get a little older, we could represent five votes.

We could be 'important' to her aspirations as Mayor, in a village where there are only about a hundred voters.

She reminds me of a strict school mistress of yesteryear, who appreciates discipline as being more important than education. I can just imagine how she intimidates people who work at the factory, where she is a supervisor.

We listen to the Notaire as he reads though the document of sale, which has paragraphs and maps dealing with the surveyors' examination of the boundary lines and the problems associated with the property. One problem is that there is a septic tank which should be connected to the embryo village sewer system, but isn't, and the other concerns illegal windows that the neighbours have inserted in their wall, which overlook the garden.

There is also a question of the drainage of rainwater off from their roofs, which is supposed to be drained back onto their properties and not fall onto ours.

"Do you understand these implications?" he asks us.

We look at each other and nod. With an entire house to reroof and renovate, small details like this seem to be inconsequential. We discuss the financial details which include all the taxes and commissions to different departments and funds. There are so many of them that we have to assume that everything is in order. At last Monsieur Fontaine gets to the end of the document and we all sign in the appropriate places.

The Mayor then hands us the keys along with a large symbolic key, which is an old-fashioned metal object as long as a forearm. It belongs to an attic of the house which can only be accessed by an external rickety ladder. The key was made this large, I imagine, so that it would be impossible to lose.

After formal handshaking and salutations all round we leave the office.

I don't have time to go and see the house again because I have to go off to work, which entails leaving on the train from Seurre within the hour. Now I have to go and earn the money to try to afford the renovation.

Marlene takes me to the railway station with my suitcase and flight bag. Our stationmaster is a tall angular man who throws his hands up in the air with dramatic gestures for the most inconsequential reasons. He has a small moustache and we have named him Basil Fawlty, because he is the double of that character acted by John Cleese in the English television series Fawlty Towers.

He is responsible for accessing the computer that books and prices the tickets for journeys by train. He is well practiced at tapping away on this diabolical machine for tickets to Dijon, occasionally to Bourg-en-Bresse and rarely to Paris.

My destinations throw him into a state of confusion. Most of them are outside France and this means codes and spellings of place names that he has never heard about.

Today I am going to Oostende. When I told him how to spell it three days ago, which is when I started negotiations to buy the ticket, he thought that I was having a joke at his expense.

"Nowhere has a name that starts with an OO!" he declared, with the finality of a man who is always right.

He was astonished to find that a place with this name actually exists in Belgium.

He told me, "No one from here has ever gone to Belgium!" as though it was my fault.

When I first started coming to his ticket office after moving into Seurre three years ago, he thought I was a nuisance, because it would take him half an hour to get my tickets worked out and printed. The difficulties, it seems, revolve around what taxes are payable on which sections of an International Line. However, as we got to know each other, procuring tickets for me became a challenge for him. Now, when he sees me coming he entwines his fingers together and cracks the joints like a concert pianist loosening up for a performance.

"Pisa, in Italy," I tell him.

His eyebrows go up and he turns to the computer with the same mannerisms as Basil Fawlty attacking the hotel typewriter, to create the day's menu. Booking train travel in France is well organised, with interlinked computers. In moments you have a reserved seat of your choosing in a clean carriage that leaves on time, and more importantly, arrives on time at its destination. However Fawlty turns the whole process into a virtuoso performance of drama, curses and insults at inanimate objects.

He fumbles for the telephone and conducts verbose conversations with some poor official in a SNCF help centre.

He pages through files of pamphlets, which only seem to confuse the issue further. Occasionally his computer goes on strike, so in accordance with that Neanderthal technique of dealing with mechanical contrivances, it gets a couple of hefty slaps on the side.

Sometimes he has to admit defeat and promises that the ticket will be ready in the afternoon. When this happens he brings the ticket to our house and we celebrate the victory with a glass of wine, after which he wobbles off homewards on his bicycle. This is why I need to give him a warning of a day or two, in order to extract the ticket out of the system.

Next time I tell him that I am off to Düsseldorf and the whole performance starts all over again. I don't think that he believes that I fly for a living, because whenever he comes to the house to deliver a ticket, I am covered with dust, paint or cement powder. I don't look anything like those uniformed mannequins that they use in advertisements for Air France. Working boots, blue overalls and canvas gloves do not give the same impression as a Captain's Hat with oak leaf clusters and a jacket with gold bars on the sleeve.

The train arrives and I climb on board from the low platform, all the while discussing with Marlene what she will try to accomplish while I am away. She has her days fully occupied with three adolescents in the house who have to be ferried fifteen kilometres to school in the mornings and then retrieved in the afternoons. She is also trying to housekeep in a building that is being destroyed and rebuilt around her.

I have compiled a list of obscure plumbing fittings that she will try to buy so that I can fit them when I return. She hates this, because the owner of the Quincaillerie (Ironmonger) loves to drag out her explanations of what she wants. It is not the explanations, so much, as the fact that all the other bored old men in the shop join in with their advice. They assemble near the till and examine and discuss each piece of plumbing, as though *she* really wants *their* advice. The taps are examined; one-way valves are treated with mistrust and ball-cock mechanisms are jiggled and condemned. In retrospect I understand why they prefer garden 'long drop' toilets. There is so little to go wrong with them.

For each piece of plumbing Marlene has to find the correct term. She is delighted to find that a 'tampon de visite' is an inspection cover for a sewerage system"

"But why do you want to visit it?" she asks the geriatric circle.

The reply from them consists of numerous, varied shrugs. They never have any desire to look down through the wooden holes they use.

They love to watch the way that she sets off on her bicycle balancing four metre lengths of copper piping, looking like a knight in the lists, charging off with multiple lances.

She has threatened to charge them an entertainment fee!

There are not many people who could cope with these tests. She is incredible in the way that she rises to challenges that I set for her, not least of which was going to sea, to sail across an ocean, with three small children on board.

Renovating two houses and a boat, bringing up three children, learning to deal with the complications of France and the French language all at the same time will be well within her capability.

If it wasn't, there would be no way that I could entertain these harebrained schemes.

I keep telling her that I am her final test.

"You have nearly completed your obligatory ninety nine lives to claim your wings," I have told her, as though I know what I am talking about. "After you pass this test, you will be a fully qualified angel."

The fact that I am still alive and well after saying this proves how tolerant she is.

She has many of the necessary qualities already, in that she smiles as a first reaction, she does not suffer with jealousy or envy and she has enormous compassion for people.

It is why she took so naturally to nursing.

She believes in that old fashioned style of nursing, in which patient care is more important than filling out documents in triplicate. Where her concern for people takes preference over hospital politics.

My three children and I are so fortunate to have her at the centre of our lives.

And, of course, I also need lots of nursing.

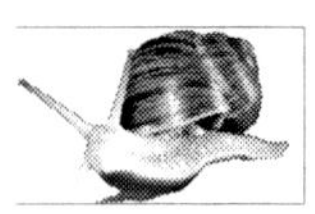

Renovation

Although the structure of the main house is sound, with brick walls half a metre thick, the amount of work that I will have to do is enough to put me into a depression.

Before I can do any sensible work on the interior I have to repair the roof. All the nails that hold the battens down have rusted away, and so the tiles are only staying in place by habit. This is one of the main problems that had put off the other potential buyers of the house. Before the French start to tackle a problem like this, they build an exterior scaffold.

Yes, we all know that old guillotine joke.

Erecting a scaffold is, of course is a good idea, but the house is three stories high, and so it means that I will have to erect a scaffold of immense proportions. The cost of hiring the equipment, and the price of the labour to erect it, could be huge. It will mean that the repair and rebuilding of the roof could cost as much as the purchase price of the entire property.

And yet, when the main house was built about a hundred and fifty years ago, they would not have had such a scaffold. They would not have had modern hydraulic lifting equipment on hand to convey the tiles the top of the house.

They would have done it all with brute force, wooden ladders and a head for heights.

Well, I shall have to do the same.

I decide that the best way to deal with the roof is to tackle the problem from the inside, by stacking all the tiles in the attic. This means that they will be close to hand when the time comes to replace them on the new beams and battens. That way we will not have to carry them down to ground level and all the way back up again. The roof of the Forge is a different problem, because the building is smaller and the roof is lower, in spite of being built to resemble a small cottage.

The roof of the Forge is the most urgent job that we have, in order that there will be no more weather damage to the interior of the building. I plan to do this by t ying ladders to the rafters and clambering around on the framework of battens with a sliding board. This is a plank to which I have nailed side guides. It will allow us to slide tiles down to the ground without dropping and breaking too many of them.

It will be a good practice session before we start work on the roof of the main house, as I have never repaired a roof before. I anticipate that there will be a few technicalities that I will have to learn about roof repair.

One of the technicalities is to try to find tiles that match the broken and missing tiles that had been used, when the roof was last repaired. This means that we have to find old tiles locally from people who have renewed their roofs. We have to find buildings that look as if they have been restored within the last few decades.

There are not many.

We start a tour of the local villages looking for 'newish' roofs, and in several cases find farmers who have stored their old tiles after a renovation. Perhaps they had stacked them with a view, sometime, to sell them to a foreigner who didn't know better? This leads us into some interesting negotiations, because there is nothing that increases the value of piles of old cracked tiles than the fact that we want to buy a few of them.

We find this same wonderful rate of inflation also affects the value of old oak beams that have been left to moulder away in a heap, in the rain. Suddenly they became objects of 'History and Art', as they represent a time of 'Disappearing Culture' or Patrimoine.

There are not many people as commercial as a French farmer who spies a potential sale of an item that he thought had no value, up until we showed an interest in it. However we have had a wide experience of bargaining from our time in Africa and during our sea voyage, so we have developed some techniques that we think may be different to the local customs.

My wife and I reverse rôles depending on the circumstances. Sometimes I show enthusiasm for a beam, a stack of tiles or a pile of bricks while she finds all the things that are wrong with it, including the price.

This means that we appear to argue with each other rather than with the seller. This technique serves two purposes, the first of which is that we do not antagonise the French seller with our arguing about the price, because we are arguing with each other. The second is that it is very good for our practise in the use of

French. We stop from time to time to ask for the correct meaning of some term or word in French, from the seller.

"But these tiles are the same type as the ones we have on the Forge," I insist in my best French.

"They are made by the same company, I grant you," answers Marlene, "but they are a different colour."

"That is only because they are stained with age."

"Yes, but!" (A favourite family expression.) "I am not going to have time to clean them all with some product or other. Those other tiles that we saw yesterday are in better condition and they are closer to home."

I shrug to the farmer.

"She is right of course, but we are here now, today! Maybe if you include a couple of those beams I will be able to convince her?"

"Ah," returns the farmer, "maybe, but I will have to discuss this with my wife and my son. They are not here at the moment. This will need some thought."

I see that he is playing exactly the same game as we are, and why not? He sees no urgency.

There is not a lot that goes on here, as time goes by, except for the change of the seasons.

The tiles will still be here next week, or next month. He rubs his face and strokes his moustache downwards. He looks mournful as though he would like to help us, but he thinks that it is unlikely that his family will agree to this giveaway price.

We stand in silence.

We look at the sky.

Then we look at the ground.

Sigh.

Life is filled with complications.

It is standoff time.

Who will weaken first?

There is more at stake than just the price. If we pay too much, then we will be considered to be an easy touch for any future transactions in the area.

The word will spread.

"I see that you have had the tiles for a long time," ventures Marlene.

The farmer extends a hand, palm down with fingers spread. He wobbles his hand in that universal way which means just about anything, except commitment. He is not agreeing or disagreeing, until he knows where my wife's comment is leading. The tiles are embedded into the ground, next to an old wooden barn, and there is several years' worth of ivy growth over them.

"There can't be much demand for old tiles around here," she says. "I would have thought that you would be pleased to get rid of them!"

I study a vapour trail in the sky overhead of a jet inbound to Paris, three hundred kilometres to the north.

"Your wife will be able to extend her vegetable patch when these tiles are moved. This soil must be good for potatoes?"

"Ah," says the farmer, "it is ***I*** who grows the vegetables, not my wife, and yes, this soil is very good, excellent in fact. I grow beans, tomatoes and lettuce also. It is perhaps the best soil in the whole of the Bourgogne. No, it is the best in the whole of the Cote d'Or!"

It is just as well we are not buying land, because with a statement like that, which he thinks is true, the price would have effectively doubled.

All I can see is a sad looking vegetable patch with the remains of last year's beans, dried and unpicked on the crooked supports.

"It is good for the health," I join in, "to grow your own food. Your family must be proud of you."

"Yes," he admits with modesty, "but the youngsters these days, you know, all they want is this prepared food. They want this fast food. It is not like the old days."

"It is important," I add, "to grow fresh food. That will encourage them to eat in the traditional way, don't you think?"

"Yes, this is true. In my mother's day we had wonderful food and fresh meat from the chickens and the sheep. That was before the War of course. When the Germans came we had to hide the animals in the cellar. But after the Liberation, well then we still had a few sheep to start breeding again."

The ancient wooden barn attached to his house looks as though there has been no livestock in it for many years. The buildings have an air of neglect that comes from generations of a family living on the same premises, without feeling the need to modernise or change the conditions. Like many of these old structures, the warmth from the animals in the barn was used as an important source of heat for the house in the winter.

"I would love to have space like this for growing vegetables," says Marlene, as she starts to pace the area next to the barn. "This is where I would put the tomatoes, because they will get the sun, and here would be a good place for carrots and peas. And here I would plough it up and put in potatoes."

She stops pacing because she is now staring at the pile of tiles which are in the way.

She stares at them for a while.

The message is obvious.

Silence reigns.

"I really think that we must be going," I say to the farmer, "we have to see someone in Bagnot who is demolishing a stable. He is building new stables to breed Thoroughbred Arab horses and he needs modern stables to impress the buyers. He has promised us some tiles and beams. It is such a pity, because we are here now and I won't have time to come back to see you for at least a month."

We start moving towards the car.

It is an elderly Chrysler Voyager which has been a faithful and reliable vehicle for us. She has transported all our building materials and has helped us move, with a trailer, every time that we have displaced the family. We have removed the seats in the back so that we have space to carry our wide variety of loads. She, like us, has a few scars of experience on her.

"Thank you for your time, Monsieur," says my wife, offering her hand in the formal way that French like to say farewell.

"How many tiles do you want?" asks the farmer.

He has weakened at last.

"Well, it depends on their condition," says Marlene.

"We will take all the ones that are not damaged," I join in.

We turn back to the pile and gaze at it.

Then we start moving the ivy away from where it has spread. We start to unpack the tiles so that we can see how many there are. Strands of nettles have grown up between the layers, so we grab them and pull them aside. We believe that getting stung with nettles is a good stimulus for our immune systems, so we are accustomed to the stings from these plants.

The farmer watches us for a minute and then asks, “Don’t you feel the stings?”

“Oh yes,” replies Marlene, “but it is not all that bad. Just a little itch, that’s all.”

The farmer suddenly seems to feel that he can’t be outdone by a woman. Obviously these nettles are not the proper stinging kind. He grabs a handful to heave them away, and then yelps.

“Ouch, Sacre Bleu!”

He looks at his hand and then with a habitual reaction, moves to stroke his moustache downwards towards his chin.

“Oh Wa Ooo!”

Now he has transferred the stinging sensation all over his face. It is already turning blotchy.

It is all I can do, not to laugh, but Marlene’s nursing instinct comes to the fore.

She is only sympathetic. She grabs at some Dock leaves that are growing next to the barn and proffers them to the farmer.

“Here, rub these on your hands,” she says, “that will take the stinging away.”

Gingerly he tries rubbing his hands and then, finding that it works, starts to rub the leaves on his face. He rubs vigorously and then looks at us with amazement.

He shakes his head and stands well back.

This is an operation that he will watch from a distance.

I wonder what he will tell his wife about these crazy foreigners who seem to feel no pain. It will be another little story for the locals to share about us, and perhaps not ***too*** detrimental.

Marlene explains to him, while we work, “The stinging of the nettles makes your body stronger. I have an arthritic nodule on my neck and I treat it with bee stings. My husband captures a bee and then he holds it to sting me on the neck. It clears away the nodule for months at a time!”

I was hoping she wouldn’t recite this story because, although it is true, it does sound a bit like ‘marital mistreatment’. Particularly considering I used to use the African bees that we used to manage once, which have a reputation for ferocity. These European bees are tame by comparison.

The farmer takes another pace backwards, as if our dangerous alternative medical methods might affect him in some diabolical way.

Within an hour we have the tiles sorted and packed into the back of the Voyager. She sits, looking a little more squat than usual on her suspension. I give her a friendly pat as though she is a horse. I have always communicated with my vehicles. I don't know how much it helps them to survive the rigours of my ownership, but all of them have served me well, so it can't do any harm.

We count out the money for the farmer, and he stuffs it into a pocket of his worn overalls. I wonder for a moment if his wife will notice that the pile of tiles is depleted. Perhaps he will be able to share a little wine with his friends from the proceeds of the sale, without her knowing. We make our departure along with effusive wishes for a good afternoon, a good appetite for lunch and good health until we should meet again.

We have had a transaction together and that should mean, for the future, that we are friends.

These commercial transactions all take time, and we have had to learn to be patient. So often we have had the urge to try and hasten things along, until we realise that we are behaving quite contrary to the norm. In a way it is frustrating, but it is also part of the charm of being in a country with so much history that nobody seems in a great hurry to add to it. We have to learn to be content and to let things flow along at their own pace.

These negotiations can be great fun, and at the same time they give our neighbours a lot to discuss about these "*étrangers*" who have come and plonked themselves into their small village.

Slowly we accumulate enough tiles and beams to replace those that we think we will need to change on the roof. Of course, a part of the cost of each pile of tiles that we buy is traded in 'information'.

This is information about us.

"Why have you come here? Why do you want to live in this place? Why don't you live in Paris? You are a pilot, yes? There are no airports here!"

This last statement is repeated to us several times, as though we must be somewhat obtuse. It took us some time to realise that many of these farming families had lived for generations on the same piece of land, and that the idea of commuting to work in some distant town is both idiotic and incomprehensible.

We parry the questions with varied answers, depending on our mood at the time, giving each farmer a slightly different version of the truth. We know that they will swap stories and compare notes. This way they won't really know what is the total truth about us. We feel that we have to hold some things back, because their curiosity about us is so blatant. But at the same time, they are not keen to reveal anything about themselves.

In a more English environment their curiosity would be rude, but here in France it is the accepted convention that all information is to be gathered, but not bestowed. The French are adept at listening to your conversations at the bank or at the Mayoral Offices, as they stand in a sort of loose queue, awaiting their turn. They are not embarrassed to offer advice and join into these private conversations. It is not unusual to have the whole queue of people offer advice and information regarding a private tax matter, or to recommend a way to avoid a tithe on the value of a new barn. This gathering of information about each other has become a national trait that some foreigners suspect goes back to the Second World War, but I believe that it is a genetical curiosity that has been honed in a rural environment.

On one occasion, when Marlene was at the Mayoral Offices registering our family details, she had to fill out numerous complicated forms. Each one needed in-depth answers. Not least of which was that she had to state separately who the father is of each of our three children. She was furious, as though this was a personal insult.

"Mais, c'est normal !" parried the Mayor.

Eventually she declared, "All this information you want! It is crazy! Do you want to know the size of my panties as well?"

"Oh yes," said the Mayor, ignoring the sarcasm. "I am sure we have a document for that too."

Information is valuable in rural communities.

After all, what else is there to talk about, when you are enjoying a four hour lunch with friends, if you are not going to talk about other people?

And farmers' lunches are lengthy affairs, even more so than the obligatory two hour breaks that the city dwellers enjoy.

So they have plenty of time to discuss minute details about neighbours, in their conversations.

****

One of the rules about renovation that I have learned in my small experience of building operations, on our first French house, is that whatever I think I need, I have to double the quantity.

This means that when I mix sand, water and cement to fill a hole, I need at least double the quantities that would fit into the hole in their natural state. This gives rise to the other formula, which rules that whatever volume of wall you demolish, the quantity of rubble is several times larger than the dimensions of the original construction. Quantity Surveyors learn this principle as they qualify, but we had to learn it by heaving what seemed to be never diminishing piles of rubble off to a land fill site. And so, applying the same principle to the roof of the Forge, we assemble as many tiles as we can find, knowing that it is better to have too many, than too few.

The day comes when I decide to start the renovation of the roof of the Forge. It is a mid February day, which is to say, in the middle of winter. There is a strange phenomenon that occurs most years in the Bourgogne, and that is that the cold weather has a break in it. Sometimes it lasts for a few days and sometimes the break will extend up to nearly a fortnight. The skies clear and the sun shines down and it is warm enough for three adolescents to sunbathe on what would, one day, be our lawn. This break in the weather sometimes occurs during the period of the midwinter school break, when most affluent families go to the mountains of the Jura or the Alps to enjoy winter sports.

There will be no such luxury for us.

Our three children are going to have to help us remove the roof of the Forge, clean the moss and debris off from the tiles and help us stack them ready for reassembly. And all this on a property that they did not approve of in the first place, because "what is the point of us moving from a comfortable house with central heating, proper toilets and a bath, to this old wreck of a place?"

So it is with a combination of motivation and threat, using techniques that all parents become thoroughly adept at, that we assemble our small work force to start stripping the roof off from the Forge. Once we start, of course, they begin to enjoy it as they become involved, with each one of us innovating different schemes to get the work done more and more efficiently.

It might seem strange that a modern family should all work together like this, but in our case we had learned to do so. There is a kind of common experience that you share with people, be they family or crew, when you cross an Ocean in a sailboat.

Together we have taken pleasure in the beauty of tropical sunsets and dawns at sea, and also we have survived the fury of hurricanes off rocky lee shores. We've watched pods of Orcas play, seen Pilot Whales in their hundreds swimming past us with purpose to a distant destination and even bumped into a Blue Whale. We've had to carry fresh water to the boat; heave supplies from Spanish markets and negotiate for lobsters from Cape Fishermen. These experiences have involved us in 'pulling together' in a way that many modern families do not have the privilege of enjoying.

We are all dependant on each other and also reliant to each other. So in spite of jibes from the other kids at school about "so where are you going for the holidays", our team start the fairly dangerous job of dismantling the roof.

I tie the ladders into place, so that we do not have to worry about them sliding sideways off the roof. We put heavy-duty plastic drums in strategic places to collect all the moss and leaves that have collected on the tiles.

I start at the peak of the roof by taking each tile and passing it to Andrew, our youngest son, who has the agility of a cat with an innate sense of balance. I don't feel nearly so at home at this height above the ground, in spite of spending my life in a cockpit of an aeroplane, but I know that I will acclimatise to it over the space of a couple of days.

Andrew seems quite at home up here.

He has the school rope climbing record, which seems a good qualification for clambering about on the roof. He controls the top of the sliding board onto which he places each tile and releases it. Chamonix catches each tile as it rockets towards her, which requires a skill and timing as they gather velocity, as they careen down the board. She develops a system where they crash one by one into a bedding of moss at the bottom of the sliding board. Marlene collects them and scrapes the moss and lichen away and then hands them to Laurence who has an eye for stacking them neatly in piles, so that they don't crack with the strain of weight of other tiles above them.

Like most jobs that we do, we find that by the time the work has ended, we have become quite good at it. The problem is that the next time we do the same job, we have forgotten the little details of how we did it last time. Thus we have to reinvent the techniques all over again.

By the afternoon we have all the tiles stacked and the Forge looks even more forlorn than before, with racks of rotten battens exposed to the sky. As we strip the roof I am astonished at how parts of it have held in place in spite of the decayed supports. It is almost as though the building is trying to survive and battling to live.

Perhaps we are here just in time to save her.

Now we can see just what has happened to the beams over the last four hundred years. The structure is secured with wooden nails that lock the beams in place, but they don't do much work. The arrangement of struts is such that the wooden nails and beams lock into place naturally, with slots and tongues that have been carved with an adze.

I enjoy putting my hand on the rough surface, to feel where someone has worked and fashioned this wood more than two hundred years before the French Revolution.

What changes this building must have witnessed.

What stories it could tell.

I wonder about where the beams came from before they were assembled here. I can see more evidence that they have been used before, from the unused holes and markings from the original roof builders. How many hundreds of years have these branches of natural oak been in the service of man?

How did they lift these huge heavy beams into place, after cutting them from the forest by hand and then transporting them here with an ox wagon?

As I sit on the peak of the skeletal roof like a bird of prey sitting on a rack of ribs in the Serengeti, I have an elevated view of the river. There is still a strong currant of water in the river from the rain that fell last week, but the air is calm and the bare trees on the far shore are reflected on the surface.

Occasionally an uprooted tree sails by in the flow, looking slightly incongruous as it passes though the inverted mirrored image of the opposite forest. There is a crow that I have seen several times recently that has taken to gathering bits of food from the surface of the river. This is dangerous for him, should he become waterlogged, but I can see him now sitting on one of the branches of a floating tree as it drifts past. He looks just like a black clad pirate on his ship. The sun is low now and the light is horizontal and softening. It doesn't look like rain so the naked forge should come to no harm tonight.

We all hope the cold weather holds off.

I see an old man standing in the road staring at us, and the roofless Forge. I wave to him but he does not see me against the light of the setting sun. I see that he is shaking his head and then staring at the ground. He turns and shuffles back to the village, using his walking stick for support. He must be wondering what all this roof renovation activity is about.

The next morning we are all feeling a little stiff from the exercise yesterday. We assemble for the next stage of the work. Now we have to dismantle the rotten wood. This means removing all of the battens and some of the struts. The beams are all in good condition although they all show varying degrees of insect damage.

"Oh, you don't have to worry about that," said the man in the Quincaillerie in Seurre, when we were buying products to treat the beams, "The insects have only eaten out the soft wood. They will never eat the good wood!"

We decide to treat them anyway because not all of the wood is old oak. Some of the struts are substitute softer wood so we decide to replace them to be on the safe side. It seems that we are not the first people to have carried out repairs here. Our collection of replacement beams has come from a variety of places. Some came from an old shed that was being disassembled on the Chalon road and some others had survived a house fire, where some gypsies had bought a house in order to insure it at an elevated price and then claim the profit.

Some others came from a barn that was being replaced by a modern house. A few had come drifting down the river during the floods and we had rescued them. Or rather, Andrew had, by paddling out into the six knot flow on a surfboard, then towing each beam to the shore.

These floating beams and logs we call crocodiles. When I was Andrew's age, in Rhodesia in Africa, I had also lived by the side of a river, but there the crocodiles were real.

All these beams, if they could communicate with us, would be able to recount a lot of the history of France.

Perhaps, I wonder, together they will create an ambiance in the Forge that I will be able to feel. Perhaps I will sense a sort of timelessness that only old buildings seem to acquire. Perhaps we will get a feeling of security and serenity that comes with experience and faith in the passing of time.

We shall see.

The naked beams on the Forge look worse today as I clamber around with Andrew. We tap at the wood with a hammer to determine the condition of each one. Solid 'clunks' denote good wood and 'dull thuds' show us where the underlying wood has been attacked by rot or beetles. We detach and throw the bad pieces to the ground where Marlene assembles them into piles ready for burning.

While we are doing this, I see that the old man who was looking at us the previous evening has returned. He watches us for a while and then wanders away. About half an hour later he returns with an old wooden wheelbarrow, which squeaks as the wooden wheel turns. The sound is almost exactly the same as the birdsong of the Coal Tits which frequent our garden in Seurre. He has loaded the barrow with sections of planking, which have bits of rusty mesh and nails attached to them.

He squeaks his way through the open gate into the courtyard, where we have the fires in progress.

"Bonjour Madame, Monsieur," he says seriously.

He and Marlene shake hands as they exchange greetings. I wave down from the roof. I know that I should climb down and formally introduce myself, which is the correct and polite thing to do in France, but I shelter behind the defence of being a foreigner. I am too pressed for time to engage in lengthy diversions, which is yet another way in which I fail to behave like the French.

"I am Monsieur Février," he tells us seriously. "I live up there, round the corner." He waves to somewhere in the village. "I see that you have a bonfire. Will it be alright if I put my old rabbit hutches onto the fire as well?"

"Of course, Monsieur!" answers Marlene, somewhat surprised at his forthrightness. Work stops.

She gives me a raised eyebrow look, small smile, which translates into: "What do you think about that?"

I return a 'hands open, thumbs outwards': 'What the Hell, why not?'

He starts to explain to us that he is giving up raising rabbits and that our bonfire will save him from the trouble of having to start one of his own. And then, unusually for a Frenchman, he starts to tell us about his 'maladie'.

He tells us how he has had to go all the way to Dijon, a distance of nearly ***forty kilometres***, to see a specialist and how the specialist did not know what the problem was.

He seems partly anxious, but also slightly proud to have a malady that not even experts can diagnose.

"They make the tests," he says, "and then I have to go back again and again. I have never done so much travelling. Five times and they still do not know what my problem is. I have these dreams, like nightmares, sometimes during the day and I have lost all my energy. No more can I keep the rabbits. Sometimes I think they turn into monsters and I fear that they will attack me with huge teeth. Me! Attack Me! Ah, everything is upside down."

Marlene realises, with her nursing background that he needs sympathy and understanding. He is a small stout man dressed in his 'blues', which are denim working man's overalls. They are a sort of uniform of the working classes in France which identify 'the people', in contrast to 'the managers' who wear white denim overalls. His black beret appears to be a permanent part of his head, because the band has depressed a groove on his forehead.

I wonder for a moment if he sleeps with it on.

Perhaps yes, in winter!

He rambles on while he and Marlene lift the planks, still thick with rabbit dung, onto the bonfire. He tells her about himself and his wife and how they have been living in this village all their lives and how he used to work at the '*usine céramique*'. It seems that this ceramic factory was the mainstay of the village economy before the war and the two decades after it. During that time it supplied employment to most of the people of the village.

"Those were the days," he reminisces, "there was work for everyone. My father worked at the 'usine' when I was at school here in the village, in the fifties, and then after school I worked there as well. The village was alive back then. The church was full on Sundays and the school was like a hive of bees."

I return to levering battens and other bits of discardable wood from the roof, while Marlene continues to listen to Monsieur Février's version of the past.

"And then they discovered plastic. Everybody started to use plastic. No more did they want proper ceramic for the drains and the sewers. All plastic! The factory closed down, we lost our jobs and the village died. All the young people then moved away, but I stayed."

He seems depressingly proud of his patriotism to the village.

By the time he has described to us about how the world is worse off without the use of ceramic drains, the fire has consumed all his rabbit hutches. He trails off back to his house with the "squeak squeak" of his wheelbarrow, which is warning everyone where he is. He has promised to return tomorrow with another load. He seems dejected and he reminds me of Christopher Robin's mournful donkey, Eeyore.

The children have had enough now and are bored with the work on the roof. We receive all sorts of ingenious stories that are supposed to convince us that they need to be somewhere else. There is holiday homework to do with a friend, there is a birthday party with another friend and there is an outing organised by a teacher from the school to which ***everybody*** will be going.

We are happy to release them, because they have done well, and there is not a lot for them to do now. It will be my responsibility to nail in the new battens. We are pleased how the children have adapted to school in France. They had been introduced into a school in the Alsace, which was where we first lived in France, speaking no French at all. We had organised lessons in French for them before we left England to come to France, but they were younger then, and had not realised the importance of the lessons.

It was a considerable shock for them at first. Laurence already had some experience of 'another' language because we had him enrolled in a play group when we were in South Africa. This had been in an 'Afrikaans' area of Cape Town, so he had learned to communicate with the other children of the group in that language. But he had forgotten all of that during our sea voyage. When we arrived in England he had a large advantage over the other children at school, because Marlene had conducted school lessons everyday as we sailed along. Sadly, he had to 'forget' a large amount of what he had acquired in order to fit in with the other children at school.

There were adjustments that all three of them had to make in England, and we had stressed to them that they should not talk about "When we were at Sea", because it would set them apart from the others. One day Laurence did mention, during a lesson, to the Headmistress that he had swum in the open ocean with his Dad and the Dolphins.

"No you didn't," she said. "You mustn't make up stories that are not true!"

We only found out about this some weeks later, but we felt that we had to mention it to her, because it was true and not an imaginary story. She was mortified and apologised to Laurence. He accepted it, but it was an important lesson for him in 'fitting in'. Now they had learned the lesson so well, that in France, when we walk down the street in the village, they insist to us that we don't speak in English, or our 'accented' French.

"Because if you do, everybody will know that we are not French." They tell us.

This isn't much of a confidence builder for us, with our slower rate of learning French. They are so adept by now that they prefer to communicate with each other in French, rather than English.

Monsieur Février returns the next day with more remains of his rabbit hutches to be burned. He is still dressed in his 'blues', still pushing his old wooden wheelbarrow, but he seems diminished somehow, as though older than his sixty five years. Again he shakes hands with Marlene as though it is the first time that they have met, but today he insists that we should call him Augustin. Together he and Marlene load his old planks onto the fire.

Today he has a little gift for us.

"Eau de Vie," he says seriously as he hands a dusty bottle of pale liquid to Marlene. "It is to say thank you for the bonfire."

"This is not necessary," insists Marlene.

"Oh, but it is! It is a special one, from my own fruit trees."

"Do you make it yourself?" Marlene asks.

"Ah no, it is my cousin who is the magician. He lives in Labergement. He has all the equipment and he is as good as any professional."

We have a healthy respect for Eau de Vie, ever since we were first introduced to it in the village of Leymen, near the Swiss border. The first time we had sampled it was at the end of a dinner that had continued for several hours. Our hosts insisted that we try some of their speciality. It nearly scoured out our insides and seriously loosened the cartilage that holds the plates of our skulls together.

We have had a very solemn respect for the liquor ever since.

"Thank you very much," says Marlene, sounding almost completely convincing.

I am able to hide my expression as I am sitting up high on the remains of the roof.

"It is nothing," he insists. "I have a supply in my garden shed. My wife? She knows nothing!"

I can just imagine that his shed is where he escapes to when he needs some peace. It seems that he has not worked at all since losing his job at the ceramic factory, which means that he must have been supported by the social system for most of his adult life. No wonder he and his wife need to find a bit of space away from each other, occasionally.

Today he has decided to tell us about his vegetable patch. It seems that this is what occupies his life.

He moans about the weather, "Always, when the tomatoes grow, the carrots don't. When the courgettes and pumpkins do well, the lettuce is a disaster and grows too fast. But the thing that always fails is my cabbages. They start well, I plant them out, but after two weeks they turn yellow and die. My neighbour? He has good cabbages, year after year. I don't understand it. I think it is because my wife is out of phase with the moon. For the last fifteen years it has been like this, ever since we started to live separately."

"Oh," said Marlene for lack of anything better to say, and not wanting to really know, added, "So where does she live now?"

"Ah, we still live in the same house, but I use the back door and she uses the front one. We don't talk. It is better that way."

I have heard snatches of this conversation in between hammering nails into the battens that I am positioning on the roof above their heads. I pause for a moment and look at Augustin Février. It would seem that he doesn't work, has no home life, farms a vegetable patch not very well, and hasn't had the yearning to travel. His rabbits that he has bred and slaughtered for years have now, in his mind, turned to monsters. What on earth has he done with his life? Has he been content to vegetate like this? He must have had some enthusiasm for life at some stage, perhaps in his youth?

He must be getting some exercise from his gardening, but he looks stiff and depressed. With his skin colour and his shuffling gait, it doesn't seem as though he and his wife will have the need to put up with each other for very much longer.

After he 'squeaks' his wheelbarrow out of the garden gate onto the potholed road back to his house, we look at each other.

"He doesn't look very well," I venture.

"Yes, he has that yellow translucent colour to his skin." Marlene says. "It is probably liver damage. Perhaps this alcohol his cousin makes for him has eaten his insides. But although he has some tissue damage below his eyes, he doesn't look like a heavy boozer. But certainly, he is not well!"

We go back to work.

We heave the replacement struts into position and secure them with long metal nails. In order to drive them into the oak I have to drill holes into the hard wood first, which I hope means that the internal wood is sound.

The resonance of my hammering echoes off the walls of the courtyard.

I take a few minutes off to watch cormorants fishing on the river. There are about a hundred and fifty of them; they are flying past and overtaking each other and then landing on the water like a sort of avian conveyor belt moving up the river. They are big birds and they splash awkwardly. Each time they touch down, they dive from view. They look like an organised gang of hooligan muggers looting shops down a main-street. The scene is eerie because they make no vocal sounds, they are feathered in black and they seem completely organised. Several grey herons are flying and landing along the bank, accompanying this raid on the fish stock of the river. They move like grey ghosts with a lumbering flight that gives an impression of great weight with grace. For some strange reason they remind me of heavily loaded Lancaster Bombers.

The killing intensions of these squadrons are the same.

Suddenly one of the cormorants sees me on the roof of the Forge. It gives an alarm squawk. The ones that are in the air turn to fly south. The others, as they surface from diving, see the alarm and takeoff to join the main mob. I know the fisherman hate these cormorants because of the fish they catch and because of the fish that they damage and cut with their beaks. These damaged fish bleed to death in the river. These raids reduce, dramatically, the numbers of young fish that are introduced into the rivers each year to enhance the fishing.

The whole raiding party of black cormorants now depart, looking like Stuka dive bombers heading for home after a raid. The grey herons, who are not on the same mental alarm frequency as the cormorants, stalk the riverbank, bemused, abandoned and elegant. They look like professors discussing the finer points of education, with their long noses pointed at the ground and their hands clasped behind their backs.

Two Kingfishers zip across the water surface like darts of blue light. No doubt they will be pleased that the raiding party has left.

Time to get back to work.

During the afternoon I see that we have another person passing by the house. He is a skinny individual with a long bony nose, dressed in a grey greatcoat. He is pushing a bicycle. His chin is buried in a grey scarf wrapped around his neck and his eyes peek out from under the edge of a grey flat cloth hat. His face looks like that of a rat as it peeps out through a gap in the folds of a blanket. He slinks past with his hands on the handlebars of his bicycle and although he seems not to see us, I get the impression that his eyes are darting about in the gloom under the peak of his hat.

I gesture at him with my hammer to Marlene.

"He looks like the Rat Man."

She looks and nods.

"Just like him! You don't think that he has followed us over here?"

She is alluding to a rather unpleasant individual who lived next door to us in England, soon after we arrived there. Marlene had started work doing night duty as a nurse at an old folk's home in Hove, before running two sheltered accommodation schemes for elderly people who were partially unable to care for themselves. This second job was grossly underpaid, but it did come with a grotty little council house and this seemed, at the time, to be a small step up from living on the boat. The children had become tired of the leaks of water dripping onto their bunks in the boat, which was not so serious in the tropics, but which made life uncomfortable for us in the wet windy weather of southern England.

It is one of the drawbacks of living on a wooden decked boat.

I contended that these hardships were good for them.

I don't think they agreed.

Our neighbour at this small house was a rodent exterminator who looked like a rat, thus we named him Ratman. One of our pleasures, when we moved to France initially, was that we would not have to see the Ratman again, and yet here he is!

Or perhaps it is his older brother?

An older greyer version of him, who looks as though he is nearing the end of his days, as a rat.

I go back to hammering and when I look up later I realise that the Ratman has disappeared. Rather like a shadow that moves into shade, so that nobody notices when it vanishes.

Over the course of the next few days we secure all the beams and battens in place. I become aware that the noise seems to have attracted various residents of the village to emerge from their houses and to wander past, to see what we are doing. Some of them pretend they are looking at the river, rather obviously not staring at us as they pass.

We are used to this rather standoffish attitude, which we had encountered when we first arrived in Seurre.

Monsieur Javelle, who has played the magnificent church organ since the fifties in Seurre, and who acts as a guardian and guide explained to us why this was.

"Seurre used to be a walled town with great battlements encircling it, in the fourteenth century. The people inside were defensive and we had a history of being surrounded and attacked. Sometimes our people held out against superior forces but, several times over the centuries, we were defeated. Each time the raiders sacked and burned the town, sometimes even damaging the church. The town was sequentially controlled by many different forces including the Austrians and the Dukes of Bourgogne. The town also suffered various plagues such as the Black Death.

"King Louis XIV, when he was in control of the town in the seventeenth century, ordered the battlements and walls to be demolished. They were dismantled with the exception of a small section which is now near the present hospice. However, because the King was impressed with our tenacity and spirit that we had displayed against the Austrians invaders, he granted the town a tax free status.

"When the French Revolution took place in 1789 and the people of France rose up against the King of France, the town lost its tax-free status and so to this day, we do not celebrate the anniversary of the storming of the Bastille. We, the people of Seurre, and a couple of the surrounding villages, consider ourselves to be separate from the rest of France!"

This isolationist attitude of the Serroise lives on. They don't take kindly to visitors. Even people from Dijon, only forty kilometres away, complain that they are treated as foreigners. The townspeople still resent the rest of France and the fact that now they have to pay taxes.

The old houses that border onto the roads of the town are built with shutters over the windows to present an impenetrable façade to the world. The gardens and family space to the rear are kept private and out of sight. So their walled-in attitude seems now to be an individually expressed, but nevertheless collective, defence against the world.

Monsieur Javelle continued to explain, "The loss of our tax-free status has been such an issue from the past that Seurre celebrates its own independence on the first Sunday of August, with an extravagant firework display. We do not celebrate the 14th of July, with the rest of France."

I am expecting the same sort of attitude from the people in this village, so it is a surprise when Jacques stops his car outside the gate and walks in to introduce himself. Jacques does not look like a farmer. He is tall and looks athletic, although this is only an illusion, because he has a cigarette in his mouth and his fingers are stained with tar. It seems, from my first impressions, that his cigarette is an extension of his hands.

He greets Marlene with a formal handshake.

It looks as though this is going to be a social visit, so I climb down from the roof.

"Bonjour." And we shake hands.

"I heard that somebody had bought this house," he tells us, "and I thought that I should come and meet you. They tell me that you are a pilot?"

"Yes." I admit.

"Ah, so it is true. I also was a pilot with the French Army. I flew helicopters for three years, but I was a bit younger back then." He smiles engagingly.

"So you are from the village?" I ask him.

"Well yes, I am living here now, but I am from near Paris. That is where my home is, but I have been here for thirty years."

Well, if he does not consider himself to be one of the villagers after thirty years, I wonder to myself, how long I will have to wait before I can think of this as being my home?

"Why did you settle here?" I ask.

"Well, I have been working for Thompson in Seurre for all that time. Recently the company was bought out by the Japanese, and the base has moved to Dijon, so many of us lost our jobs, so now I am on chômage. We used to make microchips and many miniature technical components, even for satellites!"

I look suitably impressed. I had the notion that these little villages were populated by hunters and farmers, who were living in a bygone age with traditions and attitudes that had not changed significantly for ages.

"I have come to show you something that I thought you would like to see," he said. "I have a friend who is building an aeroplane in his cellar."

Now it is my turn to give a Gaelic shrug.

Not of 'disbelief, but of 'surprise'.

I try number 44: Eyebrows high, head tilted slightly back.

The equivalent of "Wow" in English.

"It's true. He has been building it for about five years and it is nearly ready to fly. Would you like to see it?"

"Of course!"

I look at Marlene.

Aeroplanes are not high on her list of interesting diversions. They are men's things, along with motorbikes, engines and contraptions that generally make a noise and spray oil over clean clothes. She has an aversion to the smell of diesel, which is one of the reasons that, during our sea voyage, I only ran the engine once per week to charge the batteries.

She gives me a "well it is time to take a break" sort of gesture.

"Is it near?" I ask Jacques.

"Oh yes, it is only five kilometres, maybe a few more. It will take only a few minutes to get there."

"But I am not dressed for visiting!"

"Oh that is no problem. Georges understands that when men are busy, they do not have time for dressing up."

And so, with a quick dusting down, I am ready to go with Jacques. He has a Renault, which is only to be expected. It seems to me that the ordinary French people are highly patriotic with regard to the cars that they buy, which is most often one of the marques that is designed and produced in France.

The more affluent people buy German cars, and thereby set themselves slightly apart, which is not to their social advantage.

We climb aboard. The ashtray is full; Jacques has a cigarette in his mouth which he seems to have forgotten about. It has a long segment of ash curling from the end. Out of habit, I suppose, he remembers it and then carefully cups one hand underneath to catch the ash while, with the other, he takes the cigarette gently to drop it out of the window. Half way the ash drops, his cupped hand misses the ash which falls onto his lap. He brushes it away towards the pedals, drops the stub of the cigarette out of the window, grabs the wheel, turns the ignition key and we are off.

I wonder if this is the sort of coordination to be expected from a helicopter pilot. I always thought that they could tap their heads and rub their stomachs at the same time without confusing the motions, with a sort of left and right brain disconnect. I wonder if Jacques really was a helicopter pilot.

As though he reads my mind, he starts to tell me about it.

"When I was conscripted into the army for my National Service," he says, and as he drives he juggles another cigarette from the pack, then opens the matchbox with one hand, extracts a match and lights it, while the other hand stays firmly on the wheel, "they made us all do an aptitude test. They decided that they wanted to train me, so that is how I became to be a pilot."

Perhaps he ***does*** have the coordination needed.

"I was in the Army for three years. It was great. I was qualified to fly with loads suspended on nets below the helicopters and we had to do all sorts of crazy things with them."

"Did you go into civilian flying when you left the Army?" I ask.

"No, they wouldn't let me leave with a licence. They said I could stay and have a career, which meant that I had to sign on for ten years, or else if I left they would tear my ticket up, and I would not have the right to fly anymore."

"Well, it would have been worth staying for the ten years!"

"Yes, I know that now, but back then all my friends were going off and making money, going to North Africa and working in the oilfields. That was much better than staying in the Army, with Army pay! My father was furious with me. He hit me right across the room when I told him."

He rubs his jaw ruefully as he recalls the experience.

"He was right, I should have stayed, but I was young then."

I look at him and wonder what quality they saw, that they should select him, from thousands of young men, for this special training. Perhaps time will tell.

He turns into a small village, weaves down a rural tarred road and stops outside the gate of a modest home that is built on two levels. Many of the new houses have been built in this way, where a hole is excavated for the basement and the soil piled up outside the walls, so that the house looks like a single level bungalow perched on a mound. I wonder for a moment if this is to reduce the taxes by making these houses seem smaller than they really are. If this friend of Jacques is building an aeroplane here, it must be a hang-glider. The house does not seem large enough for anything else.

We walk up the gravel drive from the gate and Jacques introduces me to a large bear of a man called Georges.

"Enchanté ," he rumbles, with a deep voice that reminds me of Barry White.

It seems that Jacques has told him about me, so he turns to show us the way to his cellar.

A man of few words, it seems.

He has double garage doors under the house which are accessed by a short slope downwards. I wonder for a moment how he copes with rainwater and snow blocking the entrance. His car, I see, is parked outside. He opens one of the garage doors which rises up on runners and slides inwards over the area reserved for parking a car. The entire space inside and under the house is taken up with silvered aluminium aeroplane parts.

There is a gleaming fuselage and tail section with a single engine and propeller installed. The wings are separate from the body of the aeroplane and are gleaming like newly polished coins. They are in a stand specially built for the purpose. Around the sides of the garage is a collection of benches, lathes and racks of tools that look like the ancillary equipment of an operating theatre.

The patient is lying under the lights, centre stage.

This is not just an aeroplane built in a basement.

This is a work of love created by an artist who has a dream.

I walk towards the aeroplane with my hands clasped behind my back, in that way which declares both ultimate respect and which affirms that I will not touch anything without permission. Each rivet on the surface of the wings has been recessed into the skin to give a smooth polished finish. The quality of the work would be the envy of Airbus Industrie or Boeing. I am humbled to be in the presence of such a work of art.

Jacques explains to me, "This is not a kit construction. He has made every piece, every former and every rib. Even the retractable undercarriage he has made, by creating a mould and drop forging it. He has even made the rims for the wheels."

The cowling on one side of the engine compartment is open, so I examine the installation with all the wiring, fuel lines and inlet and exhaust systems. Every surface is polished with a patina that I would expect to see on a grand piano. And there isn't a speck of oil or dust on the floor.

I am clearly in the presence of a superior engineer.

We discuss the construction and technical aspects of the aeroplane for what seems like a few minutes, but which is actually over an hour.

Later, as Jacques drives me home, he explains that Georges was also working at Thompson and had also lost his job, when the company condensed its operation in Dijon.

I express my astonishment that a company can let skilled people like Georges slip away from its workforce.

"Ah, it is like that in France," explains Jacques. "The companies try to save money by getting rid of the older experienced people and then they employ the cheaper younger ones. The government gives the Enterprises special incentives and tax breaks to give young people work. It is because there are not enough jobs for the qualified youngsters who are leaving university. Many of the people you see working as secretaries and cashiers in supermarkets have university degrees. And then, when the youngsters get these good jobs, they pay more than 50% tax so that the people like Georges, who have been displaced, can be paid chômage! Crazy, hey? It is not surprising that many of our qualified young people are going out of the country to find work."

He gives a shrug while keeping both hands on the wheel, which is an interesting contortion.

We arrive back at my house and I stare at the work that I still have to do on my property. There are piles of tiles and heaps of moss, with old oak beams lying to one side like a giant's discarded game of fiddlesticks. Bare trees gloom overhead as if overseeing the slow progress with disapproval.

The Forge is exposed to the sky like a carcass with ribs stripped bare of flesh. The contrast between this project, which I am just starting, compared to the culmination of the dream that we have just seen, is extreme.

Jacques must see what I can see, but is too tactful to mention it directly.

"Bon courage!" he smiles.

I shake his hand, "Thank you for introducing me to Georges. I am so impressed. I thought that all the people here were farmers."

"Oh no," he answers. "I must introduce you to my wife's cousin. He is a sculptor. He carves wooden creations from tree trucks and stumps that he finds washed up on the river banks. He is a great artist. I think that you will find him interesting. He likes wood, like you. I think that he would like to see your boat."

"Ah yes, the boat! She is moored in St Jean de Losne at the moment. I will bring her here when we move into this house, but that will not be for eighteen months. I have to get this house ready so that we can live in it, and also finish the other one in Seurre. When I have done that then I will bring the boat here. I shall be happy to show him the boat, but it will not be for some time."

"Oh, that is alright. He is not going anywhere. There is time."

I climb out of the car and wave goodbye to Jacques.

He drives up the potholed road back to the village.

I am left alone for a moment to reflect on the complications that I have set for myself, simply to have my boat anchored in front of the house.

When I embarked on my voyage from South Africa, I didn't have a fixed destination in mind. I simply wanted to leave the wars and politics of Africa behind and to give the family a new start, somewhere, anywhere, else.

My thought was that, with a boat, we could go to where destiny led. We would be mobile and flexible.

But instead it is the boat that has stopped me moving. It is the boat that has fixed us in this area.

I am now anchored to this little village. I now have to learn about life, the characters, the customs and the history.

It is as though I have thrown a dart at a map of the world, to decide a destination, and it has landed, for better or for worse, in the middle of France.

So here I am with an ocean going boat, far inland, as distant from the sea as it is possible to get.

Clearly illogical!

Perhaps life has some strange lesson in store for me.

Monsieur Le Duc

Monsieur le Duc lives with the retired headmaster of the village school.

He has lived with his host, Monsieur Fabien Lafarge, for five years. The house they share together is in a prominent position overlooking the farmers' fields to the south of the village. From here they have a view over the fields to the trees that border the Sâone River.

In early spring the river floods over its banks and spreads across the farmers' fields, so that the flat land resembles a large lake several kilometres across. Copses of trees between the fields now appear to be small islands in this temporary lake. The residents of houses who are affected by this annual flood have adapted their homes and their attitudes to accept this inevitable inundation. They move themselves upstairs after they have moved their heavier bits of furniture up towards the ceiling with pulleys. When the floods recede, they sweep out the mud, drop their furniture back into position and carry on with life, with stoic acceptance.

During the flood, water birds float on the shallow water, over the crops of germinating wheat, so that they can feed on the shoots. When the snow in the mountains has finished melting, the flow of water in the river decreases and the floodwater drains back into the confines of the river. This annual spectacle is observed with interest by the headmaster, but Monsieur le Duc is indifferent about it.

The headmaster has taken care of Monsieur Le Duc for these last five years and now refers to his friend as 'Le Duc'. This is in no way a form of address that indicates disrespect.

On the contrary, it is Monsieur Lafarge who had given Monsieur Le Duc his distinguished title, after he had observed his friend's aristocratic air.

One might say that Monsieur Lafarge owns Le Duc, but that is a misrepresentation, because nobody had, or will ever, own Le Duc.

Le Duc is an independent spirit who considers that he is superior to all other beings in his life. His experiences have not given him any doubts as to his true calling or importance.

He ensures that everyone he meets knows that he is superior to them, which is not difficult for him to do, because of his size.

He is, without question, the largest cat in the village.

His coat is as black as a coal mine and his eyes are like lamps in the dark. He terrorises village dogs into submission by clawing them as they sleep. He knows exactly where each dog is tied up, and how long their leads are. This allows him to pass unmolested around the village at night by keeping a single bound away from these chained up mutts. His progress can be traced around the houses, when he permits this, by the baying and howling of frustrated hunting dogs that are restrained by their chains.

He saunters past, just out of reach, of each ravening dog while the leashed canine gnashes its teeth and gargles against its restraint. The impertinence of his behaviour is accentuated by the way he carries his tail vertically as he walks, as though he has not a worry in the world.

He is a bully of a cat, and he has acquired this behaviour from Monsieur Lafarge, in the same way that dogs are frequently mirrors of their master's behaviour.

There are occasions when Le Duc chooses not to be seen on patrol and these are the times when no animal knows of his whereabouts. Where, to us, there are fences and barriers between properties, these present no obstacle to Le Duc. He has, in his mind, a map of all the three dimensional routes to any destination. He knows exactly where he can trot across a roof to save a tiresome journey around a barn which contains smelly cows or chickens. He knows where there are holes in fences and where drains provide access under roads. He knows the time and place of houses where food is put out for animals and what is worth fighting for, and which residents leave only scraps.

He knows which of the cats in the village are the result of his past liaisons. He makes sure that they all know that he is their chief. He is a cat who promenades by himself, but only through personal choice, because a true King does not need the adoration of a court to convince him of who he is.

A true King just ***is***!

He is in good condition in spite of a few scars and a couple nicks out of the tips of his ears. When I first meet Le Duc I know immediately that he is the village 'Battlecat'.

I know that he would be able to tell me more about what goes on in this village than any of the people who live here. What a pity I can't ask him.

The information and scandal that we humans have to verbally swap about each other, Le Duc acquires from personal experience.

He must know where the lovers live, because of the pheromones that he smells on his excursions. He knows where the human fights take place because of the shouts of rancour that rent the night air. The smell of stale wine from piles of emptied bottles tells him where the alcoholics live, as if the sound of inebriated snoring from those same houses is not enough information. He knows the whereabouts of colonies of mice that do not keep a proper lookout, and where the bats live and where ducklings can be found along the river bank.

He also knows who is up and about at four o' clock in the morning, which is the time of night that cats like most.

This is the time when the village baker makes bread for the morning rush.

Le Duc likes the bakery, because it is a place where he can warm his paws in winter. The outer swing door of the bakery, where the ovens are situated, does not close properly and Le Duc knows that he can push it open to gain access to the warm interior.

The baker seldom sees Le Duc when he slips in, because he is usually preoccupied with his ovens. Occasionally he sees Le Duc as he leaves with a captured mouse. He likes Le Duc and wonders if the big black cat prefers mice fed on flour, because they taste better.

Only Le Duc knows.

Le Duc does not get the same approval rating from the Baker's Wife, who is known to hate all animals and most people.

For some reason Le Duc likes to provoke her.

He sits and waits on the raised flowerbed outside her shop and then, when a customer pushes the door open, he darts in and out of the shop.

It seems that he does this only to annoy her.

It works.

Most often she throws a stale bun at the cat. She keeps a few of them below her counter top, ready to shy at him. Le Duc is always too fast for her, so the only result is that she has to sweep all the crumbs out the shop, yet again.

She is a person who is almost always in a bad mood, and on the rare occasions when she isn't, this fact is discussed in the village in the same way as the weather or the phase of the moon.

Both of these phenomena seem to have an influence on the dark mood of the Baker's Wife.

She can best be described as a scraggly woman, whose inner unhappiness has etched a cobweb of lines and wrinkles on her face. She mutters to herself, but seldom greets anyone else. She is usually dressed in a sombre cotton dress with a pattern of large dull flowers. Her large apron has a faded 'Bienvenue' (welcome) logo, which is in complete contradiction to her scowl. She ties her hair with a headscarf, as a token gesture to the regulations that require that she should wear a hat, because she is serving food.

There is a strange connection between the scrawny Baker's Wife as she chases this large black cat with a bristle broom from her premises, at the time of the full moon, which escapes all of us.

Messieurs Lafarge and Monet

Marlene and I decide to visit Monsieur Lafarge, because he is the authority on the history of the village. We want to find out where the Romans used to cross over the river, because of all the artefacts that had been found over the years, along the banks and in the riverbed. Monsieur Lafarge had been a teacher in the village school in the late 1930's, in the days before World War II, up until 1965. He lives alone at the top of the hill to the south of the village, and his dislike of the villagers seems as strong as their dislike of him. He has bought a strip of land alongside a field from a farmer, so that he has a private road which he can use to access his home, because he does not even want to drive through the village.

We organise a 'rendezvous' and armed with dire warnings from his ex-pupils, we walk up the hill to his isolated house. We are met by a tall, lean intimidating man, who has an air of authority. It turns out that we are his first visitors for years.

He leads us into a sitting room that is lined with shelves of books. It seems that he fills his solitude with reading and research.

Instead of telling us about the village, he tells us about himself. It is as though he has a reservoir of conversation and recollections that he has to share. We had been warned that he was a tyrant, by his ex-pupils, but perhaps because we are foreigners he is very civil to us. Possibly because we speak English, he decides that we will be more interested in the War.

"Back then," he tells us, "I had to attend regular army training call-ups. I was given a commission as an officer in the Territorial Army. At each military 'call-up' I gained further points and experience towards promotion. By 1939 I was a Captain in the French Territorial Army and then I was conscripted fulltime into the forces. This was during the panic recruitment of soldiers during the last months before to the invasion of France by the Germans.

"In France we were not prepared. We were let down by our leaders. We were unable to present a meaningful defence against the German Blitzkrieg. The German forces advanced through the

Ardennes, around our defences, and the French Army and the British Expeditionary Force were swept aside.

"I was sent by train to a town in the north west of France, with my company, to try to stop the German invasion. We failed!

"The orders and lines of communication were so inadequate for the situation that I had to leave my men under the control of my Lieutenants, while I searched for a serviceable telephone. I found one in the village tabac (corner-shop) which seemed to be the only place with connections to Paris through the local exchange. The lines were jammed with calls and it took me two hours to get through to my headquarters. I managed a confused exchange of information before the link was cut with a series of bomb explosions nearby.

"We heard a roar of aircraft overhead. Airborne machine guns tore at the air with the sound of ripping canvas. We could hear squeals from the tracks of tanks, as they manoeuvred themselves at the approach to the village. Everyone in the tabac cowered at the sound of big guns detonating nearby. The crackle of gunfire announced that the Germans were here. They had come faster than we could have ever expected.

"I ran back to where I had left my troops, taking cover in alleyways. By the time I got there, the tanks had already passed on. Some of my company of men had been killed and the rest of them were captured. All of us were unprepared for the speed and savagery of this advance.

"The survivors of my men had already been marched away by the German captors. They shot those who were unable to move. I saw the final rout of his men from an upper floor window of a house where I found a vantage point. I realised the hopelessness of my situation and I decided that it would be stupid to rush into battle against these experienced troops. I would have been killed for nothing.

"I chose to change myself back into a civilian. I took off my uniform and ransacked the bedroom cupboard of the deserted house where I was hiding. I dressed myself with clothes that I found. I kept my service revolver inside my stolen jacket but left my uniform under the bed."

I look at Marlene and wonder if this man has ever told anybody else that he deserted the army. Is it because we are foreigners, and that it is so long after the event, that he is telling us? Perhaps he has been so lonely, that he has feels the need to tell someone, like a sort of late confession, to justify himself.

He continues, "The road out of the town to the south was filled with people as they ran away with their possessions. They were using every type of wheeled contrivance from bicycles and horse drawn carts to cars and tractors. Everybody was fleeing to somewhere, or anywhere, without any idea as to where that 'somewhere' was.

"I started to walk south. I used tracks through the countryside and paths through the forests and I foraged for food along the way. There were orchards with ripe fruit near abandoned houses. I found chickens that had been left to fend for themselves. I discovered deserted vegetable gardens with lettuce and tomatoes, ready for eating. I ate well. It seemed that whole areas of the countryside had been abandoned. The people were in a panic.

"I followed the route of the canal that connects the Marne to the Sâone for part of my journey. I kept away, whenever I could, from the main roads where everyday there were fighter planes strafing the refugees.

"Every time we saw an aircraft, we ran for cover under the trees or hid in the ditches at the side of the road. I saw an abandoned pram on a road, with a baby in it, explode in a hail of machinegun bullets, while the mother cowered in the ditch next to it, with all her other small children. She was so busy, in the terror of the moment, with her other children that she forgot the baby.

"By the time I arrived back home, France had surrendered.

"Fortunately I still had my 'papers' which identified me as a schoolteacher. In the confusion following the occupation, I managed to slip into the system by presenting myself for inspection to the German Lieutenant, who was posted here to control the village.

"This Lieutenant requisitioned a double storey house at the entrance to the village for himself, and a large building across the road for his troops. From there his men could monitor and control movements of people and vehicles as they passed over the bridge on the Sâone River.

"I had to stand with the Mayor, the Deputy Mayor and the rest of the villagers to witness the erection of a flagpole in front of the small hotel, the one that burned down a couple of years ago.

Do you know where it was? Yes, that's right, where the new 'Salle des Fetes" stands now. The Germans hoisted the flag of the Third Reich there. The Lieutenant made a short speech in German to instruct everyody what he expected of them.

He told us "Now you are under the supervision of Germany and your cooperation is expected and required!"

"Nobody understood the German speech except me," Monsieur Lafarge continued, "So I became the translator for the Bo ch[illegible]I knew that the villagers would be watching me carefully with regard to my sympathies. Most of them have relatives who were killed in the First World War.

"The German Lieutenant boasted to me, "Hitler says that the Third Reich will be in power for a thousand years! We are here to stay! We will reorganise this whole country for you, and you will all benefit. However it is essential that you recognise that I am in charge here, so it is imperative that you convince the villagers to cooperate with me. Is that clear?"

Monsieur Lafarge reminisces to us about the days during the war and how they coped with the shortages. "This part of rural France was relatively unaffected by the ongoing war. Until, that is, the summer of 1944, when the Germans started to get very nervous."

Perhaps Monsieur Lafarge had been alright, but we knew that some of the people had had a miserable time. Annette, our village gossip and information service, had told us about when the village shop was raided by the German contingent from Seurre. They removed every single item of food so that by the time the owner of the shop back then, Monsieur Futin, returned from tending to his allotment, his 'tabac' was stripped clean. The only item missed by the Germans was a few packets of sugar that were in a box that Madame Futin was commanded to sit on, while she witnessed the raid. The news of the theft spread though the village, so later that night everyone took their valuables outside and buried them.

Monsieur Lafarge continues with his story, "Now that we were under the control of the Germans, I felt obliged to ease any misunderstandings between the conquerors and the villagers. It was like walking a tightrope. I had to behave in an authoritarian manner towards the villagers when the Lieutenant was watching me, then I had to explain to them afterwards that I was merely a cog in the wheel of administration."

Apparently he lived under the constant threat of 'denouncement'. I imagine that his deserted 'army' connections would have been enough to condemn him, if there was somebody wanting to inform on him, to settle an old score.

He tells us, "In Seurre, the German Captain who was in charge of the town rounded up five villagers on suspicion that they were assembling to receive secret supplies that were about to be dropped from an RAF aircraft. They were shot out of hand, with no trial. One of the murdered men was the town Doctor, which made the Serroise hate the Germans all the more.

"In fact, the men had assembled for exactly that purpose and had been hoping to receive arms and radios that were going to be parachuted to them. The Stirling bomber that had been carrying these supplies was shot down and had crashed in a nearby forest at Brazey-en-Plaine. The pilot, Squadron Leader King, and two of his RAF crew died in the crash. Flight Sergeant Squance escaped with the aid of the farmer who was first on the scene of the wreckage. The rest of the crew were captured and tortured by the Gestapo, who wanted to get information about the flight.

"They were murdered at the end of the interrogation.

"They all lie in the cemetery of Brazey-en-Plaine.

"The German Captain in Seurre was charged with rooting out other members of the Resistance, who were suspected of operating there. He had to show a result, so he cornered the owner of the only small vehicle repair garage in the town. He shoved the 'Garargiste' against the wall of a building, grabbed a rifle from one of his soldiers, cocked it and aimed at his prisoner and pulled the trigger.

"The rifle misfired.

"He swore and threw the rifle back at the first soldier and grabbed another weapon from a second soldier and repeated the procedure.

"The second rifle misfired as well.

"All he did then was to scream at the 'Garargiste'. The wretched man was allowed to scuttle away, but later he became a revered figure, as we all believed that God had undoubtedly had a hand in his reprieve.

"In fact, by chance, the Officer had been right to select this 'Garargiste', because he had been an important member of the Resistance. He was responsible for storing fuel and repairing vehicles for the Maquis. He was also responsible for helping a group that had procured a van and based themselves at St Jean de Losne. He had painted a logo representing the 'Department of Geographical Surveys' on the side of their van which helped them transit the roadblocks. The last time we saw the van, was when the group was heading away for central France. It was riddled with bullet holes. Two hours after the van had left, we all heard a huge explosion from the direction of Dole, as a large ammunition dump blew up. We never heard what became of that group."

It was time to leave and I could see that Marlene had heard enough. She is not interested in war stories so we take the chance, in a break in his story, to make excuses to leave. As we wander back to our house, we discuss what he had told us. What was extraordinary was that he had told us all about how he had deserted the army, but he said nothing about his role in the Resistance after that.

It is Jacques who fills in the details about Monsieur Lafarge for us. Jacques had not grown up in the village, so had not been one of Monsieur Lafarge's pupils, but his wife knew all about the old headmaster. We enjoy Jacques' history lessons, because he speaks a very correct version of French, and leaves out local colloquialisms, so we find it much easier to follow his stories. One afternoon, shortly after we had met Monsieur Lafarge, we are sitting in the garden with Jacques having tea.

"Unknown to almost everybody," Jacques tells us, "During the war Monsieur Lafarge was the secret head of the local Resistance. They had to plan their sabotage activities to seem like accidents, because of the fear of reprisals by the Germans. If there was a raid involving a convoy, it was normal that several people in a nearby village would be shot, because they should have known about the raid, and should have reported it to the German authority.

"On one occasion," Jacques continues, "One Jura village was selected by the local commandant for reprisal. A detachment of Germans was ordered to kill all the inhabitants and burn the buildings. The Mayor pleaded with the troops that nobody in the village had committed any acts of aggression. He offered himself as a hostage. Eventually the troops decided to ransack the village instead. They took everything of value that they could find, but at least the inhabitants were spared.

"The 'Maquis' (Resistance) knew that there were people who would 'tip off' the Germans to save themselves, and also that even their own families might give them away. Families knew how they could be executed for simply being related to a captured resistance fighter.

"My wife knows the story of the Deputy Mayor here during the war. He was Monsieur Seguin. He had a boundary dispute with his neighbour, which had been going on for more than thirty years before the war. This quarrel was about the exact boundary line between their two properties.

"The dispute had started over a field which he owned on the outskirts of the town, up there near the cemetery. On one edge of this field was a track that had been used by the postal carriage service back in the days when horse drawn carriages were in use. When the new tar road was built, it was constructed to be above the winter flood line, so the old carriage road had fallen into disuse. The deputy Mayor had started to plough along the edge of this road each season with his horse drawn plough, thereby slowly claiming it to be his.

"His neighbour on the other side of the road saw what was happening, and so he had also started to plough along his side, in order to encroach on his side of the edge of the road.

"Eventually the two fields came into contact and that is when the confrontation started, as each farmer claimed that the other one had stolen the road. There was no way, by this time, to define exactly where the original road once lay, because all the markers had been ploughed up.

"The two farmers had taken to attaching their old pre First World War rifles to their horse drawn ploughs, so that when they met they could wave their weapons and threaten to kill each other. Occasionally they would discharge their rifles over each other's head, all the while screaming insults. They would not have been the first farmers in France to murder a neighbour, over a dispute of a few centimetres of land.

"It didn't take long for the Deputy Mayor to figure out that if he could denounce his neighbour as a partisan or a Jew to the

Germans, that then his problem would be solved. He managed to communicate his suspicions to the German Lieutenant in charge of the village, that his neighbour was a Jew.

"The Lieutenant, although he did not believe the Deputy Mayor's claim, knew that he should take action, if only to stamp his authority on the villagers. The following morning at three 'o clock, six soldiers under the command of the Lieutenant surrounded the farmer's small house on the edge of the village. The Corporal bashed open the door with a rifle butt.

"They took the farmer away in a truck and he was never seen again. Suspicion is that he was sent to an internment camp near Strasbourg called Natzweiler, where 12,000 people were murdered. Everybody knew who was responsible for this arrest and denunciation, because of the long standing feud between the two farmers.

"Within a week of the arrest, a message arrived at the Deputy Mayor's house, addressed to Monsieur Seguin. It declared that he was needed for a meeting in Beaune. The message was handwritten in French and indicated that this meeting would promote him to a new status in the community, now that he had chosen to become a part of the Third Reich.

"He departed the next day on the scheduled bus service which operated from the village hotel. He had his letter, which he thought would give him the authority to travel, along with his identity documents.

"Monsieur Lafarge also boarded that same bus.

"Neither of them arrived in Beaune.

"The bus driver, when he was questioned later, said that he had no recollection of either passenger. Years later, a skeleton was discovered in the forest of Montmain five kilometres from here. A tree fell over in a gale and the roots tore up the ground. The hole in the ground exposed a cadaver. Nobody 'officially' knew whose body it was and so it was left there, with just a small cross to mark the spot.

"Most people here believe that Monsieur Lafarge was involved in this disappearance of the Deputy Mayor, but nobody made an official statement. Some are uneasy about him because, when he had a chance to fight the Germans at the beginning of the war, he failed. After that he was acting as the German interpreter. That alone was enough to put him under suspicion."

It seems to me as though people gave him the benefit of their doubts as regards his allegiances. I wonder to myself what his real role was. Nevertheless, his dual existence could only have existed because of his forceful personality. Having met him, we realised that he must have been a tough character when he was younger.

We gathered that he was feared and not trusted and so people found it safer to exclude him socially. He had the status of a headmaster and so was associated with authority, and as all rural people know, authority means trouble of one sort or another. They let him know his status in the community by the way they greeted him.

There is a huge variation in tone and meaning in the two simple words 'Bon Jour' that can convey anything from respect to contempt. Of course the angle of the head, position of the eyebrows and arrangement of the hands is all part of the semaphore. In this way, it seems, the villagers were able to remind Monsieur Lafarge that he would never really be a part of them and their community. No wonder this animosity between Monsieur Lafarge and the village became such a serious issue.

It was Annette who told us about how Monsieur Lafarge countered this passive aggression in a much more meaningful way, by subjecting the children of the villagers to a reign of fear in the school. He was never accused of blatant cruelty, because nobody stood up to him. He inflicted intellectual abuse on the children in-between bouts of ear twisting and hair pulling.

Annette told us, "He specialised in pulling the delicate hairs just in front of the boys' ears. He said he was trying to instil some backbone into the new generation because, he said, the lack of guts of the French after the losses of the First World War was the reason why the country had been overrun so easily during the second. One day he hit one of the boys on his head with the edge of a thick heavy ruler. When the boy died six weeks later of a brain trauma, nobody came forward to make an accusation against him. On another occasion he assaulted his wife in front of us pupils. Again, nobody protested. But we all feared him. People muttered but nobody ever did anything about it! That man was never happy in his skin."

It seems that Monsieur Lafarge was a bully and he had that first requirement of a bully, which was that he thought himself to be superior to everybody else. Perhaps he was in many respects, in this farming community, but this attitude did not ingratiate him with his neighbours.

While he was still employed as a teacher, he was part of the education system and could not be displaced. He had to be tolerated in the village because of the power he had to control the grades and exams of the children. His comments that he made on the children's school reports could influence their chances of employment in later life.

After he retired, his wife died which was a blessed release for her, as far as everybody was concerned. He then enlisted a prostitute to come each week from Dijon to service his needs.

Annette told us, "This is just for show. She does nothing except have cheese and wine with him. And maybe she cleans up the house a bit! He is past it, thank God."

Monsieur Lafarge's authoritarian attitude had a particularly strong effect on one of his pupils, Claude Monet.

Claude Monet was a boy who learned from his schoolmaster what force of character meant, when applied to others. In the early fifties Claude Monet formed a small gang of louts in the school and then used them as his backup in dealings with the other children. His gang members stayed as part of his gang, because it protected them against becoming victims themselves.

Monsieur Lafarge did nothing to control this behaviour in the schoolyard between classes. That was when Claude Monet persecuted the other children.

Initially his bullying consisted of forcibly acquiring all the lunch-packs and treats from the children and then pooling the collection. He then reallocated the proceeds according to his own desires. Most of the children came with food for their midday meal, as their parents were working out in the fields or at the factory and did not have time to return to cater for their families.

Young Monet saw himself as the rightful arbitrator of who would get what, and for simple 'peace in life' the children fell in with this practice. It was not a large step for Claude Monet, when he left school, to realise that he endorsed the principles and ideals of Communism, as long as it was *he* who had control of the allocation of assets.

There was only one child who resisted the Monet gang with any real show of character and this was Marie Rufin. She decided that she was not going to share her lunch with the others. Her father was the village baker and her Papa always prepared special patisseries for her lunch. As far as she was concerned, she had the best and she was not going to give it away without a fight. Sadly, that is what sometimes happened, so Marie started eating her food during the last class before lunch, so that there would not be so much for the gang to steal from her.

Marie preferred to go home for lunch. Her home was over the baker's shop in the main street next to the small hotel where the buses stopped. But her mother was always busy in the shop before lunchtime. This was the peak period for customers at the bakery. Her father was also busy during this period, as he had deliveries to make to the nearby villages of Bagnot and Broin. So there was nobody available at home to supervise Marie.

The school was supposed to take charge of the children for the two hour lunch break and that arrangement was good enough for Marie's parents.

Marie, although an only child at home, thus learned to deal with other children at school, and learned to stand up for herself. She also developed a deep and abiding loathing for Claude Monet, for his gang and to a lesser extent for the other children who stood by and did not take her side, nor help her in her adversity.

She was lean, but not slender. She was fine boned but not pretty. There was nothing that stopped her being beautiful, except for that indefinable misbalance of features that didn't quite gel. Her mood and her circumstances gave her a mouth a resentful look and her eyes were wary and defensive.

She had a passive aggressive character, so she enjoyed nurturing her resentment against young Monet. Although she knew she would never have the opportunity to hurt him by any means, she fantasised nevertheless about him suffering some or other misfortune.

She dreamed that a crazy horse might bolt and gallop over him and pummel him with its hooves, or that one of the 'autobusses' might go out of control and run over him.

She dreamt that he might slip down a muddy bank into the river and drown. When she saw him she would smile her secret smile and imagine him falling out of a tree. Her maudlin glee on the inside was like a grimace to the world outside.

Equally Claude Monet could feel these waves of resistance from this younger girl. He realised that any gain he might achieve by bullying her into submission could prove to be counter productive in the long run.

He knew that to be a successful bully, he had to choose those who were not prepared to defend themselves. He made sure, however, that Marie was not included in any of the games in the school yard. He took to calling her 'Acnette' which was an allusion to the acne spots that she had on her face. Sadly, her spots were partly due to the chocolate treats that her father put in her lunch packet.

When Claude Monet left the school, the blemishes on Marie's face cleared miraculously.

Claude Monet departed from the village when he was offered an apprenticeship with a printing works on the outskirts of Paris, where he worked and stayed until retirement. The printing company was to regret many times over the years that they had offered employment to this young boy, because he became the leader of the trade union within the company. He was an aggressive negotiator. He was in a continual battle with the management, who were unable to get rid of him. He developed the power to call all the workers out on strike, on the slightest pretext.

He was not shy however to ensure that he accumulated a tidy private pension and retirement fund. His Communistic ideals seemed to be only fully applicable to others, in that what they earned or possessed should be reallocated for the common good. Whereas it was right and proper, he thought, that he should benefit personally from his own organisational skills, in order to be better off than they. He also ensured that, when his retirement from the printing works became due, he retained a position on the Union Committee. This position ensured that he earned a consultancy retainer, which was not declared in the union's annual audit.

Claude Monet had high hopes when he retired and returned to the village of his birth and his youth. He thought that he would be able to carry on in the controlling position that he had once enjoyed at school. He bought a house on the main road and had it renovated up to his standard by the local artisans, three of whom he knew from the past. He arrived with two new cars in order to impress the lesser mortals of the village.

He made his first big mistake, after his arrival back in the village, when he called into the Baker's Shop to buy his daily baguettes. He saw Marie Rufin who was now married and known as Madame Marie Peron.

He did not know this and he certainly did not care.

He said, without thinking, "Bonjour Acnette! Give me two baguettes!"

Why this became his first big mistake would only become apparent later, because his other big mistake was more obvious, and caught everyone's attention at the time.

This second mistake he made was when he decided that he was going to run for the position of Mayor of the village.

He had no idea of the political skills that the Lady Mayor had developed, in this apparent rural backwater.

Claude Monet made his presence felt initially when he attended a meeting in the village hall.

This 'rendez-vous' was called so that representatives of the Departmental Water Board, or SDEI could explain the problems with the water supply to the village.

They made it clear that the main supply line needed to be replaced because, when there were peak demands such as when the Firemen needed water in emergency situations, then the increased flow caused the pipelines to deliver soiled water.

"This is due to the rusting and breakdown of the interior of the pipes," explained the official from the SDEI, "and is not due to the filtration plant not working properly."

The SDEI man delivered his speech, with his pointer and display board, in the same way that he had given the same information to other villages in the area. He had practiced this oration and it had been accepted elsewhere and he had no reason to doubt that these villagers would accept his findings and conclusion. But he had not encountered a Claude Monet personality before. This was a man who enjoyed disrupting meetings for the sole purpose of using the occasion to bring attention to himself.

Claude Monet accused the official and the SDEI of negligence in allowing the situation to become this bad. He queried the costs of the renovation and how the villagers were going to be forced to pay for the mistakes of the past.

This argument got most of the villages on his side.

"Why?" he shouted at the official, "must we pay more than anywhere else in France for water. Water is the essential life blood of the community! Why does the government not pay for this renovation? Why must we pay for the errors of the past made by your department? Why are we not equal to everybody else in France? We should all pay the same price for water throughout the land! The water prices should be subsidised by the government!"

It was no coincidence that a little over two hundred years before, another Monet with the same aggressive attitude had also been at the centre of public meetings.

The only difference was that two hundred years ago, the meetings then convened were to find out who in the area needed to be put on trial and then led to the guillotine.

Claude Monet's distant relative had been known as 'The Executioner' during the French Revolution and had traversed the Bourgogne with a mobile guillotine. At each town or village he had set up his horse drawn contraption, in a suitable open space, and then had been ready for business. As 'The Terror' spread and anarchy took control, the trials became farcical. The majority of people murdered in the later stages of the Terror were those who were supposed to benefit from the changes taking place.

These spaces, where the executions were carried out, are now called 'La Place de la Libération' in these villages. In some cases the cobblestones, which were stained with blood all those years ago, are still there.

Claude Monet was only following his instincts from his family background, which meant creating dissention and mob unrest in the community. He became more excited as adrenalin coursed through his body, giving him a feeling of power. He began to lose his coherence as he started to shout invective at the nonplussed SDEI man. The difference between past and present was that this technique had worked when the downtrodden peasants had been called to take up their scythes and axes and march on any local chateau, to capture and kill the Bourgeoisies.

But the villagers of today are from a different background.

They can follow the SDEI official's reasoned arguments and explanations. They begin to be embarrassed by Claude Monet's behaviour. Monet shouts down interruptions to his tirade until the meeting breaks up in disorder.

Nothing is changed by the disruption of the meeting, as the water tariffs are increased anyway to pay for the renovations. Villagers cut down their water consumption as much as they can, in order that they personally do not have to bear the whole cost burden.

This isn't hard for the elderly residents, because they are used to deprivations they experienced during and after the war. They only turn on one electrical light at a time in their houses, and that is in the room which they are using. They have a practice of switching off each light as they leave one room to go to another. It is a routine that is normal to them, so that economising on use of water is a fact of life that they accept.

"What else can we do?" they shrug.

Claude Monet however is on a high.

He sees the abandoned meeting as yet another example of how he can gain control, and increase his influence. The Mayoral elections are due later in the year and so he starts to canvas the villagers, to gain support for his campaign, to oust the Mayor and install himself.

The Mayoral position in France is an executive one and carries considerable power and responsibility, so the people know the importance of electing a suitable candidate. However there is always the problem that the incumbent is in a strong position to influence the vote, by introducing popular projects and reforms during the final year of the six year cycle.

Monsieur Monet searches for people who hold resentment against the Lady Mayor for decisions of the past. In this way he slowly recruits followers for his campaign.

Some people are annoyed about the money that the Mayor has spent to install a little traffic roundabout in the village.

She claimed, "I authorised the roundabout because the government gives a subsidy for each new roundabout, and the village needed the money for road improvements."

However the roundabout does not fulfil its function, in that it confuses the traffic flow, and the residents.

In France the normal traffic rule is that all vehicles must give priority to those vehicles approaching from the right hand side. However at roundabouts the priority now switches so that drivers have to give way to traffic approaching from the left hand side. This causes consternation and argument, particularly when the roundabout in question is merely a pimple in the middle of the intersection, which means that some drivers ignore it and the reversed priority. Perhaps it is why it has taken so long to introduce roundabouts in France, as opposed to Britain where the traffic priority remains the same at all times.

Thus this little roundabout has caused feuds between friends and fights between foes. Neighbours who have coexisted for decades are drawn into confrontations where this new order is now supposed to replace the old order.

Their natural rustic conservatism encourages them to resist.

Tractors and Combine Harvesters have always had priority in farming villages, and now they have to give way to bicycles.

"And what about the priority of cattle and geese?" queries Monsieur Monet.

This one small roundabout forms the cornerstone of Monsieur Monet's campaign. And it is not only because of the traffic confusion, but also because the verges of the streets leading to it had been upgraded.

"This road improvement," claims Monsieur Monet "clearly indicates favouritism on the part of the Lady Mayor towards the small wood working business next to the roundabout. Do you know where she bought her doors and windows for her new house? From this menuiserie! Why? Because they gave her a discount! So she arranged for us all to pay for their road outside their factory to be improved, so she could save money!"

Some of the villagers reckon that, with typical French cunning, they would have done the same thing if had they been Mayor.

They complain about, but secretly envy the way she uses the municipal mower and driver to cut the grass on her smallholding.

When they are in an expansive mood after lunch, with a little wine, they approve of these advantages that officials appropriate for themselves.

"After all, look what President Chirac does!" they claim. "He makes jobs for his friends and accommodations in Paris for his family. President Mitterrand had girlfriends all over the place. He even had an illegitimate daughter. She and her mother were supported with public money. And look at that Prefect in the Jura who uses the Air Force to fly his girlfriend to his chateau in the mountains. I would do the same if I could!"

But they are also quite happy to become indignant about these same issues, when aroused.

Like some political claimants, Monsieur Monet doesn't bother too much with the truth and also, like some over zealous politicians, he begins to believe his own lies.

Monsieur Monet pursues his cause with revolutionary zeal, and soon he has a committee to whom he promises changes and favours in the future.

"No more roundabouts, and there will be a new cycle track to Seurre for those villagers who can not afford cars and who are a bit wobbly on their bicycles!"

He promises that, "The track will be paid for by the government, because I will present it as a scheme to enhance tourism."

He also promises, "A new 'Piste du Pétanque' which I will install near the church in the centre of the village."

"Then my friends," he exhorts the elderly players, "You will not have to go all the way down to the riverside to play."

When the earthen roads had been tarred in the upper part of the village, some of the farmers there had lost their traditional recreation areas. These were the places that they used as their 'pistes'.

The Mayor had complained to them, "When you throw your metal 'boules', you are making dents in our new tar roads."

"Well, we didn't want these new tar roads anyway! We didn't ask for them. They make the discs on our cultivators blunt!" they retorted.

"This is another uncalled for piece of modernisation that the Mayor has introduced!" complains Monsieur Monet as he tries to turn the situation to his advantage.

Monsieur Monet is confident, when he holds his first public meeting, that he will sweep the rest of the villagers into his support. He books the village hall and his acolytes post pamphlets through all the post boxes in the village. These circulars declare that the present unsatisfactory state of affairs will be rectified by electing a new Mayor.

The Town Crier, Hugo Bouviet, would normally have carried out this traditional function of disseminating information and news. However, he had been laid off some years before, on his sixty fifth birthday. This now elderly man had volunteered to continue his duties, free of charge, but the village council had to ask him to stop because they could not cover him for insurance purposes, as he was now over the official retirement age.

The real reason they wanted him to stop was because nobody could understand him anymore.

He used to stand and shout "Hear me! Hear me!" and then bang on his drum. Then he would go into a confused reading of the proclamation or notice that had been issued to him.

The fact was, he had never learned to read, so in the past he used to rely on his memory to repeat the announcements. He had to remember, as best as he could, what was on each proclamation and then spread the 'word'. Sadly, he had started to have memory lapses as he approached his sixty fifth birthday and as a result he had become increasingly unreliable.

Villagers used to complain to the Mayor about incorrect information, but as the Town Crier was an official position under the jurisdiction of the 'Département', there was not a lot that the Mayor could do.

She was also politically astute enough not to upset the official purveyor of news in the village by retiring him early. However, as he is now safely out of the way communication within the village is by means of printed messages, posted in all our letterboxes.

Monsieur Monet sits in his chair on the platform in the village hall while his 'Shadow Deputy Mayor' introduces him to the meeting.

The hall is partially filled by people who have seated themselves from the rear forwards, because they are not ready to commit fully to this new faction just yet. Anyone who sits near the front might imply to everybody that he is declaring opposition against the old order and he is supporting the new order.

This could be risky if the old order remains in power after the election! Particularly if one needs a favour.

As Monsieur Monet rises to address the meeting there is a flurry at the entrance to the hall. Madame the Mayor and her entourage enter the hall and they stride, with determination, towards the front seats.

They take their positions directly in front of Monsieur Monet.

He looks startled for a moment but then gathers himself for the challenge.

Before he can open his mouth, Madame Beringer stands and calls with a loud voice, “What are you going to do about the Nuclear Dump that the government wants to put into place at Nuits St Georges?”

Monsieur Monet has no idea what she is talking about. He has not heard anything about any proposal for a Nuclear Dump.

“And what are you going to do about the bypass?” she continues, “It will take away all the trade from the shops here in the village! What are you going to do?”

“Madame Beringer, please take a seat. I will explain.”

“Monsieur Monet, have you told the people what your proposal to install Village Gas will cost? There are only twenty seven houses here that have said they want Village Gas but the cost will be thousands of euros. We don’t have the money for that! Are you going to increase the taxes Monsieur Monet? Well are you?”

“Madame Beringer, this is not your meeting. I will answer your questions about costs later!”

“And you want to sell our Church Bell! That is part of our heritage. It is not yours to sell!”

At this point Monsieur Monet loses his temper. He starts to shout about favouritism that the Mayor has displayed towards certain businesses. He bellows that she has done nothing to get the government to pay for the new water system for the village.

“Why haven’t you got money from the government to install a port on the river for visiting boats? Why did you let the owner of the Chateau sell it to the Japanese?”

These are all points that he wanted to present in an orderly and meaningful way, but now they are all jumbling out.

The villagers are embarrassed by this outburst. They can understand a part of Monsieur Monet's rant regarding the water supplies, but they also support the Mayor's position because she has encouraged the businesses of the village. She had organised the upgrade of roads outside the wood working 'menuiserie'.

"And that will encourage trade... will it not?

"After all, we all depend on each other, don't we?"

Exactly as he had done at the SDEI meeting, Monsieur Monet becomes incoherent with rage. His arguments may have had a basis of fact, and they may have been appealing to his followers when they had their discussions in the village pub, but in this public meeting his points seem puerile and vindictive.

"And even if these are good arguments, this is not the way to present them." murmurs one spectator.

"This is not diplomatic." says another.

"This is not the way that people who are seeking positions of importance should conduct their affairs."

French is the language of Diplomacy.

Monsieur Monet's tirade is insulting, both to decorum and to the meeting. Slowly people at the rear of the hall start to stand and leave the building. The panic rises into Monsieur Monet's voice and the crowd can detect his discomfort.

Monsieur Monet is being defeated by a woman, and one from a little village, where he should have been in command and treated with respect.

Madame Beringer knows, with the instinct of a predator, when the moment of the kill occurs.

Precisely then she stands and leads her followers from the hall. Monsieur Monet remains on the platform and shouts his political career into oblivion.

But still this is only his second big mistake.

His first and more serious mistake is when he buys his bread from Madame Marie Peron, for the first time, after his return to the village, after living in Paris.

This is the first time, since she was nine years old, that anyone has called her Acnette.

This is the mistake that will cost him his life.

Mademoiselle Marie Rufin

Madame Marie (Acnette) Peron is a deeply unhappy woman who did not like children when she was a child, and does not like people or children now that she is an adult.

She has been forced, by life, into a situation where she is required to deal with people everyday. This is further proof, as far as she in concerned, that life is to be endured and not enjoyed.

The only small pleasure that is available to her now is to make sure that she makes life as unpleasant as possible, for all those who are forced to come into her zone of influence.

Her zone of influence is considerable.

She is the Baker's Wife of the only bakery which supplies several villages in the surrounding area. Bread is the staple diet of many French men and women, who go every morning as a ritual to their local bakery to buy their baguette and croissant. This means that her bakery is the main centre for the distribution of both nutrition and news.

That is what it should have been and could have been.

It is the rôle that is played by the purveyors of patisseries in the rest of France.

But this is not so in our village.

Here it is quite different.

Madame Peron had grown up as the only daughter of the only baker and so, even with her difficult character and moody temperament, she was a 'catch'. Many young men had introduced themselves to her when they heard about her potential to inherit a business, but they had departed just as quickly, when they got to know her.

It was not that she was spoiled as a child or had high expectations of life, or that she had been denied anything.

She was simply an unpleasant child who had grown up into being an unpleasant woman.

The old marriage adage that 'every pot has a lid' seemed to be wishful thinking at first in young Marie Rufin's case. There did not seem to be anyone who would find her attractive enough to overlook her attitude flaws. But there was one 'cover for her pressure cooker' in the form of a young man called Pierre Peron, who was also known by the nickname of 'PP'.

This pet name could have been derisive, but that did not affect young Pierre in any way. It didn't bother him at school in the early sixties, nor did it seem to worry him when he came of age. He had a happiness inside that overcame the gloom around him. For some almost inexplicable reason, except perhaps for the observation that sometimes 'opposites attract', he gravitated towards Marie Rufin. He was several years younger than Marie and so was not at the village school at the same time as her unhappy scholastic period there.

He was therefore not a member of Claude Monet's gang, which had broken apart following the bully's departure from the school.

PP approached school leaving age without any great dreams or preconceptions, except that he knew that life was going to provide for him, because of his innate optimism. All the way through his schooldays he was allocated the duty, by his family, to buy the breakfast bread. This was a task that he carried out without any resentment that his brothers or sister should sometimes do the chore. He whistled as he walked on his way to the bakery, he smiled at Marie Rufin's mother, he passed the time of day respectfully with his 'Olders and Betters' who were also buying bread and then he whistled as he walked on his way home.

Madame Rufin had her eye on this young man for some time, so that when he was about to leave school she approached her husband with a proposition.

She suggested to her husband that they should take the young Pierre Peron into the family business as an apprentice.

"After all," she appealed, "We are not getting any younger, and we need someone to take over here eventually. Marie can not do it all by herself and anyway she hates baking."

Monsieur Rufin readily accepted this idea, because he had a far more realistic view of his daughter's personality flaws than his wife. He was in no doubt that the business would be lost soon after he and his wife stopped working, and young Marie took charge. The result would be the loss of all the good customer relations that they had built up over the years, which had effectively stopped any other bakeries setting up in opposition.

And so PP started work with the bakery, and his attitude to life brightened even the most gloomy winter mornings for the Rufin family. In between the preparation of the ovens, mixing the different ingredients and then putting the hot trays onto the cooling table, he had time to pop around from the side of the bakery to the front entrance to greet some of his friends.

He was both a cheerful worker and a wonder at public relations.

Even Marie came under his spell and although he was younger than she was, when unwanted pangs of womanhood began to afflict her soul, she started to be halfway pleasant to him.

She caught a glimpse of who she might aspire to become, as though with his eyes. She saw herself in the way that she could possibly be, that is to say, without malice and doubt. He helped her to glimpse herself as someone with worth and with a future.

This was such a radical change from all of her life up until then that even her parents could see the change in her. Her mother glowed with the certainty that at last there was going to be the chance of grandchildren. This was a dream that she had realistically doubted would ever happen, when she took time to contemplate her life and Marie's character.

PP passed out as a fully qualified patisserie chef after four years. He did not formally ask Marie to marry him. It seemed inevitable that they would marry and then both carry on the family business as though they needed no further discussion. Slowly PP took over the duties in the bakery from old Monsieur Rufin, in that he did the early morning shift and then drove the bread deliveries to outlying villages, while Monsieur Rufin prepared the ovens for the mid day rush.

The Rufin parents began to entertain the idea of a holiday.

This was a very exciting concept, as they had never been away together, even for a weekend. There was always the responsibility of the family business hanging over them, coupled with the fact that some of the elderly people in the village depended on the bakery for their daily bread.

These people had no transport to go elsewhere for bread.

The Rufins' small commercial concern was not only a business, but also an essential service to the community. But now, with PP qualified and Marie bathing in the glow of infused optimism from his personality, there was a chance for the Rufins to see some of the rest of France.

With characteristic caution, their first expedition was to Chalon. They had to take the bus to Beaune which was twenty kilometres away and then make a connection with the train to get to Chalon. This was high adventure for a couple who had been denied time away together, up until then.

They were away for three days and two nights. Their holiday was a great success, although Monsieur Rufin still woke up at 4am both mornings because he was worried if PP had everything under control. They stayed at the Hotel de la Gare in Chalon, where the noise of trains and traffic did not disturb them, because they were used to the disturbances of vehicles on the main road past their home.

They enjoyed gazing at the river which gave them comfort, as this water that was flowing here had passed their village only a few hours earlier. Because of this they did not feel completely severed from their roots. They had decided, before they left on the journey, that they would not telephone Marie and PP to ask if everything was alright with the shop. However they were tempted to call each time they encountered a public telephone, as they promenaded around the town. They stuck to their decision as they knew that the young couple had to fly a ‘first solo in tandem’ without interruption.

When the Rufins returned home they found that everything had gone smoothly in their absence, which was both a relief and a disappointment. It disturbed them a little to think that they could walk out of their lives and that Life would continue on, without missing a beat. Monsieur Rufin was concerned that they would not even be missed.

This disappointment was soon swamped by Madame Rufin declaring that now she would like to see the sea!

This remarkable idea was shared with, and had to be discussed by, the patrons of the bakery, all of whom had various pieces of advice and warning.

“There’s no good that will come of such a crazy idea. I’ve never seen the sea and nor do I want to. It’s full of pirates and English ships. They are both the same thing really!” complained one customer.

"What is the world coming to, that people want to waste time and money travelling about like that. What a way to squander money. I always said that the price of village bread was too high. This proves it!" said another.

Monsieur Rufin started to make patisseries with marine motifs, with little pastry shells decorating strange looking starfish, which he glazed with bizarre colours. His masterpiece was an octopus with curled baguette sized tentacles that Madame Rufin left in the display window, until the sunlight turned it hard and stale. The octopus was a rather incongruous sight in this landlocked department of France, hundreds of kilometres from the nearest sea.

Their first decision concerning their holiday was to choose which 'sea' they should go to visit.

The choice was between the Mediterranean to the south, the Atlantic to the west, or La Manche (the Channel) to the north.

One customer warned them, "If you want to go to Nantes or Brest, then you have to take the train to Dijon first and then go to Paris. Then you have to take a taxi in Paris and do you know what happens in Parisian taxis? Then, when you get out of the taxi at the Gare Saint Lazare, the driver will take all your money. I know about this because Daniel Trudeau from Asserey told me. You take your life in your hands if you go anywhere near there. That is a dangerous place, Paris. You'll not catch me going anywhere near it."

An elderly First World War veteran shouted, "La Manche has bad weather all the time, I was there during the Great War. Noise, rain, sludge and mud. Miserable place. Much quieter here!"

It was much quieter here, for him, these days, because he had been partly deafened by the artillery during the war.

That left the Rufins with the only acceptable alternative, which was to go to the South.

They had heard lurid stories about what went on in Nice and Marseilles, so eventually they decided that they would visit Arles. This quiet town has the added advantage that it is connected to the river and canal navigation system, thus it is still connected tenuously to their little village via the Rhône and the Sâone Rivers.

However, they had something important to do before they could go away for such a long journey. Anything could happen in the ten days that they planned to be away, not least of which was that Marie would be left unchaperoned.

The Rufins needed to get Marie and PP married, because who knew what the villagers would say otherwise? And what the villagers think is important for the future of any business, in a small community.

"If people are not happy with the way the bakery is run," warned Madame Rufin, "they might go elsewhere."

"It is a well known fact," she continued, "that in rural areas, sinister 'family lives' of bakers will affect the bread."

"'Bad bread' can taint the health and life of a whole village!" agreed her husband.

Madame Rufin started to drop hints whenever she spoke to PP and to her surprise he acquiesced and asked her if he could marry Marie. She was surprised because he asked her rather than Marie herself, or her father. However Madame Rufin decided that this showed that PP thought that a woman's decision was important.

'And that,' she confided to her husband, 'is not such a bad thing!'

This forthcoming wedding was going to be a significant event in the village, because any marriage which concerns a local business has repercussions that last long after the bridal couple are dead and buried. They had to consider past amalgamations between the two families and the possible complications that this marriage could cause in the future. Ancient feuds and present ongoing fights had to be scrutinized for many reasons, not least of which was to decide who should, and who should not, be invited to the wedding.

"Should we include our long standing customers of the bakery?" asked Madame Rufin, "And if so, what is the cut off time for a customer to be considered for inclusion on the list?"

"Should we ask all your school friends Marie?"

"Absolutely No!" retorted Marie.

"What about the Mayor?" asked Monsieur Rufin. "If he comes, he might want to make a speech. Maybe it would be simpler to ask him to make a speech anyway! If we do that perhaps we could ask him for a discount from the price of hiring the village hall."

The Mayor, in those years shortly after the war, was a garrulous man who always went on interminably when he had the chance. He waved his arms and twirled his moustache for emphasis. The village hall was underneath the Mayor's Offices, and it doubled up duties as a class room for the school. It was also the only viable hall available for a function of this importance.

Also, there was the question of whether to invite the new Deputy Mayor, who was known to get maudlin when he drank too much wine. However, he was the owner of the village hotel, and so maybe, if he was involved as well, and invited to the wedding, he would give a discount to some of the people attending the wedding.

"We are going to need somewhere for all my friends from school to stay." declared PP. "Many of them have left here and I know that they will want to come back and be here for the reception. By the time the party is over, the last train and the last bus will have left. I am sure that if I talk to the Deputy Mayor, I will be able to get a discount for them, so I think it would be tactful to invite him."

They discussed if they should get a marquee erected outside for extra space.

"We can ask our cousin Pierre about that," said Madame Rufin. "He owns half of that company now, you know, the one with the marquees and tents? Well, they specialise in advertising promotions and political rallies. I am sure that we can get a special price for a marquee."

Slowly, as the discussions carried on, the form of the celebration began to take shape. It was governed mainly by the friends that could be called upon to help, because of their special skills or connections at their places of work.

One thing that the Rufins did decide early on was that they were not going to do the catering. They would hire the village 'traiteur', who had a van with which he delivered his catering foods for parties and functions. They soon realised that the 'traiteur' would have to combine his efforts with a colleague, because this wedding party was going to be too big for him to cope with on his own.

"I think we should have the wedding at the end of May," suggested Madame Rufin. "There is no chance of frost then and the risk of the Bise (the cold North Wind) will be over."

"I agree," answered Monsieur Rufin, "because also, it will not be too hot for the guests in the marquee, in the afternoon sun."

One big difference from tradition with this wedding, they decided, was that after the ceremony and reception, it would not be the 'happy couple' who would be leaving on honeymoon.

They would have a business to run together.

It would be Monsieur and Madame Rufin themselves who would be 'going away'!

And for a whole ten days too!

The planning and the preparations occupied the conversations in the bakery in the mornings, when the villagers collected for their bread purchases.

The possible seating plan at the reception was discussed at great length.

They had the never-ending problem of who was talking to whom and which disputes could be set aside for the duration of the festivity. There were some feuds that were too deeply ingrained to be allowed to be eroded, even though, in some cases, the original reason for the dispute had been forgotten.

The day drew closer and the excitement in the village grew as the invitations were sent out.

These invitations alone were potential sources of dispute in the future. There is nothing like the divisions of who is invited to a wedding and who is not, to determine the battle lines for upcoming conflicts in a small community.

"Zut Alors!" Exclaimed old Monsieur Corbonier, "Zey 'ave included me, 'owever I will not go if zat Pascalle woman eez going to attend! I 'ave said it before and I say eet again: I will not be seen in zee same room as 'er!"

This particular spat went back some fifty years to one of the harvests of the houblon or hops. Monsieur Corbonier was then a dashing young man of forty two years of age whose wife had declared that their six children was enough for one family, and that she was restricting his conjugal rights forthwith.

No amount of pleading would make her change her mind.

"There is No Way, you randy old goat!" she declared.

There was no other choice for Monsieur Corbonier but to look around and see what other potential sources of amorous diversion were on offer.

He decided that Pascalle Vincent was going to be the lucky recipient of his attentions.

Both of them, along with several other villagers including Pascalle's younger brothers, had signed on to help with the harvest of the houblon (hops). This temporarily enlarged work force was needed to cope with pulling down of the dried vines and their twine supports from the huge structures of poles that supported them.

The harvest was a great success that year, as the weather was dry so the flowers were not impregnated with mould. There had also not been any catastrophic winds from thunderstorms, which could wreck havoc with the spider-web of twine between the poles. The supports and the cobweb of lines moan in the wind and the sound is interpreted by the old men as their method of forecasting the weather.

The workforce was divided by gender. The men were in charge of lowering the poles to the ground with care, so that the flowers were not shed prematurely from the vines, nor trampled underfoot. The ladies, who had among their group some nuns from the Congregation of Saint Joseph in the village of Chamblanc, had baskets in which to place the sticky flowers. The nuns were wearing their habits with their distinctive headgear which gave a sense of decorum to the proceedings. The other women all sported large sun hats decorated with garlands of flowers and they had long dresses for protection.

Monsieur Corbonier was wearing his special wooden clogs which his father had worn before him. They had carved motifs of bunches of grapes. Monsieur Corbonier's father used to be a vigneron and had worked in the vineyards above Beaune.

Pascalle Vincent was approaching her prime age as a young woman. In England this might be considered to be eighteen but in France is appreciated as thirty, which is an age when a woman has experienced life and has a mind of her own and is more than just an ornament. It seems that the French men are not shy of comparative competition from the past, when it comes to matters of close intimacy and procreation.

However, procreation was not uppermost in Monsieur Corbonier's mind, when he decided that Pascalle Vincent was gong to be the lucky girl to be the recipient of his attentions.

He was far more interested in the preliminary mechanics of procreation, rather than any final fruition.

He ensured that he was always in Pascalle's locality in the fields. He was on hand to cut away the vines from the twine and the poles, around which they twist in a clockwise corkscrew. He was there to help her carry her overflowing basket of flowers to the horse drawn wagon. At first she was flattered, but his attentions became embarrassing after a while, particularly when the nuns started to give her censorious glances.

He followed her into the still standing crop during one lunch break, when she went to relieve herself out of sight of the others. He returned a few minutes later, after they had all heard a resounding slap from the direction in which he had disappeared.

Monsieur Corbonier's face was bright red on one side and he was in a foul mood for the rest of the day. The ladies later discussed this with giggles, out of earshot of Pascalle Vincent, and decided that the ruddy cheek of Monsieur Corbonier was not caused by sunstroke alone.

Monsieur Corbonier, by accident, heard the incident being discussed in the village bar, along with guffaws from the patrons. He never forgave Pascalle Vincent for the insult, even when she got married and raised her own family.

"Which goes to prove that he is not a great lover," was the opinion of the bar flies in the village pub, "because if he was, he would not let one small setback destroy his ardour and his effort."

"Look at Monsieur Jolly for example. He is eighty seven and he has a double hernia, but that does not stop him from trying to get off with the ladies!"

So the invitation of Monsieur Corbonier had to be carefully considered as the Rufin family knew of the problem between him and Pascalle Vincent, who was now Madame Theron. The fact that they were now ninety two and eighty respectively did not diminish this complication of the past.

This was only one of the histories that the Rufins had to mull over.

On the day before the wedding ceremony in the church, the families of the bride and groom assembled in the offices of the

Notaire in Seurre. The Mayor of Seurre was in attendance because he had to officiate at this, the legally accepted wedding ceremony.

The Mayor had kindly acceded to the request to carry out the registration of the vows at the lawyer's office, because there were other legal documents that had to be signed at the same time. These were the documents that were to make PP a partner with Marie in the bakery, so that Monsieur and Madame Rufin could officially retire. They would still be involved in the business of course, but this way, when either or both of them died, there would no be complications with the estate.

Everybody, except the State, would benefit from the reduced death duties that would be payable some time in the future.

The Notaire, Monsieur Fontaine, was originally from Italy where his family name was Fontini, but he knew that the French people would regard an Italian lawyer with suspicion, so he had changed his name by Deed of Poll.

He had explained to the Rufins all about the dangers of ceding their business over to their children, because of an experience he had witnessed in Italy. He told them about a mother who had ceded her house to her son, whereupon the boy had evicted his mother and sold the house. The son had invested the capital gain from the house in an expensive Italian sports car. He had killed himself in an accident with the car one week later. The son had no valid driving licence and the car was not insured.

Madame Rufin was vaguely aware of her daughter's character flaws as regards her lack of popularity, but she was certain of Marie's integrity with regard to business. As for PP, both she and Monsieur Rufin were sure that he was completely trustworthy.

Nevertheless, Notaire Fontaine drew up a document citing the parent's rights under the new partnership. All these contractual and marriage documents had to be signed at the same time because they were all linked.

The whole formal procedure was in compliance with the French love/hate relationship with bureaucracy.

The day of the church wedding and reception dawned bright and clear.

PP's family were all up and ready, filled with eager anticipation. The men collected chairs and tables from friends to furnish the hall. They prepared the canvas marquee with sufficient seating for the anticipated overflow of guests. The women collected flowers from invited guests who had gardens that they had made available to supply the church and the hall. Irises were in full bloom so they formed the main displays. Even the farmers in the village, who did not consider growing flowers was a productive way of spending their leisure time, had self perpetuating beds of purple irises lining their driveways for the decorators to use. The ladies used Garlands of wisteria, which were slightly past their best, to festoon the pews along the aisle in the church.

The men set up a bar in the marquee which was going to be their destination once the dancing started. Most of the men that is, because there was still Monsieur Jolly and a couple of other 'Romeos' in the village who considered that a wedding was an excellent venue for an amorous fling. They planned to escort the village belles to the dancing area one by one, to assess their chances. The four-piece band members set up their miniature orchestral platform in one corner of the hall.

The musicians were friends of the Peron family and they consisted of a piano accordionist, a drummer, a pianist and a double bass player.

This unlikely quartet made up for lack of facilities and instruments with their enthusiasm. Their one drawback was that the drummer was an alcoholic whose drumbeats slurred if they didn't keep him off the sauce. The danger period, at weddings, was during the speeches when the drummer made excuses to leave the room, in order to search for reinforcement. It was up to the others in the quartet to try to keep him under control during this period, after which he was usually reliable.

The pianist delivered his piano to the church. PP's friends manhandled the instrument inside so that there would be music for the service. After the ceremony they arranged to carry the piano to the hall, so that it would be ready for when the newly married couple's arrived at the reception.

Monsieur Rufin's sister had married into a vigneron family in the village of Mersault, so they arranged between them for a barrel of Bourgogne wine for the celebration. This family had several small 'parcels' of vines on the slopes above the town. They delivered the barrel well before the reception, so that it would have time to 'settle'. The barrel was one of those secret ones that slip past the strict controls that govern the quantities and qualities of these premier wines, as supervised by the authorities. That is not to say it was not of the best of the Burgundy wines, it was simply a part of the unaccountable 'angel's breath', that is one of the perks of being a vigneron.

The Pastis for the wedding was supplied at a discount rate from a bottle store in Seurre, which was owned by a family that had long connections with the Rufins. The complex web of these shared biological cousins, aunts and uncles was beyond even the abilities of the tax office to unravel.

Some of these composite relationships could be traced back to the time of the French Revolution, so they claimed. In reality, everyone was related to everybody else in some way.

Of course the Pastis was going to be supplemented with quantities of 'Eau de Vie' from local clandestine stills. The liquor makers siphoned their Eau de Vie into Pastis bottles for the occasion. This was to disguise it, so as not to embarrass the sensibilities of the guests. It was only going to be available to the 'inner circle' of men.

A wedding like this is a fine time for the men to compare their products and to swap hints on how to achieve an even better quality. Each bottle had a numbered sticker as a code, so they knew who had produced which blend.

In those days, the legal licence to distil alcohol was handed from father to son, but old Monsieur Grogan who operated the travelling 'Alambic' (alcohol still), was the last of his line.

Monsieur Grogan arrived every year with his tractor drawn chariot, which before the War had been towed by a fine pair of horses. The chariot was an ingenious affair which unfolded to reveal a fruit press, several large barrels and a huge copper flagon into which the fermented fruit was poured for distillation. The whole contraption was covered by a canvas tarpaulin. Because the distillation of everybody's' fermented fruit took some weeks, it meant that the Alambic became a fixture in the village square for the duration of the distillation.

This gave Monsieur Grogan time to sample the product while it was reaching maturity. The villagers, whose fruit he was processing, watched him carefully to ensure that none of their production was diverted to somebody else. They also took advantage of the fire that Monsieur Grogan kept glowing under the still, to cook their homemade sausages. Eau de Vie production was an important social event in the village.

Monsieur Grogan could tell the exact moment that the first dangerous alcohols, which had to be discarded, had burned off.

"I do it by the smell of the vapours from the still," he announced. "When the "good stuff" is condensing in the coils I have to keep a constant quality check. I have to try a sample every hour."

The result was that Monsieur Grogan spent a lot of time sitting in a chair, while he listened to the burps and belches of the bubbling mixture. This lack of exercise, coupled with regular imbibing of carbohydrates, meant that Monsieur Grogan's shape was very similar to his pot bellied still. He didn't care about his shape or anything else. He had one of the most serene occupations in the world. He was at peace with everyone.

The sound of the ambrosia dribbling into bottles was like orchestral music to a symphony conductor. Except that, in Monsieur Grogan's case, his supervision was less physical and infinitely more soothing.

He was a very contented man.

Although he was virtually pickled in alcohol, the villagers knew that Monsieur Grogan would not last for ever. It was going to be a catastrophe when he died. This was because he had no 'legally accepted' son to take over his licence to distil liquor. This was why there were a number of pirate and illegal stills at work in the department.

"Because," the villagers agreed, "What is going to happen when he passes away? Where will we get our supplies then? Is it not better that we practice the techniques now, so that there is no interruption in quality when he passes on?"

One interesting feature of these clandestine clubs was that they enjoyed their illegal activities just as much as they enjoyed the dangers of obstructing the Germans during the war.

The difference was that the penalties after capture were different.

During the war, to be caught as a member of the Underground meant execution. Now the penalty for making illegal Eau de Vie consists of a hefty fine. Although informing on neighbours has been an intrinsic part of survival, and sometimes personal gain, in France, there are some activities which, if betrayed, will cause a backlash against the informant. Telling the authorities about an illegal still will ensure that the informant will never be buried in the village cemetery and that his name, whenever mentioned, will be followed by spitting on the ground.

One way that illegal still owners have found to disguise the aromas from their illicit activities is to burn laurel leaves in the fire under the stove. This pungent smoke rises and removes almost all the olfactory evidence.

It is no coincidence that clandestine distillers have large laurel hedges surrounding their properties.

All those villagers who had not been invited to the wedding found excuses to not be seen on this day. Some went fishing, others went to town and a few closed their shutters and pretended that they were not at home.

Marie Rufin was in a bad temper.

"She got out of her bed on the wrong side", was the excuse that her mother made for her.

Her wedding dress didn't fit properly, because she had initiated a row with the seamstress in Seurre who was in charge of the final adjustments. The seamstress had, in a pique of retaliatory temper, taken in the waist of the dress two centimetres too tight in order to punish Marie. The result was that Marie could not slouch when she sat down, which was her customary attitude when taking the weight off her feet. She had to sit upright in order not to burst the buttons from their positions down her back. The seamstress had unwittingly done Marie a favour, in that she was being forced to be more elegant than normal, by sitting up straight.

PP was in his customary good mood in spite of being led astray the previous afternoon, by his brothers and a group of his school friends. They had come back to the village for this special occasion. He had insisted on having a bachelor party in the afternoon, rather than the evening, because he had to have an early night in order to be up and active for the early morning shift at the bakery. Minor things, like getting married, could not be allowed to get in the way of him having the bakery open with bread in the morning, after his bachelor party.

Unlike English bachelor parties, where the objective seems to be to get drunk, misbehave and then to get the groom on a non-stop train to Edinburgh, the French bachelor party is a more mature affair.

The friends arranged to have lunch at a small 'auberge' in Villars Fontaine which is in the countryside, in the hills behind Nuits St Georges. The proprietor agreed that the party could continue after lunch. Following a meal of beef bourguignon, the friends sipped wine and reminisced about their school days, and what had happened to everyone that they knew.

They passed the cheese platter around until the sun softened in the west. The fields of wheat in the valley below the auberge glowed with the ambiance of good wine in the golden light. When they parted to go to their various lodgings, it was with bonhomie and promises of endless affection. Some of PP's friends feared that their access to PP was going to be far more hazardous in the future, once he was married to Marie.

Their private thoughts were that PP was going to be beaten into submission by this new wife. Some of them had already had a look at Marie, and they had decided that they were not brave enough to sign up for a 'lifetime voyage of hurricanes' with her.

In a way they were saying farewell to a friend who was going voluntarily to his own execution. He would emerge reincarnated in another life, in which he had every chance of being alarmingly different from the old PP, their loveable and optimistic friend.

Father Ferdinand de Govier was asked to be the minister in charge of the ceremony, which was by special request of the Rufins. He was another ex-pupil of the village school, before he had taken up Holy Orders. His parents, who were now living in Dijon, had a small printing business and they supplied the wedding invitations and the service hymn-sheets. This was their wedding present to Marie and PP.

The owner of the large Hops drying building in Seurre still had his horse drawn wooden wagon, which he used to use to collect the houblon flowers before the War. Now that it was the sixties, he was using a Peugeot tractor with a metal trailer for the transport, but he had kept his wagon and his horses for nostalgic reasons.

His horses still grazed in the walled enclosed field around the drying barn. The Rufins asked him if he would let them use the wagon for the bride to arrive at the church and then for the couple to go to the village hall for the reception. The Houblonnier was very happy to oblige, but he pleaded that the wagon was not in a good state of repair, and that the wooden spokes of the wheels were at risk of collapsing.

His wagon was now a decoration in his garden and was loaded with cut wine barrels filled with earth and dahlias. His horses, although now rather portly with lack of exercise, were still fit enough to pull the wagon.

The Rufins found another wagon in a good state of repair in one of the barns in the village.

The farmer who owned it was invited to the wedding, and thus the problem of bridal transport was solved.

The Houblonnier delivered the horses during the morning of the wedding day, fully harnessed. PP's brother led them down to graze by the river until they were needed. The road down to the river was called the "Watering Place" road because, in the old days of the village, all the village cows used to go down to the river to drink.

A cow herder who lived next to one of the barns in the village walked through the village every morning. All the cows used to file out of their open biers in turn and follow him. The cows then grazed all day along the river bank while he sat under the shade of a tree. When the church bell tolled the time of the evening, he would return home. The cows used to follow him back without any fuss to their respective barns, to be milked by their owners.

At two in the afternoon PP and his new father-in-law closed the bakery and started to ferry their extra baguettes and snacks to the village hall. PP's brother drove the horses up from the river and secured them to the wagon. Helpers finalised the seating in the hall and placed the cards with guests' names into position. Monsieur Jolly sneaked in later to rearrange the table where he was going to sit, to his own satisfaction. It was no coincidence that two of the most comely young ladies in the village were now allocated positions on either side of him.

By four in the afternoon PP's brother had the wagon ready to take the bride to the church. He parked it in front of the bakery. His parents remembered with nostalgia, the sight of horses in harness with carriages here. That was when this 'relais' used to be an important stopover between Dijon, Dole and Beaune.

Marie was fashionably late at the church, but not though prior design. Her nervousness had caused her spots to erupt and she had made it worse by having a row with her mother, who was trying to disguise the damage. Monsieur Rufin managed to calm her down by the time they arrived at the church. It was just as well, because the photographer was waiting to capture the moment with his large tripod mounted camera. They stood in the bright sunshine while he fiddled with focus and aperture, disappearing like a conjurer below the cape that covered his equipment.

At last his bespectacled bearded face appeared, like a gnome peering out from under a mushroom. He had a small cable in his hand which was connected to the shutter.

"Ouistiti" he commanded, " le petit oiseau va sortir!" Most of his work came from schools recording their pupils on photographic plates, so his patter was really more suitable for children.

The camera clacked.

The pianist struck up Mendelssohn's March and Marie whisked her father down the aisle with 'undue alacrity'. That was the opinion of the social critics among the congregation.

It was unfair because Marie had never been the centre of attention at any time of her life, except when she had been bullied at school. For her, this entire day was fraught with an unrecognised dread. She was only going through this ordeal for the sake of her parents. And, of course, also for PP, who had been anticipating this day with enthusiasm.

Père de Govier led the fully packed church through the service. He gave a well received sermon concerning the sanctity and responsibilities of marriage, which was interesting because his information and advice were rather theoretical. He had never been, nor would be, married himself.

PP and Marie exchanged rings and the deed was done. They turned to go back down the aisle while guests threw confetti and wheat seeds in all directions.

Now the village was in a party mood.

PP and his new bride clambered aboard the wagon, along with several of the village hunters who started playing their French Hunting Horns. These are huge circular instruments that are worn over the shoulder when riding a horse and are balanced on the outside of one arm when they are played.

Their blaring chords are directed behind the musician. Several horns together make a resonance that carries for miles. By wobbling the horns the musicians achieved a warbling chorus, which carried to the far extremities of the village. All the chained hunting dogs started to bay and howl at the sound.

PP's brother urged the horses into a trot and the entourage, accompanied by several cars sounding their klaxons, started a tour of the village. Pigeons and doves on the rooftops took to the air, alarmed at the din. Eyes peered through gaps in shutters from houses apparently deserted. Two dogs attacked the large wooden wheels of the wagon. One caught a paw under the metal rimmed wheel and its yowls of pain were added to the cacophony.

The gaggle of wagon, cars and children on bicycles took twenty minutes to tour all the streets of the village, by which time the piano had been man-handled to the hall.

The French Horn players managed to keep an almost continuous announcement of their progress around the outskirts, by blaring from the back of the wagon. Occasionally the volume reduced as one or more players stopped blowing in order to drain their instruments of condensation. This involved removing the mouthpiece and twisting the instrument against the direction of the coils and then shaking out the moisture. This pause also gave the players a chance to swig at a mug that they replenished from a barrel of beer on the wagon, which added to the 'condensation' in the horns.

The horses were streaming with sweat, from their unaccustomed exercise, by the time the revellers arrived at the hall. Their bygone working days had consisted of standing between the shafts of a wagon in the fields and then pulling the load of hops along a flat road to the drying barns. This high-speed trot up and down the slopes and grades of the village was fun but exhausting for them. However the horses loved being part of the excitement and they stamped their vast iron shod hooves on the ground, as though displaying the pride of war horses.

PP swept Marie down from the wagon. She was now allowing herself to enjoy the day, as she knew that the ordeal of critical examination by her peers was over. By now they would have judged her dress, her makeup and PP's two little nieces, who were decked out as bridesmaids. Marie was a pragmatic woman and knew she could do nothing more to save any impending pitfalls. Now it was up to the rest of them. PP had to make a speech and dance with her, but they had already practiced for that.

Marie could feel the wave of goodwill from the guests.

Corks of Crémant de Bourgogne exploded from their bottles as she and PP entered the hall. The band played and PP led Marie into a waltz around the floor. Their parents joined in and within minutes the guests were dancing.

The proverbial ice was broken. Everybody knew each other from the village anyway. Monsieur Corbonier chatted to Pascalle Theron. The Mayor made a speech but had to cut it short when he was drowned out by boisterous, but well intentioned, heckling.

Monsieur Rufin welcomed PP publicly into his family.

He had already come to regard PP as his son and of course knew him better than most real fathers know their sons. Monsieur Peron, PP's father, returned the compliment by saying flattering things about Marie, after which the guests burst into noisy communal singing, accompanied with banging on the tables and hand clapping.

The tables were laid out in long rows so that guests could sit on benches and chairs opposite each other. As the party progressed and some of the people danced, so the others moved along the benches to talk to friends. The hall now had more young people in it at the same time than anyone could remember.

The children who had grown up in the village, and who were now young adults, had used the occasion to return and meet with all their friends. Their children in turn played under the tables in exciting games of 'tag'. One little boy went missing and after a frantic search was found curled up asleep under Marie's chair, where her voluminous dress, as she sat, had formed a tent which covered him.

As the light faded outside, the members of the unofficial 'Eau de Vie' appreciation club lit their kerosene pressure lamps in the marquee. They continued to examine the finer points of their high proof liquor. The secret, they decided, was that the products of their labours should be sipped at a young age.

"It is better, so that the full flavours of the fruits can be enjoyed. If you wait for maturation in a cask, to give it body, the fruit flavour is lost."

This sentiment was voiced over and over, in different ways as the levels in the bottles dropped.

They passed their bottles around and refilled their glasses as they discussed their lives, their wives and their friends on ever more personal levels. They would all remember this occasion as one of the finest wedding receptions they had ever attended.

One of the bottles of Eau de Vie appeared miraculously under the drummer's stool. Nobody knew how it got there, but when the accordion player saw it, it was already too late. Already half of its contents was missing and the drummer's beatific expression gave away where it had gone. He had to retire, suffering from injury, twenty minutes later.

The band played on.

Slowly some of the older guests began to filter away to their homes, some humming tunes from the band's repertoire as they walked.

Others had to concentrate as they walked past the imaginary potholes that suddenly appeared before them, which made them swerve on an otherwise completely familiar road.

The horses pulled the wagon with the Houblonnier and his wife back to their home in Seurre.

There was no traffic on the road to see the two hurricane lamps that they tied to the wagon to light up the way. The horses knew the route, which was just as well because the Houblonnier and his wife both fell asleep on the straw in the back of the wagon. They only woke up as dawn broke, still on the hay in the back of wagon. The horses had stopped at the gate to their small estate and had waited, with equine patience, for the barrier to be opened.

Monsieur Jolly did not achieve an assignation as he had hoped, which was just as well for his health as well as for his probable disappointment, if he had failed to rise to the occasion. Monsieur Corbier revised his opinion of Pascalle Theron who, he realised with reluctance, was quite right to have slapped him all those years ago.

At a few minutes to midnight a taxi arrived to take Monsieur and Madame Rufin to the railway station. They had a 'sleeper' compartment, booked all the way to Marseilles. From there they had reserved seats on a bus to Arles.

The guests gave them a rousing send-off as though they were the newlyweds.

Madame Rufin threw a bouquet to her daughter Marie, who caught it and then, on an impulse, she gave her mother a huge hug in front of them all.

It was an uncharacteristic explosion of love from Marie and caught everybody unawares.

Their friends cheered and yodelled.

As the taxi departed the elderly couple wept quiet tears of joy that their daughter was married and that everything had gone so well. Even the weather had been perfect.

It was wonderful that they could leave on such a high note, with a future of so much promise.

They had found and adopted a son.

Their business was secure for the future and they had hopes that soon there would be more than 'buns' in the ovens of the bakery.

Surely it was not too much to hope that Marie and PP would soon announce the arrival of a grandchild?

That would be wonderful.

What a fantastic send-off they had.

That last hug that Marie gave to her mother was to stay fresh in her mother's memory for the rest of her life.

The taxi delivered them to the railway station in Dijon in time for the train from Paris to the South. They had a compartment with two bunks which they hoped would give them a good night's rest. They wanted to be rested and alert for their first sighting of the Mediterranean Sea.

They saw the sea for the first time as they were eating their breakfast in the dining car of the train. Madame Rufin was impressed by the almost impossible blue of the water. Monsieur Rufin was impressed that the croissants that they served on the train were hot and of good quality.

They arrived in Marseilles in mid morning.

The bus was waiting outside the main entrance to the station and they presented their tickets to the driver, who loaded their baggage into the under floor luggage compartments of the bus. They set off for Arles and they backtracked the last part of their train journey, so that again they had a view of the sea from the windows of the bus.

Shortly before noon as they approached Arles, the bus swerved off the road and crashed through the roadside barrier. It careered down the embankment, turned over and came to rest upside down.

The driver had suffered an acute heart attack.

Monsieur and Madame Rufin, who were seated in the bus just behind the driver, were killed instantly.

Madame Marie Peron

PP was up and working in the bakery by four in the morning, in spite of only having had two hours sleep. He had managed to keep going at the reception party for another hour after his new in-laws left in the taxi to go to the railway station.

His friends were prepared to carry on with the party until dawn, so he had to sneak away before the band stopped playing, so that they wouldn't notice that he had disappeared. The older guests had already filtered away by the time he retired, and Marie was ready to go to bed as well, but not for the normal reasons that young newly married couples want to get away from the wedding reception.

She was emotionally exhausted from being the centre of attention. She had to play the part of the happy bride, and it didn't agree with her nature. She knew that she wasn't one of the prettiest girls in the hall and she found herself staring at some of those who were. She wondered if she envied them with their carefree cavorting.

Those three older sisters of the Chazelle family were being particularly shameless, she thought, probably because their mother didn't care how they behaved or what they did. Marie didn't want any of the Chazelle family at the reception, but her mother had insisted that at least some of them should be invited, because the family had been good customers of the bakery over many years.

Marie had compromised by inviting these three sisters.

"Look at the way those Chazelle girls are behaving," she complained to PP. "They are brazen and disgusting. We should never have invited them."

"Well, Pierre and Dido don't seem to mind!" answered PP, which was not the response his new bride wanted to hear.

Marie, as an only child, had never experienced this sort of competitiveness and complicity that exists between sisters. At the beginning of the evening the three Chazelle girls were working in unison, by standing in a group and pretending to laugh with each other at little private jokes. All the while they were watching the boys, who were fortifying themselves with wine, before trying to pick one of the girls out from the group.

Why the Chazelle girls should put on this coquettish behaviour was obviously for the benefit of PP's out of town friends, who perhaps did not realise that there was nothing these girls did not know about sex. As the evening had progressed, the girls had disappeared for varying periods with different partners. Marie could only imagine what they had been doing at the back of the Mayoral building in the dark.

She felt no jealousy of them, because she did not understand what the addiction was that these girls had for the chemistry of sex. Marie's own forays into that area had been very limited. PP was an outgoing and sociable man, but he did not seem driven with a desire to inveigle himself into her bed. Early on in their relationship with each other she had been concerned that he would try 'something', but as the months passed it had not materialised.

She wondered if perhaps he might never try 'anything'.

Perhaps her mother was right when, on the only occasion that the subject had come up, she had said, "Don't worry dear, when the time comes, you will know what to do!"

Marie's experiences, in the normal youth sex education in a farming community, were essentially lacking. All the farmers' daughters knew about what stallions, bulls and rams did, but daughters of bakers grow up without any of this 'hands on' experience. Marie was never a part of the 'cliques' when she was at school, so she did not learn the rudiments of sex from the giggled conversations of the girls in the playgroups.

It seemed to Marie that PP was almost disinterested in her in a sexual way. She surmised that their marriage was going to be rather more of a close business arrangement, than a torrid relationship in the bedroom above the bakery. Well, that would suit her fine. But having to watch these Chazelle girls misbehave was enough to give her a headache. She was very happy to slip away from the reception with PP, when he suggested that they go.

They had already discussed their sleeping arrangements for their wedding night. PP was going to get up early in the morning as usual, so they had decided that he would use the spare bedroom, so that he would not disturb her when he rose for the morning's baking.

In the morning, Marie was a bit later than normal when she opened the Boulangerie. By the time she pulled the front door curtain aside and unlocked the door, there were three people waiting for bread. None of these three had been invited to the wedding, so none of them asked how she was.

Each of them showed a stiff disapproval of having to wait and each one acknowledged her with only a taut 'Bonjour' as a punishment. Inside themselves, however, they were revelling in the daring excitement of being rude without showing any obvious sign.

Marie's headache from last night was still bothering her, so she scowled at them in return.

PP was in revoltingly good spirits, which only made her feel worse. Her next customers were a straggle of fishermen who were getting their bread to take down to the river so that they could have their breakfast by the water. They wanted to be away from their wives, who did not want to be disturbed on this, or any other Sunday morning. Particularly on a Sunday morning that followed a noisy wedding and reception, with noisy car klaxons and singing guests.

None of the fishermen asked Marie, with innuendos, what married life was like because they already knew what it was like from their own experience.

They were not much impressed with it.

That is why they were fishermen.

Or rather, they were men who used fishing as an excuse to get out of the house. Golf for them was too expensive, too physical and too gregarious. As fishermen they had all day to brood upon, and take pleasure in, the miseries of life, which includes not catching anything and arguing with the licence inspectors.

What a satisfactory way for them to reinforce their depression.

There was a flurry of activity at the bakery at ten o' clock amongst whom were clientele who were visitors to the village. They had come to use their holiday homes for a week or two. There were also a few campers who had erected their tents in the fields near the river, where the village cows graze every day.

Marie was able to spend her day being satisfyingly grumpy to everyone, which caused considerable amusement to the older wives. They knew from her demeanour that she had not broken her 'duck' as regards PP.

And they were also shrewd enough, with sufficient experience of life, to understand why.

"PP is such a ***nice*** chap!" they snickered to each other.

Which he was. He had time in between bakes to pop out of the bakery for a breath of fresh air and to exchange greetings with the customers. He just seemed to be such a happy fellow, content within himself and almost immune to the negative attitudes of cantankerous people.

He was the ideal partner to compensate for Marie's negative mannerisms.

By noon PP had packed the little blue pre-war Citroen van with bread and was ready to leave on his scheduled rounds to the nearby villages to deliver orders. He waved, with a big smile, to Marie through the front display window of the shop, squeezed himself behind the wheel and started the engine. Then he had to unravel the variable mysteries of the gearbox, which was controlled by a lever mechanism that had been designed by an engineer with a perverse sense of humour. After some interesting gnashing of gears he was off, leaving a haze of oil impregnated exhaust smoke in his wake.

An hour later Marie left the shop to prepare some food for herself, because she had no customers. In true Gaelic tradition, the timing of her midday meal was sacrosanct, so that anyone who wanted bread, in the middle of 'déjeuner', was obviously a tourist or a foreigner, and therefore of no consequence in Marie's estimation.

She was very annoyed therefore to be disturbed by rapping on the front door an hour later.

Anybody who knew anything should have already collected their bread. Interrupting her during lunch was, in her opinion, inexcusably rude. She remembered that she had forgotten to close the curtain to indicate that the shop was shut.

She clutched her napkin in her hand so that the disrupter could see that she was in the middle of her meal, and so he would therefore be suitably chastised.

She walked through from the kitchen to the shop.

There were two uniformed Gendarmes standing outside the glass front door.

"Oh God," she thought. "PP has gone and done something wrong."

They looked serious, as though they were going to arrest her, or at least give her a severe warning about something. Perhaps it was something to do with declaring tax from the bakery? Maybe someone had complained about the noise last night? Had the Mayor complained about something that had happened in the hall?

Whatever it was, it was bad news.

She opened the door and stood with her arms akimbo and the corners of her mouth pulled down, as if she was a little girl about to receive a scolding at school.

The Sergeant saw the napkin and said.

"Bonjour, Madame Peron."

She was slightly shocked, because this was the first time she had been addressed by her new married name.

"Is your husband here?"

There she knew it. It was PP in trouble already. Maybe he ran over somebody's' chicken, or dog. They could not have caught him speeding, because the van couldn't go fast enough to earn a ticket.

"No, he is not here."

"Madame, we have some bad news."

Well that is obvious. Whoever heard of two policemen calling around with good news?

"It is your parents Madame. They have been involved in a road accident."

"No it can't be." She said. "It can't be them. There're not here. There're on a train, not in a car. We don't have a car. We only have a van, and PP, I mean to say my husband, is using it."

"Madame, there is no mistake. Your parents were on a bus near Arles and it has crashed off the road. Your parents were on the bus. They have been identified from the papers that they were carrying. I am sorry Madame, but there is no mistake."

"So where are they now? Are they in a hospital? Can I get hold of them?"

"No, I am sorry Madame. That will be impossible. They were both killed. There was nothing they could do down there. The Chef of the Gendarmerie in Arles told us that the bus went over an embankment. The driver and five passengers were killed and three were seriously hurt. It is a very sad affair. I am very sorry, Madame."

Marie stared at the huge revolver on the Gendarme's hip while she tried to gather her thoughts.

Wasn't it so bloody typical of life!

Nothing was ever designed to go smoothly.

Everybody said that these plans that her parents had to go travelling were crazy, and they were right! It just goes to show, once again, that any optimism in life will always be rewarded with disappointment. How reassuring it is to know that life is such a miserable affair.

There is always something going wrong with it.

Why do we put up with it?

Stupid. Stupid. Stupid!

She refocused her eyes onto the Gendarme's face.

"What happens now?" She asked.

"Well perhaps Madame you can contact Monsieur Fontaine, the Notaire in Seurre. He will know what to do and how to proceed. Do you know him?"

"Yes I do! I was in his office only two days ago. On Friday, in fact."

"Madame, the accident will have to be investigated before Monsieur and Madame Rufin will be allowed to return here. The Gendarmerie in Arles wanted us to tell you that. They have to have an inquest into the cause of the accident before the bodies are released. I hope you understand?"

"Yes, thank you Monsieur. Who do I contact there? Who shall I speak to?"

"Madame, we will do that for you. We will tell you the date for the inquest and where it will be held. Do you think that you will want to be there?"

"Yes… No… I don't know. I will have to speak to PP… my husband, first."

"Very good, Madame Peron. We will call by tomorrow to see if there is anything you need, or any information you want."

"Yes. I'll tell you what I want to know, that is, what company is it that operates these busses? These ones that operate between Marseilles and Arles?"

"I don't know Madame, but I will find out."

There was nothing more that the two policemen could do for Marie, so they climbed back into their little blue Renault and returned to Seurre. Somehow their car looked miniaturised by the large blue light fitted to the roof. It looked out of proportion. How these large policemen fitted inside was a puzzle. Marie stood in the doorway of her bakery with her napkin still clutched tightly in her hand.

One thing she did know and that was she did not want to see anybody. So she closed the door and hung her 'Fermé" notice so that it could be seen from the outside, through the glass panel.

Her first thought was to recapture, in her mind, the last moments that she had spent with her parents. It was those few minutes when they were departing for the railway station. They were her best and closest memories. She knew that, as they were leaving, her parents would have to treat her as an adult from then on, rather than as their child. She was a married woman, and her mother would have to treat her as such. She wouldn't just be the daughter of the family anymore.

And now, in a single instant, her whole world had changed. She would never be that adult in the eyes of her parents.

To them she would always be their child.

The child who her parents had thought that they had to teach and guide. The child who always had to be improved and made better for some destination that existed only in *their* minds.

All of a sudden, the reason for her resentment of life, that she had to be better than she was, for her parents sake, had been taken away. She had never been given the chance to win. She would never have the chance to prove herself to them. She would never be able to show that she could do things, like run the business and run her life, without their constant corrections and supervision. Always, in her mind, they would be her supervisors and so never would they all be equals, or even friends.

By dying they had taken away her main motivation in life. Now she could never prove that she could do anything she wanted, without them. Here she was straddled with this bakery business, and a new husband, and nobody to show how she could do it all, if she really wanted.

What is the point of it all?

She didn't want to be a baker's wife like her mother. She had only gone along with this whole plan of getting married and becoming partners with PP in order to prove to her parents that she could achieve; so that they would leave her alone.

And now they had!

Forever.

She was more furious than sad.

She was cross that they hadn't given her the chance to establish herself in their estimation. They had straddled her with PP, as though they thought she couldn't manage life by herself. But she knew that it was going to be *she* that would have to lead *PP* through life, rather than the other way around.

She felt as though she had been preparing for an examination and now, when it was the moment of the final test, the question papers had been taken away.

It was so damned unfair!

Why couldn't they have just retired like other sensible people, instead of getting this ridiculous urge to gallivant, in this unproductive way, around the country?

She sat down at the table where she had her half finished meal and started to bash her clenched fist on the table, still holding the crushed napkin in her grasp.

Why? Why? Why?

She heard the familiar spluttering "phut phut phut" of the Citroen van, as it drew up outside the side door of the bakery. She knew that PP was back from his rounds. She stood up and walked through the shop to the adjoining bakery, where the ovens were still warm from the morning's production of bread.

PP was already heaving the sacks of flour from the back of the little van to the door of the bakery. He had made an arrangement to collect the flour from the mill at Bragny on this Sunday rather than on Friday, because of the need to use the little van for moving things for the wedding reception.

"Oh," he said as he saw her, "Do you remember Madame Pettier from Bragny? She has had twins. Yesterday! Her husband said it is because of our bread! He is so excited that he gave me a huge hug!"

Marie was neither interested nor concerned. These were people that PP met on his rounds and had nothing to do with her. She only had to put up with the people that came into the shop, not those that had deliveries.

They were only names on a list of invoices and balance sheets.

Nor real people.

Just names.

"My parents are dead!"

PP froze in mid stride.

"What? … No! … No, don't joke about things like that, Marie. It's not funny!"

"I'm not joking PP! The Gendarmes from Seurre came here. They have a message from some Gendarmerie in the South. There's been a bus crash with my parents on board. They've been killed. It's true!"

PP dropped the sack of flour. Tears welled out of his eyes and streamed down his cheeks. His face seemed to break into disjointed pieces as he absorbed the news. He shook and his hands found each other and he began to wring them unconsciously. He started to wail.

He was displaying more than enough emotion for both of them.

Marie stared at him, determined to not let herself go. True, her eyes did moisten in sympathy with PP's dramatic distress, but she blinked them dry because it was a sign of weakness. She was still clutching the napkin with unconscious strength and her arm was beginning to shake with the strain. She could feel that her forearm muscles were beginning to cramp. She put the serviette onto the cooling table in the bakery and shook her arm to ease the strain of tense muscles, while PP sagged against the side of the doorway for support.

He was shaking his head as the enormity of the situation came to him. He had never had anyone close to him die before. His parents and grandparents were all still alive and well. Although his entire family did gather on All Saints Day to go to the village cemetery with everybody else in the village to honour the dead, the family graves there all belonged to ancestors who had died before he was born.

He had worked with Monsieur Rufin now for more than four years, and they knew each other, oh so well. Old man Rufin had been like a father to him. In fact, now that PP was married, he *was* a father to him.

And Madame Rufin was like his own mother.

She had always been so kind to him.

She had always been there.

Always in the shop for as long as he could remember.

Always greeted him.

Always there as a sign of permanent reassurance that nothing would ever change.

And now it had.

Everything had changed.

PP tottered through the shop to the kitchen at the back of the house and sat on a chair next to the kitchen table.

He wept.

His shoulders shook and he rubbed his eyes with his hands. The flour dust on his hands and arms from the sack he was carrying now smeared over his face. Tears streaked his cheeks, and he looked like a wretched portrait of misery; like a child with a clown's face blurred with sniffles.

Marie looked at him and almost despised his weakness.

She had learned at school not to show emotion. If she had shown only one glimmer of fear when the boys had pushed a spider in her face, she would have been marked for life. They would have never let up. Everyday they would have tried to frighten her again with something else. She knew how to not display any sign of weakness, no matter what the situation. And here was PP, who was supposed to be a man, yet snivelling like a child.

Oh, God, she thought, I am saddled with him! Is this what he is going to be like whenever something goes wrong?

"Oh PP! Pull yourself together!" she demanded.

"We've got to sort this out! There is no point whimpering about it. I've got to go and see Monsieur Fontaine tomorrow morning. Are you going to come with me?"

"Yes, well… No. I don't know. Why there? Why do you want to see him? He isn't going to change anything!"

"Of course he will. He will know what we are going to have to do."

PP just looked at her astonished that she could think of anything that concerned the future, when all he could feel was the wave of pain that engulfed him now.

'Don't you have any feeling?' he thought, 'Don't you realise what has happened? You must be numbed out of your mind.'

He nodded his head and then shook it. 'She hasn't caught up with the reality and she is finding things to do, so that she does not have to think about it.'

"No," he said, "I'll stay and look after the shop. You go and see him. Do whatever you have to do. I don't want to see anyone."

And so, with one statement PP handed over the reins of his life to his wife. It would have happened at some stage anyway, because she was the stronger character of the two, but with this first emergency of their married life, the decision was accelerated.

Marie knew she had won an important point, although the significance of it would only become apparent to her later. For the moment she was fully engrossed in weighing the possibilities that this new development had introduced and what steps she should take to make the best of it.

She realised that she had to lead and stay ahead of the situation and that the best way to do that was to issue commands. She looked at PP and felt a touch of sympathy for him, in the same way that she might have felt compassion for an animal that had hurt itself. The problem was that she didn't like animals very much, so it was easy to quash this small weakness and continue to gauge the situation.

"PP, go and wash your face and then get all the flour out of the van. I have to use it tomorrow to go to Seurre to see Monsieur Fontaine. In fact I must ring him now to make sure that he is there. PP, come on now, we have things to do."

PP looked at his wife and acquiesced.

It was so much easier this way.

He had never forced his personality on his brothers and his sister, all the while he was living at home. He had found it easier and more pleasant to go with the flow and ignore the stresses and uproars that they introduced into their lives all the time. All the sibling squabbles had concerned the others, and he had simply been there without taking sides or becoming involved. His whole nature was non confrontational, and this is why people liked him. He was no challenge to them.

And he was certainly no challenge to Marie.

He went through to the kitchen behind the shop and washed his hands and face in the sink and then wandered to the outhouse to urinate into the dark hole, through the stained and cracked wooden toilet seat. As he stood there he watched a small group of wasps which had started to make a nest of fine papery material suspended on a stalk. They looked so involved and busy. They seemed completely unaware of the disaster that had overtaken him and Marie. Their lives were completely unaffected. Rather the same way that Marie seemed completely unaffected.

Because of the gentle nature of PP's mind, he did not see that the character of his wife showed similarities to these insects, in that she also occupied herself with tasks, and yet carried a sting in the tail. He did not realise yet that he would have to show her the same respect that these insects required from the world that surrounded them. He had not realised yet that she was the dominant force of their marriage and that as long as he occupied himself with his duties, all would be well.

He wandered back to the kitchen and remembered to rinse his hands in the sink again. He cleared the flour sacks from the back of the van and swept it out. Then he stacked the flour in the store room that was adjacent to the bakery. There was enough flour for the next month. He would have to remember to order some more when it began to run low, because old Monsieur Rufin, Dad, used to do that.

Tears blurred his vision as he thought of the old man who had taught him how to become a patisserie chef.

How the flour used to dust his grey hair and collect on his moustache.

How he used to have to remember to put his hat on when the inspectors called, because he despised them and their rules, which dictated that he had to wear a hat because he was preparing food.

PP smiled as he thought of the old man.

He looked at the shiny brass handles of the oven doors and he knew that the old man was there with him. The old man's hands had polished the handles with use, and each time that PP pulled the doors open he would be duplicating the old man's movements.

Yes, the old man, his old man, Monsieur Rufin, would be here with him in the early mornings taking care with the morning's bake.

Together they would prepare the flour, warm the ovens and dust the trays on which the baguettes sat, when they were pushed into the mouth of the oven.

The old man had spent his life in here and PP felt secure that he would do the same.

Monsieur Rufin would be closer now than ever he was, when he was alive. PP and he would continue together with the tradition of baking and Marie could take care of the business side with the lawyers, the accountants, the inspectors and the taxmen.

PP would continue to make the gallettes in January, fruit tarts on Saturday and brioche on Sunday.

People of the village would come to buy, as they always had. He, Pierre Peron, would be there with the spirit of Monsieur Rufin behind him to continue the tradition and the trade.

The Pains, the Baguettes and the Croissants would continue to come alive and give life to the village. PP could see purpose in his life, and he used this to assuage his despair and his loss.

Marie hand-cranked the telephone to contact the exchange in Seurre and demanded to speak to the Notaire, Monsieur Fontaine. She explained to him in a few words what had happened and made an appointment to see him early on Monday morning. She was not prepared to wait any longer than this because she had a business to run.

"I can only see you between ten and eleven o' clock," she informed the Notaire. "Earlier than that, I have my regular customers and after that, there are the others who need bread for lunch. The afternoon is out of the question, because that is my private time."

She was not going to give that up for the convenience of the Notaire.

"So why can I not see you in the morning?" She demanded.

"Well, Madame Peron, I have to get papers together and consider the circumstances. This is all very sudden, and the papers that you signed on Friday are still here in my office. They have not been posted and registered at the Prefecture yet."

"But they are still legal, aren't they?"

"Oh yes Madame, from the moment that they were signed. It is just that normally they are registered with the offices in Dijon before they are acted upon."

"Monsieur Fontaine, I have to see you in order to get the bodies of my parents released by the coroner in Arles. I need to organise funeral arrangements here in Seurre. I have to ensure the smooth running of my business. I do not have time to waste waiting for the Prefecture to register receipt of documents. I will see you tomorrow morning at ten o' clock."

Marie hung the telephone on the hook, thereby cutting off Monsieur Fontaine before he could reply. She did not hear the other clicks on the line, which were from the exchange operator as she disconnected the line after listening in to the conversation.

One of the perks of being the telephone exchange operator is to be the first in the village with news. Calls to the Notaire, although normally boring and full of jargon concerning contracts, did occasionally yield news of importance to the community.

The exchange operator did not consider that she was infringing any protocols in disseminating information, because it was all in the public interest. And it did inspire people to use their telephones to spread the news and gossip, and that was good for business, was it not?

After all, she had helped spread sensitive news during the German occupation and now they had left, they had been replaced by petty bureaucrats who were, in her mind, rather worse.

By the time Marie arrived at the Office of the Notaire in Rue de la République, most of the community in Seurre knew about the deaths of Monsieur and Madame Rufin.

The flower shop proprietor, Monsieur Simmoneau, whose establishment is directly opposite the entrance to Monsieur Fontaine's office, saw Marie entering through the old oak door. He knew that he would soon be getting orders for wreaths. The exchange operator, who was married to his cousin, had said that the bodies were going to be brought back from the south. That meant that the funeral would be held here. Perhaps it would take place in the church in Seurre, because the church in Marie Peron's village might be too small to accommodate all the mourners who may come to this important event.

Monsieur Simmoneau called across to his wife who was busy sorting out her stock of ceramic vases, in which she was arranging the flowers that had not been sold over the weekend,

"Cherie, we have some business coming our way. We will need several wreaths and bouquets, maybe later this week. Do you think that I should put an order in for more roses?"

"I think we should wait until the day of the funeral is fixed. With this warm weather, the flowers will go off too quickly. We can ask Roger if he knows when it might be, because they will probably need his ambulance to collect the bodies of Monsieur and Madam Rufin. I wonder if his ambulance will make it all the way to the south. It's never been quite right since he took that huge truffle pig of Antoine's to the forest to search for truffles and got it stuck."

"Yes, you are right," agreed Monsieur Simmoneau. "If they use Roger's ambulance, it will take him two days to get there and two days to get back. It is already making a funny noise from the differential. I think he bent something on that tree stump that he hit. That pig was far too heavy for the vehicle and anyway I think that pig eats more truffles than Antoine gets. It is too big to control. And now everybody knows where Antoine's secret truffle ground is. That Monsieur Chazelle from over the river, you know the fellow who says he is going to have fifteen children, he will be down there with his truffle dog and he will steal them all."

"True, he is always trying to sell his wild mushrooms here," replied Madame Simmoneau. "But I think they are wasting their time looking for truffles. There can't be any good quality ones. Mushrooms? Yes! But if they want to get good truffles they need to go down south. Did you know that Henri said that Monsieur Chazelle stole that truffle dog?"

"You might be right, but I think that Antoinette Falage, you know, the old lady who walks in the forest and says she can see the spirits of dead people there? Well I think she knows where to find truffles. She told me that she smells them. Her father taught her. He used to use a divining stick of laurel, and she said that you have to face the rising sun and then the stick will bend towards the trees where the truffles are. Then you have to smell the ground and *if* you know what you are doing, you will find them."

"I don't like them," grumbled Monsieur Simmoneau. "They smell too much like compost to me. I prefer the smell of flowers. Flowers turn the smell of compost into a beautiful scent. That is why they are so special."

Monsieur Simmoneau went back to arranging his display on the tables outside the door of his shop, where the pedestrians had to step off the pavement in order to pass. He kept an eye on the Notaire's office door so that he could intercept Marie Peron with a greeting as she left.

The baker's family from over the river was turning into this month's best customers, with a wedding and a double funeral.

Monsieur Simmoneau breathes deeply of the scent of his flowers and smiles.

There is always someone who needs his flowers.

The Adventure of Roger du Bois

Marie Peron commissioned Roger du Bois to take his ambulance to Arles on Tuesday afternoon.

It took Marie from Monday morning until after lunch on Tuesday to organise the release of her parent's bodies from the morgue in Arles, for the permits to transport them back to the village and for the mortician in Arles to arrange for the correct coffins for transportation.

Monsieur Fontaine had a headache.

He had never achieved so much is such a short space of time. With the complications that he foresaw in Marie Peron's case he imagined that it would take the better part of a month to achieve what Marie achieved in twenty four hours. His entire practice revolved around letters, consultations, negotiations and drawing up contracts.

A typical example of his ability to procrastinate concerned the deceased estate of a young man who died unexpectedly at the age of forty two. He was the second son of Sandrine, a widow in the village. He was recently divorced so he came home to live with his mother.

One afternoon he decided that he was slightly tired, so he went to lie down.

He never woke up.

The only thing that the young man owned in his own name was a car that had been bought for him by his mother. She was still making the payments on it. As her son was divorced, the proceeds of his estate were bound, under Napoleonic Law, to go to his two children who were too young to drive. That case had taken Monsieur Fontaine three years to finalise during which time Denise had to continue to pay for a car that she did not own, and could not drive, nor sell.

His real estate dealings were legendary, because there were times when signatures of over fifty people were needed to finalise a contract. The rewards that he could glean from these transactions had made him a wealthy man. The confrontations that he liked the most were ones where a builder defaulted on the building of a house, either by running out of money or not building to the specifications. Usually the builder would declare bankruptcy and then the whole 'affaire' could continue for years. One such house, on the outskirts of Seurre, had a twenty year old tree growing through its half finished foundations.

Most of the villagers lived in awe of their Notaire and they were too frightened to urge him into action, because he was always the final authority in a dispute. Many situations were negotiated by him and never did get to court, because of the villagers' deep mistrust and fear of the complications of the legal system. He was like an unofficial prosecutor, judge and enforcement service to most people.

That was until he was forced into action by Marie Peron.

She was on the telephone to the coroner's office in Arles within five minutes of entering Monsieur Fontaine's office on Monday morning. She had several conversations with the Chef de Police in Arles and by Tuesday morning they were all happy to sign all the relevant documents in order to get rid of this demanding woman. Where Marie's sudden surge of confidence and assertiveness came from was not clear. It was perhaps that the sudden release of parental control had triggered a desire to have her own way for once, and no petty bureaucrat was going to stand in her path.

Certainly the officials had sympathy for her situation, and so they jumped some of their own administrative hurdles to facilitate her desires.

Roger du Bois had warning on the Seurre grapevine that he might be required to do this epic journey to the south, so he had spent the day preparing his Peugeot van, which doubled as a hearse and ambulance. Because either of these rôles would require the vehicle to be painted either black or white, he had compromised by painting it blue. This gave it an official appearance, because it was the same shade of blue that the Police vans were painted.

One advantage of this was that cars following him did not hoot and flash their lights in frustration, when he was puttering along the National Roads, just in case he *really was* driving an official Police vehicle.

Roger drained the oil and replaced it. He removed the rocker cover box and reset the tappets, which was a job that he had been putting off for over a year. He checked the brake fluid levels and the acid levels in the battery. He decided to get some distilled water from the Quincaillerie to top up the battery, rather than use rainwater which he collected from the roof gutter in a wine bottle. This was an important mission and nothing must go wrong. He pumped up the tyres and borrowed a spare wheel from his brother for emergencies. He put a five litre metal container of water in front of the passenger seat, in case the radiator should start to boil.

He was ready for the longest trip of his life.

He left early on Wednesday morning armed with the permits to transport dead bodies, the authorisations to take possession of the bodies from the morgue in Arles as well as his licences, insurances, identity documents and enough cash for petrol and expenses.

His route took him through Chalon and Macon to Lyon where he got lost.

He had never driven in such a big city before, but fortunately the sun was shining and so he had a sense of direction of where south was, until he saw the signs directing him to Marseilles. Now the road, which he knew would follow the Rhone, descended into the valley where flood waters of the past had scraped a gorge through the hills. He managed to find places to stop to eat the snacks of bread, cheese and cakes that PP had prepared for him. It was late evening before he reached the flat plain south of Avignon, which extends towards Arles and the Camargue.

At last he found the centre of Arles and following his directions, located the river Rhone. From here he found the hotel Porte de Camargue, which overlooks the river on the Quai de la Maritime. This was the same hotel that Monsieur and Madame Rufin had booked. Marie had confirmed that their room, which had already been paid for, was available for Roger. He had a rather uncomfortable feeling when he entered the room, after checking in at the reception, because he felt as though he was coming into somebody else's territory.

He had not known the Rufins well, because he always bought his bread in Seurre from the bakery in the Rue de la République. Like many French people, he was faithful to his Boulangèrie, because that was where he could swap news and anecdotes with his friends.

This room was supposed to be occupied by people who were now dead. There was nothing, Roger decided, that could not be overcome with a bottle of Southern Rhone wine and a good meal. He decided on having a treat, so chose a Gigondas wine to go with a rump steak from a Camargue bull. He thought that the Gigondas would suit his palate better than the local Chateau Neuf du Pape, because his taste preferred the delicacy of the Bourgogne wines.

He ate on the balcony of the Embargo Café, which gave him a view over the market square. It was a good choice and the combination of free-range meat and sunny wine, along with the fatigue of driving, ensured that he slept well.

Next morning he presented himself and his papers at the town morgue. Miraculously, for a country that enjoys paperwork, the gears of officialdom ran like oiled cogs and in half an hour Roger was ready to load up his cargo. The coffins of Monsieur and Madame Rufin were brought to the side entrance of the morgue, which gave access to a narrow alley which was just wide enough for Roger's blue van. The attendants positioned the coffins side by side in the back and Roger covered them with a blanket. He strapped the coffins in position to securing rings that were designed for that purpose.

Now that he was ready to go, Roger decided that he would like to see the site of the accident. It was only a few kilometres from Arles on the road to Marseilles, and then after that he could cut across the countryside towards Avignon and the north. He negotiated the cobbled streets and alleys of Arles that had been laid out long before the motorcar was designed. He found a sign indicting the way to Marseilles. The countryside is flat, and the road had been built to ensure that it would be above the level of the plain, in the event of flooding.

Roger found the site of the accident which was still marked by the broken railings where the bus had careered through them. It was the only part of the road that had a larger than normal embankment because it was where one of the meandering rivers crossed under the road on its way to the sea. Had the driver of the bus crashed off the road a few hundred metres before or after this position, it would have been unlikely that the bus would have turned over, as it had.

Roger examined the railings and saw the yellow lines daubed onto the road which indicated where the bus had swerved. The whole episode was so sad because it was so unlucky. He shook his head at the fragility of life and then clambered back into his van to continue his journey towards Marseilles.

He drove into the town of Saint Martin and decided that he should ask someone for directions. He wanted to know if it was better to try and find his way through the networks of small roads to Avignon, or to carry on towards Marseilles until he got to the National Road. He also felt in the mood for a coffee and a chaser to settle his nerves.

He saw a café which looked suitable for a quick coffee. There was a parking area half a block from the café, so he pulled into it. It seemed to be a site where a building had been demolished, as the houses on either side had bricks and the remains of beams jutting into the gap where the building had once stood. Perhaps it had been bombed during the war, or had just fallen down and nothing could be done until the multiple owners decided what to do about it.

There were no signs declaring that it was a private property. Several rather decrepit cars had been parked in the space at odd angles, as though they had been abandoned. Roger locked the van and walked back to the café. It was a rather seedy looking place filled with swarthy individuals smoking Galloise cigarettes, while they fingered small glasses of pale liquid.

The proprietor was an overweight man with a sour expression that seemed to display his contempt for both his life and his customers.

Roger asked for a black coffee, which the proprietor prepared from a machine that resembled a small church organ, with complex pipes and handles. As the steam squealed and hissed through the coffee filter Roger asked for directions to the road to Lyon.

The café owner knew from Roger's accent that he was not a local and so took his time before answering. He asked Roger what he was driving and where was he parked, before going off to find a pencil and paper to write down the directions. A couple of the characters leaning against the bar, who looked like they had a North African ancestry, shoved their coffee cups away, looked at each other and walked out of the café.

The owner came back grumbling about losing things, that seemed to disappear of their own accord, and then started to sharpen his pencil with a wicked looking knife that appeared, as though by magic, in his hand.

Roger was used to the French habit of not displaying a sense of urgency, particularly for strangers but this man seemed to be making a point of being obtuse. He lit yet another Galloise from the one dangling from his mouth and then started to draw a map of the road system of Saint Martin.

"You take this road here, Rue de la République, until you come to the Avenue Nostradamus. If you get into this road you have gone too far. Anyway this road is blocked today because of the street market. So you must turn right by the church and then go to the Rue Alphonse."

He started to write out the name in an illegible scrawl.

"Then you find Rue du Soleil and you take this one until the Avenue Nostradamus. Here you cross this one but I don't know the name of this road. Hey Alfredo!" he called one of his patrons.

"What is the name of the road that turns into Rue du Soleil?"

Alfredo came to join the conversation but contributed nothing.

Roger was impatient.

It was typical.

These people were arguing about trivia and something concerning the bus station. Roger wanted to leave and find his own way, or perhaps go back towards Arles and take the small road that he had used when he came down.

Now they were discussing different ways to get to Avignon and what the proposed bypass round the town was going to do to business.

No wonder men hate asking for directions. It always ends up with too much detail, or else becomes a conversation about something else.

Eventually he managed to interrupt their discussion about the new road and what the effect was going to be on the life of the town.

"Thank you," he said, "But I think I'll just go back to Arles and then go to Avignon from there."

This started another discussion until Roger pulled a ten franc note from his pocket, placed it on the counter and walked out. He muttered to himself on the way back to the van about the idiots from the south, how their language was unintelligible, how they had no sense of time and how they were just generally unhelpful.

'Too much olive oil and sunshine', he decided. 'That is the problem.'

He had already forgotten about the cooperation and help he had received earlier that morning in Arles.

He turned into the parking area and stopped in astonishment.

His van was gone.

He turned around to make sure that he had not walked into the wrong place. No, everything was the same. The same unserviceable cars were scattered in the same positions as they were when he had parked his van.

The enormity of the situation struck him.

What was he going to do?

How could he explain this?

He must report it immediately.

Fortunately he had his identification papers in his little portefeuille along with the documents and his cash. He knew with the instinct of long practice that these documents must stay with him at all times. The Germans, during the occupation, were constantly asking for "papers" and so it was second nature for him to carry "papers".

The thought of going back to the café and having to deal with the disobliging proprietor seemed to be too daunting a proposition. Roger asked a woman pushing a bicycle where he could find the Gendarmerie and was told to continue down the road where he would find it next to the Town House and Mayor's Office.

When he entered the Police Station the Officer in Charge gave him a quick 'once over' glance. It was like being categorised by a prospective father-in-law. He felt guilty, as though something indefinable was already his fault.

"Bon jour," he started, "I have lost my van. It has been stolen."

"When was this?"

"Just five minutes ago. It was parked just down the road there, while I went for a coffee, and then 'pouf' it was gone!"

"Did you lock it?"

"Bien sur!"

"Ah bien! What kind of van is it? What colour?"

"It is a blue one, a Peugeot, fifteen years old."

"Yes these ones often get stolen. The locks are too simple. They have only about ten different keys for the whole range. Have you got the papers?"

Roger gave him the "Carte Grise" and the insurance papers. The policeman started to fill out the stolen vehicle document, as he had done so many times before. He half suspected that Roger had arranged to have it "stolen" so that he could claim another van from the Insurance Company. It wouldn't be the first time that had happened.

When he saw the registration number, he said, "You are a long way from home!"

"Yes," said Roger, "but I must tell you, there is a problem. There are two dead bodies in the back of the van."

"Bodies? Human bodies?"

"Yes, I am… I *was* taking them back to the Côte d'Or."

Suddenly the policeman was electrified with the significance of the situation.

"Why?"

"They are victims of a bus accident and I am taking them home to be buried in their home town."

"Is that from the accident last Sunday?"

"Yes, that is the one. It was on the road to Arles."

"I know the accident. We were called to the scene as well. Have you got permits for this transportation?"

The policeman stared at Roger with an accusatory glare.

"Of course!"

Roger handed over the papers and permits. The whole situation had now changed and the policeman was full of concern and zeal.

"Do you think that the thieves wanted to steal the bodies?"

"No. They couldn't know that there were coffins in the back. I had covered them with a blanket. Anyway, why would they steal an old van? I was only parked for ten minutes."

"Ah, there are many reasons. The drug traffickers from Marseilles are always on the lookout for vans that look like local farmers' vans. The local thieves like them for transport, if they raid a store or if they want to move stolen property from a house. There are many empty holiday homes in the south that are easy targets for thieves."

"What will happen to the coffins of Monsieur and Madam Ruffin?"

"That depends. Probably when the thieves discover the coffins they will abandon the van, because they will know that we will be after them with all haste. I hope they do not dump the bodies. Excuse me."

The Gendarme started to call the police stations in Arles and other local towns and also reported the theft to the 'Département Centrale' in Marseilles.

Roger pondered whether he should telephone Marie Peron to tell her about this complication, but decided against it. Maybe the police would find the van quickly, in which case there was no point to raise the alarm at home and get everybody worried. He didn't think that they were expecting him back today. The distance back home was far and they might suspect that he could have had some difficulties with the clearances.

It seemed to Roger that everything had been done that could be done to recover the van. The question was what he should do while he was waiting for some news. He decided to walk around the town and then come back to the Gendarmerie early in the afternoon to see if they had found the van. He gathered his personal papers but left the vehicle documents with the police and agreed to return after lunch.

The market in Saint Martin was in full swing with stalls displaying everything from clothes to food.

The clothing stalls had a range from Spanish style dresses to Italian suits.

The food stalls had cheeses, local olive oils and walnuts. The range of breads included ones made with nuts and olives and herbs, all quite different from central France. There were stalls with equipment and saddles for horse riding, and stalls with collections of vinyl records of traditional songs and modern popular tunes.

Roger would have enjoyed himself more, had it not been the nagging worry about how he was going to explain the loss of the van and the bodies of the Rufins. He had his lunch at one of the stalls where they featured Spanish style fish paella, which was the first time he had tasted it. He thought that he was being most adventurous. Like many French people of that era he was suspicious and cautious about foreign foods. But he offset the danger by having a half bottle of 'La Chasse du Pape Prestige', which is a very acceptable southern Rhone white wine.

He was in a rather good mood when he returned to the police station, only to find that there had been no sightings of his old van, in spite of a general alert.

The gendarme explained to him, "The problem is that there are many thousands of vans like yours all over this area, on the farms and in the villages. It will take a few days to check out all of them, but we are giving it a big priority. Perhaps I will have some news for you in the morning."

"Thank you, Monsieur," replied Roger, "but I have been thinking. That café on the main road back towards Arles is where I went to ask for directions. I remember that there were two people who left after I started talking to the owner. Maybe they were involved with the disappearance. They didn't look quite honest to me, somehow."

"Oh yes, we know all about him and the clientele there. That is quite possible. I will go and interview him as soon as my relief arrives to take over here. I suggest that you call back tomorrow morning to see if there has been a sighting of your van."

Roger agreed to return the following day, because there was not a lot he could do otherwise. It would be silly to take the train home and then find out that they had found his van nearby. On the other hand, if they didn't find it soon, then there was every chance that it would never be found. He walked back down the Rue de la République past the seedy café to the village two star hotel. The gendarme had asked Roger not to alert the café owner that he was coming, so Roger took care to pass the café on the opposite side of the road. The patron would be unlikely to see him through the dirty windows.

The next morning there was good news. The van had been found but there was a problem. It was in Bordeaux!

The thieves had taken it there to bring back a load of smuggled goods from a fishing boat in the docks. When they opened the back they had discovered what lay under the blanket. They had abandoned the van on the outskirts of the industrial area. The police in Bordeaux had received an anonymous telephone call to say where the van had been left. It was now in the police vehicle pound and they had requested that Roger come immediately to collect it, as otherwise they would have to open a dossier and that could delay everything for weeks.

The gendarme gave Roger all his vehicle papers and told him how to get to the railway station.

"You will have to take the regional train to Nîmes and then you can get on the express through to Bordeaux via Toulouse. You should get there by this evening. You must hurry because by tomorrow they will have to start the paperwork. They are expecting you! Here are the contact numbers for you to call when you get there."

Roger left before asking what had happened about the café owner and his dubious clients. It seemed that, as far as the police were concerned, the case was closed and they did not want to start an investigation that could become overly complicated. They had experience in these matters. As far as they were concerned, the matter had been resolved. To pursue a felon, who had given up his booty and then had tipped off where he had left it, was enough reason to slip the folder into a drawer and forget about it.

The trip to Bordeaux by train was uneventful and on time. As Roger left the railway station he was intercepted by two gendarmes. It was obvious that they had been waiting for him in the Bordeaux station. They must have been given a description of him from the gendarme in Saint Martin. They took him directly to the van which was in an enclosure with a number of accident vehicles that were under investigation. They shook his hand, wished him a 'Bon Voyage', unlocked the gate and waved him on his way.

It took him two hours to find his way out of the sprawl of the city into countryside, with its numerous vineyards. He had to take the road to Clermont-Ferrand, because the road to Paris and back down again to Dijon would have added another three hundred kilometres to his journey. And now he was in a hurry!

By midnight he was exhausted with driving and knew that he had to have a rest. The road was congested with trucks.

'There really is a need,' he thought, 'for the new motorway system that was being proposed by the government even if you have to pay tolls to use these new highways.'

He was not prepared to leave the van for a moment, in case something else happened, so he decided to sleep in the passenger seat.

The passenger seat was uncomfortable and he felt rather weird trying to sleep with the bodies of Monsieur and Madame Rufin so close by. Before dawn he was on his way again, stopping only for fuel and a croissant, which he bought from a bakery where he could watch the van at all times.

He passed through Autun where he had to negotiate complicated diversions. They had piles of cobblestones that were being re-laid, because the weight of new heavy trucks had distorted the road surface. When he weaved through the hills approaching Beaune he began to feel that he was getting back into his own territory.

He was tired and yet exhilarated as he crossed the Val de Sâone towards Seurre.

He had never been so far from home before. There had been times during the trip when he had wondered if he would ever find his way back. He drew up in front of the funeral home in Seurre shortly after lunch time with a sigh of relief. He decided that he would not tell anybody about his route, his delay and his problems.

'If that is what travelling is all about then,' he decided, 'that is enough for me.'

He would not be tempted to travel again, with all the dangers and uncertainties that were involved with it.

'The villagers who keep themselves to themselves are quite right,' he thought. 'What is the point of confusing oneself with other places? They eat strange food and behave in peculiar ways. It is quite enough to cope with the problems at home.'

And so it was that the Rufins did complete a journey to both the Mediterranean and the Atlantic Ocean.

Madame Rufin did accomplish her dream to travel.

It was just a shame that she was not alive to see it all.

Marie Peron takes charge

Marie closed the bakery door and placed the 'fermé' sign so that it could be seen through the glass. Someone had telephoned her from the funeral home in Seurre, near Monsieur Fontaine's office in the Rue de la République. Apparently Roger du Bois had arrived, at last, with the coffins of her parents and they wanted to know what she wanted to do next. Marie had chosen this funeral parlour because it was the most convenient one to hand after she had left the Notaire's office last Monday. There are three 'Pompes Funèbres' in Seurre, which all compete for business from the Hospice which has been in existence for over three hundred years.

Marie was annoyed, because 'what to do next' was their job, not hers.

She had spoken already to the Mayor of the village about two plots in the cemetery at the top of the hill. She had wanted to arrange to pay for 'perpétuelle' sites. However the cost had been such that she had gone for the less expensive option of paying for one concession with the other as 'superposition'. This meant one grave whereas if she had she decided on two, side by side, then she would have to go for the thirty year or the fifty year option, because of the expense.

Because the bakery building was rented and because Marie's parents had never owned their own house or land, she felt that she would like to ensure that they had some permanency at last. They had been together throughout their lives, so what was wrong with ensuring that they stayed together forever?

"Anyway," she reasoned to PP, "if they had separate graves, then the cost of the funeral would exceed the cost of the wedding. So together in one grave they will have to be, for all eternity."

She had agreed terms with the Mayor to spread the payments for the sites over the next few years.

PP arrived back at the bakery from his distribution rounds to the other villages, but Marie did not feel the necessity to discuss the funeral arrangements with him. After all, what was there to discuss?

She had unilaterally decided that she was going to be the decision maker and without so much as a discussion on the subject, PP had cooperated. After all, it was her parents' business that he had come into, and it was her parents who were now going to be interred, so who else other than she had any say?

He parked the bread van at the side of the bakery outside the swing door to his dough preparation room and came in with his satchel of receipts and cash. He smiled at Marie and gave her a 'peck' on the cheek. She turned half away from him in a gesture that, to an onlooker, would have been rather like the way a sister would receive an obligatory kiss from a least favourite brother.

PP did not seem to notice, because this was friendlier than they had been to each other before the wedding. It seemed to be enough, and it was, because their relationship was falling into the pattern of a brother and sister working together.

As it was, they had been in this association with each other for over four years now, before getting married and neither of them seemed to feel the urge to step up to the next level of intimacy.

They had already decided on continuing the pattern of using separate bedrooms because of their different working hours. Marie's parent's room was still filled with all their clothes and personal belongings. After the news of their deaths, Marie had simply closed the door to their room with the intention of dealing with it later. She decided that she would continue to use her room, and PP would use the spare room at the back of the building. It was near the head of the stairs and so it was convenient for him to get the ground floor.

The sexual consummation of their wedding had still not occurred and now neither of them was in the mood. It seemed that duty and attention to the more serious matters of life and death took precedence over these frivolities.

'After all,' Marie reasoned to herself, 'our wedding is more of a business arrangement than anything else.'

Marie announced to PP, "I have spoken to the funeral home in Seurre and I have arranged for the funeral to be on Wednesday, at four in the afternoon. They will arrange all the transport and they will make sure that the church is organised and ready. I don't want Père Ferdinand de Gouvier to do the funeral service so soon after our wedding, so I have arranged for Père Chatalon of Seurre to do the service. He has known my parents for years. I have ordered the flowers and I have placed the death announcements in the 'Bien Public'. I have got Hugo Bouviet to go and announce the time of the funeral around the village so that everyone will know when it is. I have made him rehearse it this time, so I don't think he will mess it up like he did when he announced the wrong date for the circus in Seurre. I have decided to close the bakery on Wednesday, so you may have to make an extra batch of bread on Tuesday, depending on the orders people want. Okay PP?"

PP nodded in acquiescence. Marie seemed to think of everything so why not leave her to do what she did best. He would be free to bake and design his patisseries as old Monsieur Rufin had taught him and Marie would not interfere with that, because she was not really interested in that side of the business.

"No," PP decided to himself, "I'll let her get on with it."

And she did.

There was a good attendance for the funeral at the church in Seurre, but the cross section of the congregation was very different from the gathering that came to Marie and PP's wedding.

All PP's school friends and cousins, who had come for the wedding celebration, had all returned back to their own villages and cities. None of Marie's school acquaintances had been invited for, or had come to, the wedding, so consequently there were none at the funeral. There were a number of elderly people who had come out of curiosity from the surrounding villages, and there was a sprinkling of attendees from the Hospice who were still able to ambulate, with assistance, to the church.

The service was sombre and even the light filtering through the stained glass windows did nothing to brighten the mood. The candlesticks, which Napoleon had given to his girlfriend nearly two hundred years before, were on either side of the altar. They had been donated to the church. All six of them had lighted beeswax candles, which marked this as a special occasion.

Marie let go for the first time since she had heard of the accident and allowed herself to sob quietly by herself, but only for a few moments and only during the first hymn. PP was more emotional in his grief and the people in the pews behind him could see his shoulders shaking as he made a huge effort to control himself.

Monsieur Javelle played the organ which had been installed in the church over two hundred and fifty years before. He was proud of this opportunity to display his prowess on this magnificent instrument. People in the streets outside could hear the chords and feel the bass vibrations rising up from the surface of the road.

When it was all over, Marie and PP followed the coffins out into the bright afternoon. The light was dazzling after the gloom of the inside of the church. Monsieur Javelle pulled at one of the bell ropes which controlled the main bell in the dome of the church. It pealed out over the village to announce the end of the service.

The funeral home had arranged two hearses which then led the procession over the bridge across the Saône to the village cemetery.

A small crowd, which included the Mayors of both villages, witnessed the interment after which they dispersed back to their cars. Marie had not made any arrangements for a gathering after the burial because she had no wish to prolong the event longer than absolutely necessary. She certainly had no wish to be on public display for the second time in a fortnight.

When she and PP got back to their bakery, she sat at the kitchen table and looked at the small pile of sympathy cards.

She wondered what she should do about them.

The whole thing was so depressing and so formalised, and seemed to have nothing to do with the realities of the situation. It was as though all these rituals were supposed to numb her mind into acceptance.

Here she was, within the space of ten days, transported from being the daughter of the village baker to being the mainstay and decision maker of a business.

She now had a husband for a partner, who had been chosen for her by her parents.

She was lumbered with following in the footsteps of her mother down a route that she had no wish to go. However, she had no other idea of what other alternative way she could lead her life. There was really no choice. In some ways it was a relief, but on the other hand she had a feeling that she was not in control of her destiny.

Why should she care about things like destiny?

Her parents had been subjected to the rigours of the war and the occupation and now, only these few years later, had not had any grand ideas about their destiny. They had tried to travel and see France, and look where that had got them.

'No, dreams are dangerous,' she decided.

'Plan the day, keep emotion and sensations at arm's length and then they can't hurt you. Look at PP, how he is snivelling and letting himself be seen to be weak. Doesn't he know what they will all say about him afterwards? Doesn't he care what they will be thinking?'

Marie still recalled how she had to keep her feelings in check when she was at school, with that dreadful Monet and his gang.

'Thank heavens he has left the village now, hopefully never to return.' Marie decided, 'I am going to live each day with no expectation of anything better, and in that way I will not be upset with the reality of disappointment.

'I won't love too much, because then it will not hurt me when it is withdrawn or comes to an end.

'I won't hope too much, because then I am sure to be disillusioned. I won't care too much, because when I find that the person I am caring about does not care about me, it won't matter.

'I shall return every enquiring glance with a glare!

'I shall scowl rather than smile.

'It is so much easier.'

Marie determined the course of her life, as she sat at the kitchen table in the small kitchen at the back of the bakery.

She decided on her own way of protecting herself against the inevitable hurts that the future was going to bring, by developing a shell that would be impenetrable to all the darts and arrows of life. She would shield herself by not allowing anyone, even PP, into her heart and so thereby she would be invulnerable to them all.

She would keep life at a distance.

And so it transpired, over the months and years that followed, that the little village bakery became known as the most unfriendly boulangerie in the Bourgogne. Campers and weekend visitors to the area nudged each other, to see who would be courageous enough to go and get the morning bread.

When the grownup children from the village returned, on their occasional visits, to see their elderly parents, they would be dispatched to get the bread. Their joke was to see if they could get a smile, or a 'Bonjour', out of the baker's wife.

They'd giggle, nudge and exclaim to each other that, "The weather is determined by the moods of Marie Peron rather than the other way around."

Some villagers decided that they couldn't cope with the negativism.

They believed that 'bad aura' means 'unhealthy bread', which is not good for the body.

They made a roster to go in turn to the other bakeries in Seurre. They then shared and distributed the bread they brought back, amongst themselves.

But for others it is a challenge to see if they can get a smile or a greeting out of Marie.

Very few succeed.

Claude Monet and Marie Peron

When Claude Monet walked into the boulangerie and said in his off hand and arrogant manor, “Bonjour Acnette, give me two baguettes!” he could not have known that the emotions that he caused within the heart of Marie Peron were the strongest that she had ever felt.

Here, in person, was the one man that she had hated and dreamed of destroying ever since she could remember. He was the bully who had taught her to contain her feelings and never show weakness or fear. She had wanted someone to hate in her life and so it had been easy for her to concentrate all that emotion into hating one particular person, and that had been this schoolboy bully.

He was so easy to hate in his absence.

But now he had come back after fifty years!

Here he was, standing in her shop with the same arrogant assuredness that he had perfected over fifty years ago in the schoolyard. He was heavier and stronger now and had developed that air of cockiness that makes even little people seem formidable. He had lost hair on his head, but that was not due to an apparent lack of testosterone. He had liver spots on his hands but otherwise he had worn his body well.

Marie responded to him in exactly the same way that she responded to most of the people who came into her shop. She selected two baguettes from the basket and wrapped a tissue of paper around them and slapped them onto the counter.

“One euro forty!”

He placed a two euro coin in the ceramic change tray and she gave him his change without a word.

“Au revoir.” He said as he left.

Claude Monet was so self engrossed that he did not realise that Marie Peron had not spoken to him, apart from relaying the price of the bread. But then he never did care about inferior people. He turned towards his house in the main road and strode off, unaware that eyes of hatred were boring a hole in his back.

Marie Peron was now in a thoroughly bad mood and she snapped at every other customer who came into her shop that morning.

She smacked the 'pains' and the 'croissants' onto the table beside her cash till, so that crumbs flew to the corners of the room. Crispy French bread has a crust that takes wings with only the slightest provocation, so that twisting a handful of baguette can cause a shower of flakes to disperse extraordinary distances. This means that Marie has to sweep her shop at regular intervals. She does this with a 'ballai' or bristle broom, with which she is able to reach between the legs of her shop furniture. She has developed a habit, over the years, of muttering while she does this unrewarding and repetitive task. The few school children in the village regard her with dread as a result.

Old Madame Pillou, who lives at the end of a row of farm labourers' cottages, uses the threat of Marie Peron to control her grandson.

"If you don't behave," she warns him with her ultimate threat, "I'll get the Baker Lady to come and beat you with her broom!"

The village children think that Marie is casting spells as she sweeps and perhaps they are not far wrong. She has found a certain amount of satisfaction in slapping the bristles of her broom at the various obstacles she encounters, which is why the paint and varnish has been worn off all the furniture at ground level.

The broom also gives her a handy weapon with which to chase that black cat which darts into her shop for no apparent reason. If only she could get hold of it she'd wring its neck. There is always a pong of cat pee near the door, and she knows it is because of that damn cat.

Today she is not just muttering, she is cursing out loud as she sweeps.

She curses Monet and all those other children who had been in his gang. They were all part of a conspiracy against her. Back then the gang always had brown paper packets filled with candy, which they used to buy from the village 'tabac'. Monet used to bribe the weaker and less assertive children into his group with these sweets. She had refused to join in and share her patisseries, which her father made for her, and so she was the permanent outsider. She didn't know how it was that these boys always had money to buy those sweets. Their parents did not have spare cash to splash out on luxuries like those.

One of the reasons that Claude Monet, when he was still at school, had developed his power over the others in his gang was that he had discovered some silver coins.

'They must have been dropped many years before, perhaps even hundreds of years ago,' he told himself.

He found the first ones in a copse of trees near the river when he was scratching among the roots looking for earthworms to put on his fishing hook. He found three that first day. They were not much to look at, because they were discoloured and looked poorly made. The edges were uneven and the embossed pattern on them looked as though they had been bashed with a hammer. He pocketed them anyway.

Later he showed them to the owner of the 'tabac' next to the hotel. Monsieur Futin took the coins, rubbed them with his finger and then, pulling on his moustache to hide his greed, said in an offhand manner:

"Yes, I will give you something for these, but I don't think they are worth much these days, because they are too old. But I don't mind because I collect old coins. Say, I'll give you a handful of sweets for every one you bring me. How's that?"

Young Claude Monet was excited, but did not want to show it. He tried to sound casual. Just imagine if he could find more! He nodded to the shopkeeper.

"But you must not tell anyone else," added Monsieur Futin, "otherwise everybody will be bringing me coins and then they won't be worth anything at all!"

Claude Monet decided to push his luck.

"Okay, but I want cigarettes and matches as well."

Monsieur Futin looked at the boy and realised that one day this kid was going to appreciate the true value of these coins. Perhaps he should give him a little bit more.

"Alright," he said, "I'll give you sweets for every coin and a packet of twenty cigarettes for every fifth coin, but this must be a secret. You know what will happen if anyone finds out. You must be careful!"

Claude Monet thought he was getting a bargain from Monsieur Futin, but the sly old man knew that he would make a very handsome profit.

Monsieur Futin deduced that the coins were probably from a hoard that had been hidden back in the days when the Romans used to ford the river. He knew there was a crossing place somewhere near the village, because the men who dredged the river for sand and gravel used to find all sorts of artefacts from the old days. The coins that the Monet boy brought to him had the head of a Roman emperor embossed on one side. Monsieur Futin was too canny to ask Claude Monet directly where he had found the coins, so he started finding out where the boys assembled after school. This meant having to leave his shop with his wife in charge during the peak periods after school and on Saturday afternoons.

When he explained to his wife why he was taking time away from the shop, she was suspicious in case he was seeing some 'fancy woman'. He had to show her the few coins that he had already traded in, as proof that he was 'onto a good thing'.

Claude Monet was too sneaky to tell any of his gang anything about the coins or where he found them, so it took several weeks before Monsieur Futin narrowed down where the boy had located the coins. During this time Monsieur Futin exchanged several more packets of sweets for coins. He knew that young Monet must be visiting the treasure trove area regularly.

Monsieur Futin took to fishing in the river because this gave him the excuse to stand and wait for the Monet boy to saunter past. By a process of observation he determined the most likely area to search, which was on the first bit of higher ground from the flood plain area along the river. He felt sure that the cache had been left by somebody in a hollow tree or buried in the ground prior to crossing the river. Maybe the owner, all those years ago, had drowned or been attacked and had never returned.

Once Monsieur Futin was sure, he waited until the children were in school and then started digging a series of holes between the trees. He knew he would only have one chance to locate the hoard before young Monet discovered the earthworks. He was partly lucky to find some coins but the problem was that the original horde had not been left in a hollow tree. It must have been left high in the branches so that when the tree died and fell, the coins had been scattered. Over the intervening centuries they had been spread further by animals and erosion.

Monsieur Futin scrabbled through the undergrowth as best as he could with a shovel and found nearly fifty of the coins before he had to abandon his efforts and try to cover the evidence of his prospecting. This gave him a fund to which he added more coins as Claude Monet brought them to him over the subsequent months and years.

He could not go to the bank with the coins, because they would want to know where he had acquired them and he was sure that there would be some sort of law against what he was doing. It stood to reason.

"There is a law against everything." He told his wife.

One day he took a chance.

There was a beautiful young woman in his shop. He knew that she was staying in the big chateau next to the river. There was nobody else in the shop, so he took out one of the Roman coins that he had put in a rear compartment of his till. He had been keeping it there so that he could feel it from time to time, and gloat. He had stashed the others behind the skirting board in his bedroom. This is the second most favourite place to hide things in France. The mattress is the favourite, and one which is plundered often in houses where old people have died.

"Excusez-moi, Mademoiselle?" he started.

She looked at him with a raised eyebrow, a slight pout and that small tilt of the head that seemed to say, 'You better have a good reason for approaching *me*.'

She was only here to get a magazine for herself and didn't want to be bothered by shrivelled shopkeepers.

"I was wondering if, perhaps, Mademoiselle, if by some chance, perhaps, your father might like to have a look at this."

Father? What father. What was this silly little man talking about? Oh, he must think that Monsieur de Gouvier is my father. Well he can think on!

Monsieur Futin held out the small silver coin that had been polished bright by his greedy fingers.

She was curious enough to take the coin and examine it. It was obviously old.

"Where did you get it?" she asked.

"It has been in family for years." Monsieur Futin evaded, "I have a small collection of them. They are quite rare. I thought that your father might like to make me an offer?"

Chandelle Charisse eyed him and was not impressed with what she saw. She knew it was a mistake to stop here for some reading matter, but it was close to the chateau and she didn't feel like taking more time than was absolutely necessary, by shopping elsewhere. She had some tanning to do and she still had to get her hair done and her nails manicured before this evening. That village coiffeuse had better be on time this time, or else she would get that other one from Beaune to come around instead.

'I am really too busy,' she thought to herself, 'to be delayed by this grubby little man.'

But the coin did look interesting.

'Perhaps I can have it pierced and have it made into a small medallion on a gold necklace?' she wondered, 'Or perhaps, with a few of them, I could have them joined up into a necklace?'

"Alright," she said, "I'll show it to him. How many have you got?"

"Aaah! At the moment I have about eight, but I can get some more if he is interested."

Not enough for a necklace then.

"Oh well, why not. And I'll take that "Marie Claire" magazine as well. How much is that?"

"Please take that as a small gift, Mademoiselle."

'Perhaps,' she thought, 'he is not quite so grubby after all.' She rewarded him with a brief smile and a flash from her eyes that would have given any twenty year old male heart palpitations, but Monsieur Futin was almost immune to the effect. He had stood behind his counter for more than forty years now and he had been cured of any optimism that was not directly linked to his cash till.

Two days later Monsieur Futin received a message on his black bakelite telephone that sat sullen and silent, from one week to the next, at the end of his serving counter.

It was a message from the telephone exchange operator in Seurre: 'Would you please present yourself at the chateau at 1600 hours on Thursday!'

There was no reply expected.

On Thursday afternoon Monsieur Futin walked down the long straight driveway, bordered by large plain trees, towards the gates to the Chateau. He was met by the grounds-man whose family had worked at the Chateau for decades. Most of the other servants and workers had been laid off after the First World War when two sons of the old owner had been killed. The present owner was the third son and he was said to be not too successful in business, but he was the owner of the ceramic factory and so he was very important in the hierarchy of the village.

Monsieur Futin was ushered into the entrance hall by a young woman whom he had never seen before. The hall had the largest expanse of tiled floor that he had ever seen. A stairway with hand carved wooden banisters curved down from a mezzanine floor which was decorated with statues in niches. Monsieur Futin could not believe his eyes. All the statues were depicting couples in advanced poses of copulation. There were limbs and torsos contorted into the most unusual positions imaginable.

No wonder that these people led such secluded lives. As Monsieur Futin stared, the girl who had let him in started to draw curtains across each of the niches, so that slowly the display was concealed.

He felt shocked. He had seen some of those magazines that had been allowed onto the market, now that it was ten years after the war, but they were kept below his counter and not on public display. Customers who wanted that sort of thing had to request to see them. He found this display of crudity obscene.

Monsieur De Gouvier emerged from one of the doors that lined the ground floor of the hall and walked towards Monsieur Rufin.

"Bonjour, Monsieur Futin." They shook hands.

"Bonjour Monsieur."

"You have brought the coins with you?"

"Yes sir, I have brought some of them. I may be able to get some more if you have a special request."

Monsieur Futin thought that he was being very savvy by controlling the flow and the quantity of these coins. He had used the same technique during the war with items that were in short supply in his shop. He had done well, by pretending that certain shortages could be circumvented by people who were prepared to pay a little more. It was a dangerous game because he had to be careful not to be accused of profiteering.

"I'll tell you what I am going to do, Monsieur Futin. I am prepared to offer you a one and only price. I will buy all of your coins here and now for a fixed price, but I will not buy any more in the future. I will offer you a good price, but only after I have inspected them all. So what you must do is go and get all the coins you have, and we will make a deal. A one time deal!"

"Yes Monsieur. I understand. I do understand. Yes, I will go and get them. But it must be for cash."

"Of course, and you must not discuss this with anybody!"

Monsieur Futin made his exit and walked briskly back to his small store on the main road. He had to tell someone about all this. He had to tell his wife at least. What if this Monsieur de Gouvier took all the coins and hit him over the head?

No he had to have some insurance.

He needed to have somebody to raise the alarm if things went bad. And anyway, what sort of offer would he get?

What were they worth?

He didn't know.

But then, who could he ask? Who could be trusted?

No one!

This was a risk, but what else could he do?

He called his wife when he got back to the shop and he explained the situation, as they closed the door and put the 'Fermé' sign in place.

They worried at the problem like puppies with a bone.

It was their one chance to make some money and at the same time it was a way to get rid of the risk of being burgled. It was quite possible that the Monet boy could tell one of his friends about the coins and then the secret would be out. It might be more dangerous to keep them than to risk dealing with the chateau owner.

With trepidation Monsieur Futin went to his bedroom and levered the skirting board away from the wall. His little bag of coins lay in a recess that he had made by removing two of the red bricks from their places. He carefully inspected his hoard and then counted out all the coins and added the ten that he had in his pocket.

He had a hundred and forty seven altogether.

They had only cost him that some bags of sweets and a few cartons of cigarettes. He was certain to make a profit out of this.

The question was how much.

He walked back to the chateau with his wife in the twilight. Some blackbirds were singing from the tops of the trees and air was fresh. His senses were heightened by the danger. This was the most exciting thing he had ever done.

Madame Futin waited by the gate. He did not want her to go into the chateau and see those lewd statues. He didn't even want to tell her about them. He tramped across the gravel courtyard and banged on the main door with one of the large circular iron knockers.

Immediately the door opened, and inside he saw that somebody had placed a table and two chairs in the centre of the hall. They seemed dwarfed by the size of the room, as did Monsieur Futin. He approached and saw that the position was floodlit from lights that shone from all around the mezzanine so the there were no shadows. It looked like the table was the focus of spotlights on a theatrical stage, except that Monsieur Futin had never seen a theatre or a stage before.

He placed the bag of coins on the table.

Monsieur de Gouvier emerged from a different door this time and strode with confidence to the table. He gestured to Monsieur Futin to take a seat and then in silence opened the bag to examine the contents.

He took his time as he checked each coin with a magnifying glass. Monsieur Futin was embarrassed that he had not cleaned and polished the coins before he brought them, but that did not seem to bother Monsieur de Gouvier.

Finally, after what seemed to be an hour, Monsieur de Gouvier put the coins into three piles, and then counted them out. He did some calculations on a sheet of paper and then left the room without saying a word.

When he returned two minutes later he was carrying a small leather case. He opened it and turned it so that Monsieur Futin could see inside. There were bundles of hundred franc notes neatly tied with twine. Monsieur Futin had never seen so much money, at one time, in his life.

The little shopkeeper did not know how to react. His heart was pumping with excitement and he was sure that the booming in his ears was from a large drum somewhere. He knew his hands would shake if he stretched out to touch the money, so he gripped them together in his lap and said nothing.

Monsieur de Gouvier said, "I offer you this cash on one condition, that you do not say anything about this transaction. If you do I will ensure that you are buried where not even the worms will find you. Do you understand?"

Monsieur Futin nodded and said nothing.

"I will know if you tell anyone, because I will have you watched. Is that clear?"

"Yes Monsieur. I understand. I have an infallible reputation. I am respected in the community. Nobody doubts my word."

This was not strictly true, and de Gouvier knew that, because he had already researched the storekeeper before he had made this rendezvous. He also knew that the storekeeper was not a brave man, and would not dare risk retaliation.

"Very well, Monsieur Futin. You will see your way out? I wish you a good evening!"

The lights around the mezzanine started to go out one by one and Monsieur Futin took the hint to go. When he closed the large main door behind himself, he found that the courtyard was almost in darkness. At the gate he could just make out the shape of his wife who was standing in the moon-shadow of a tree. He crunched his way across the gravel of the courtyard, slightly worried that he might be called back inside, and that the whole thing was an elaborate joke.

"What happened?" she asked.

"It's okay; he's made me an offer. For everything."

"How much?"

"I don't know."

"What do you mean you don't know?"

"Well, it's all in this case. More money than I've ever seen. Those coins must be worth a lot. More than I thought. Maybe I shouldn't have sold them all at once."

Monsieur Futin's natural Shylock tendencies were beginning to emerge from hiding. He quickly cloaked them with cowardice. He didn't want to risk the wrath of the most powerful and wealthy man in the village.

When he got home to his little shop he explained everything to his wife. Now they were in even more risk of being burgled and what was worse, they could not take this money to the bank. There would be questions, and they knew that secrets about accounts and amounts in them were open for discussions in the cafés and bars.

The couple discussed the problem late into the night and eventually decided that they would buy a property somewhere far away from the village, where nobody would know about them. They would hide the money in a 'maison secondaire', and then they could think about selling their shop and moving away in secret.

After a series of covert journeys to the south of France the Futins bought an apartment in Contes, a small village occupied by artists in the hills behind Nice. He knew full well that if he showed any display of wealth in his home village, then somebody would report him to the authorities, and then they in turn would want to know how he had found the money.

Monsieur Futin regarded his fellow villagers as if they were all a murder of crows, all of whom watch each other to make sure that not one of them can gain an unfair advantage over the others.

He could just imagine the cackling and cawing that would result, if they knew he had made a profit out of a child.

When Claude Monet returned to the village for his retirement he was not the first of the old gang of schoolboys to return. Charles Vincent had left the village after going to college and become an engineer, had married and had raised a family and had now returned. He was keeping himself to himself in a large house in the centre of the village and did not seem inclined to have much to do with his old acquaintances from school. Monet had a suspicion that now the rôles of the two schoolboys might well be reversed, because an engineer is somewhat more important than a union leader of a minor printing company.

There was Augustin Février who had never moved away, but Claude Monet had never thought of him as an important member of the gang, although Augustin Février thought he was. Février had not come into the full glare of Marie Peron's hatred, because she seldom saw him. Madame Février had collected the bread every morning while he was working and she had continued to do this after he had been laid off.

Jean Corbier had moved away and become a Gendarme and Presidential escort and Marie had forgotten about him to a large extent, in his absence.

The two Peltier brothers had gone off to join the army and Marie had no idea, nor did she wish to know, what had happened to them. Then there were the girls, like Michelle Pepin who married the fat Post Master Michel Bonnadot, but she stayed in her house almost all of the time these days. Marie could not remember when she had last talked to her, although she saw her everyday when she came for bread. Michelle Bonnadot was one of those people who get swept along by the others and now she is one of those who are swept under the carpet, by life.

Marie could, and did, successfully ignore her.

Anyway, Marie felt that she had accomplished so much more than being the downtrodden wife of a foncière, so whenever she did see the Post Master's wife, it gave her self esteem a little boost to think that she had achieved more than Michelle.

Marie had never kept her distain for others a secret, but she had kept her hatred of Monet to herself. She never shared this particular emotion with PP because he would not have understood the meaning, or the feeling, of her hatred. It was not an emotion that he had in his character.

PP had no malice and so did not recognise it in others. He had been born without envy. When he smiled and greeted people, they were disarmed by his apparent innocence.

The widows and wives on his rounds looked forward each day to the moment when he would stop outside their houses and toot the horn of his little van. He had time to greet each one of them and ask about how the chickens were laying, and if the new calf was doing well. He knew all their grandchildren's names and when they had last come to visit from the big cities where they lived with their parents.

Even the guard dogs wagged their tails when PP stopped and called to them.

Everybody was pleased to see him.

Every day he had a comment about how beautiful the roses were, that festooned Madame Fournier's entrance, or how well the geese that Monsieur Faupin was breeding, were multiplying. He complemented each of his customers and they loved him. They all thought that he must be a happy man with a lovely family of his own. They imagined that he came from a village where the sun always shone.

It was a village that, of course, they had never had a reason to visit.

This meant that they had not met Marie.

PP was never aware of the cesspool of hatred that Marie carried inside herself. He knew that she was moody, but she was also private. In the same way that a dog knows when its master is having an off day, PP knew there were times to keep a low profile, until Marie's mood changed.

After Monsieur Monet left the shop with his two baguettes Marie swept the pile of crumbs and flakes of bread through the door of the shop, and then across the pavement into the gutter at the side of the road. The residue would eventually be swilled by rainwater into the drain. As Marie turned and re-entered the shop, a rather well to-do lady alighted from a parked BMW across the road and then followed Marie inside.

Marie recognised the lady as the wife of one of the Pharmacists in Seurre. She was a chatty person who carried on a conversation with everybody she met. She was known to be indiscrete, because her conversations often concerned prescriptions that people presented at the Pharmacy. This was information which should have been confidential but, to the Pharmacist's wife, it was the grist that made up the dough that resulted in the bread of conversation.

She was known, behind her back, as the 'Cuisinière' because of her ability to 'cook up' a scandal out of the most basic of ingredients.

She swept into the bakery with her scarves fluttering and her hat placed 'just so'. Her expensive clothing was out of place in this village bakery and her high-priced perfume competed successfully with the aromas of baking bread.

Marie wondered to herself why it is that wealthy people were so convinced that they smelt so bad, that they had to use such large quantities of scent to disguise themselves to ordinary people like her.

"Bonjour, Madame Paris."

"Good morning Madame Peron. May I have a selection of pastries? I have the ladies from the committee of the 'Restos du Coeur' coming for a meeting and I have to have some tarts to go with the coffee."

Marie, privately thinking of Madame Paris as being a tart herself, silently made a selection of PP's best pastries.

Madame Paris chattered on as though Marie was one of her ardent followers of gossip.

"They are all coming around to discuss the fête that we are holding next week to raise funds for the organisation, and we have to make a roster to collect donations at the supermarkets. You know how hard it is to get people to stand and ask the shoppers to leave some sort of donation for those less fortunate than themselves? I would do it myself, but I am so busy these days organising everything. Oh, Madame, don't put any of those mushroom tarts in with the others, please. We had a scare at the Pharmacy last week. That Chazelle boy, you know the one who sells mushrooms in Seurre? Well he sold some mushrooms that made several people ill. Three of them had to go to hospital and the others had to have anti-nausea tablets. What a performance! And that was after my husband told him which ones were poisonous and which he should throw away. Stupid person, he should have known that just rubbing those poisonous ones with the good ones would cause people to get ill, even if they ate the good ones. So nobody in Seurre wants to eat mushrooms now, in case there are some more bad ones from that basket. Good; that will be all, thank you! How much is that? Fifteen euros fifty? There you are! Au revoir!"

And Madame 'Cuisinière' swept out of the shop unaware that Marie had not returned her departing salutation, and also unaware that she had planted seeds for a macabre plan in Marie's mind.

So simple!

So easy!

Marie felt the thrill of excitement that was, for her, almost as good as an orgasm. Well, perhaps more like what she thought that an orgasm would be, if she had ever experienced one.

A part of Marie's bitterness with life did revolve around the fact that PP, although a pleasant enough person to have around as an unpaid provider of bread and labour, was nevertheless not a person to inspire thoughts of sexual fantasy in a practical woman.

Marie had wondered at the way in which other people found this subject of sex so fascinating.

She was at the hub of many of the lines of communication in the village, in that conversations in the shop often reverted to who was having an 'affaire' with whom. She had found that her non-participation in the village scandal mongering had led to the belief among her clients that they could discus all sorts of indiscretions of the neighbourhood with each other in the bakery shop, and that Marie would not relay them onwards.

This was because Marie found the subject boring.

An opening gambit of conversation by many clients who had a juicy bit of information about a neighbour would be:

"Did you hear about what Michelle Fubin said about that daughter of the rich Japanese man who bought the Chateau, after Monsieur De Gouvier absconded with the salaries and the pension monies?"

Or another would say:

"You know? I saw that Danielle Jolly getting into a car last week. That girl is just like her grandfather! She is as promiscuous as hell. And do you know whose car it was? I'll bet you'll never guess!"

Well that was always true, because Marie never did guess, but she often had a very good idea about who it was from the other snippets of information that came her way.

"It was that Peltier boy, you know, the one who married that girl from Dijon. I knew that marriage wouldn't work. Taking on a stranger from that distance away, to be a wife, never works! Those big city girls don't know how to behave properly in the country."

"Three euros forty five!"

"There you are, but don't say it was me who told you. That Madame Peltier still hasn't forgiven me for not going to that boy's baptism twenty five years ago. Well 'phut' to her, I say!"

And the door of the shop slams shut behind another happy customer who has offloaded today's load of malice and innuendo.

Marie rearranges her bread and wipes the counter surface until the next customer pushes the door open with another snippet of gloom and despondency.

Sometimes there is a break in the stream of customers, and Marie stares at the odd cars which pass by outside on the road to Dijon. Occasionally one makes more noise than another, but there is nothing that ever makes her wonder about where they are going, or who is driving them.

But now, today, she is actually excited.

A plan has unveiled itself with all that dreadful simplicity of an insight, as though the germ of it has been waiting for just the right combination of hate and opportunity to combine.

She wipes at the surface of the counter with her worn cloth, and she actually smiles.

It is so simple.

All she has to do is to find out where that Chazelle boy found those mushrooms. After that it will be easy. She will be able make a 'special' bread and keep it on one side. Under the counter perhaps where she can reach for it without attracting attention. It will not be the normal baguette mixture, because they will taste the difference.

She will have to promote a new type of bread, one that has other things in it. Perhaps she can make nut bread like they do in the south. That was according to that truck driver, who was the son of old Monsieur Roger du Bois, who had started that taxi and ambulance service in Seurre after the war.

He had said that those people in the south put herbs and olive oil in the bread, along with the nuts. Crazy! But those sorts of ingredients would disguise the taste of the mushrooms.

But how can she get that Monet man to buy the bread?

Maybe she can ask him to try it?

Perhaps she could ask him for his opinion?

But what if he didn't like it?

Maybe she should try to get him to buy it regularly before giving him one with poison mushrooms in it?

But what if he didn't want it anyway?

Perhaps she should just make it and wait for the right moment and then just give it to him as a gift?

He would be sure to be suspicious about that. Marie knows that everybody is aware that she does not give away bread, even old stale bread!

Perhaps this might not be so simple after all.

She carries on wiping her counter on autopilot while she ponders the complexities of how to encourage someone to try a new type of bread. She knows that the natural conservatism of people in the countryside, against anything new, will make it difficult to get any of the villagers to try anything different.

They will be more likely to pick it up, feel it, prod it, smell it and then put it back with a moue of the mouth and maybe even a shrug.

"Sometimes," she remembers her mother saying "to get a fellow Frenchmen to try a new food is as difficult as making a cat catch a cabbage."

But, on the other hand, Monet had been in Paris all his life. He had adopted that arrogance of a Parisian on top of his already superior attitude.

Then Marie has a brainwave.

"I can tell him that the herbs in the bread will be good for his sex life!"

Now there is an idea!

She knows, from her village informants about 'Life', how many of them complain that their husbands have lost their ardour by the time they come to retirement age. She had heard that there were products one could buy to enhance the ability and the desire for these activities. Maybe these products worked like the green grass of Spring, which made the animals get randy.

She knows what those bulls and cows do in the field on the way up to the cemetery, when the farmers let them get at each other.

It is positively embarrassing.

Whenever she walks up there to renew the flowers on her parents' grave, she knows that, at that time of the year, she has to walk on the opposite side of the road.

Disgusting.

'But maybe I can get that Monet man to buy the bread,' she schemes, 'if he thinks that it will enhance his prowess. On the other hand, how about if I get Madame Monet to buy it for her husband. That will be a much better way to ensure that he tries it!'

'His wife will nag him to try it, or maybe even sneak it onto his plate when he is watching television.'

Marie finishes wiping the counter with a flourish.

That is it!

'Everybody knows how those Parisians, who live in apartments, never sit down to eat a proper evening meal in the kitchen, like country folk. They either eat in a restaurant or they sit watching that stupid television box, while at the same time getting indigestion from eating packaged food.'

She decides to prepare the bread first and then get Madame Monet to buy it. She is a 'Parisienne' and Marie knows from the grapevine that she is not happy at being transposed to the village. She is dissatisfied with life down here in the country, so if Marie can find a way to make life more interesting for her, she will probably go for it. Marie is sure that, at some stage, Monet's wife will come into her shop to buy the daily bread.

All Marie has to do now is to find out where to get the mushrooms, and then to develop a recipe for the bread. She will be ready for when Madame Monet comes to the shop.

For the first time in forty five years of selling bread from her little shop, Marie Peron starts to hum a tune.

In the afternoon, when PP leaves to collect the flour for the month from the Bragny Mill, Marie wheels out her father's bicycle from the shed at the bottom of the garden. It has been there ever since her father died, and has not been used. There is a film of rust on the wheel rims and the rod and lever mechanism of the brakes is stiff but seems to work. Miraculously the tyres are inflated and in good condition.

'It must have been PP,' she thinks, 'who has kept it in a usable condition.'

She sets off on the road towards Dijon. She passes the entrance to the chateau, opposite which is the scruffy house of the Chazelle family. Then she pedals up the incline that leads past the cemetery. Now she is in open country. Normally she walks up here when she comes to visit her parents' grave, so she is surprised at how much steeper it seems now that she is pedalling a bicycle. She begins to enjoy the sensation of breeze and the view of fields of wheat as they fold away into clefts in the countryside.

In the distance is the forest of Montmain, which is her destination. She pedals onwards until she gets to the trees. She can see where woodcutters have been at work. They have cleared paths into the forest to access their neat stacks of wood. She dismounts and carries her bicycle across the ditch at the side of the road and then pushes it between the trees. She props it against a young oak, and wonders where she should start looking.

Her problem is that she does not know quite what kind of mushrooms she needs. She knows that people come up here to look for mushrooms. There had been people from the Alsace who had come into her shop who said they came all the way here to hunt for mushrooms. So there must be mushrooms somewhere. She knows that this is the right time of the year.

She stares into the clearings between the large oak trees. It is almost like a park now, where the smaller scrub wood has been cleared away by the woodcutters. She sees a small marker in the shape of a cross. It looks like somebody's grave. There is no writing on it. She removes her scarf that she had used for protection against the wind while she was riding her bicycle.

How is she going to tell which mushrooms are which? She knows the normal ones, which are called the 'Champignons de Paris'. They look like the ones for sale in the shops. She knows the Cèpe because her mother used to use it for cooking, and the 'Trompette des Morts' or black Death Trumpets which her mother had used in Omelettes. But where did Marc Chazelle collect the poisonous mushrooms and what do they look like?

She thinks that it is most likely that they are similar in appearance to the edible ones and that is why those people got sick in Seurre. They couldn't tell the difference.

Marie is distrustful of the claims of mushroom hunters, concerning how many mushrooms they find. She reckons that their claims will be like the fishermen's tales: full of exaggeration without the proof in hand. But now she has a reason to be interested in what they had been saying over the years.

She selects a stick that had fallen to the forest floor and uses it as a staff to push the bushes and twigs aside. Most of the trees in this part of the forest are oak and ash and as she walks she sees that there are plantations of other different types of trees. She knows that some types of mushrooms are found near certain species of trees, but what type of tree and where to find them is the puzzle.

Then she sees a spectacular mushroom. It is red and has an attractive speckle of white spots that look like minute meringues spread over the head. It is like the mushrooms she had seen in illustrated children's books. It is growing near the roots of a large pine tree.

Marie crouches down and pulls it from the ground. It is very attractive and has a white stem with a bulbous base. It looks promising as something to try, but it can't be mistaken for a cultured mushroom. She continues to search and finds several more of the red ones with white dots. She picks them and puts them into her folded scarf. She finds some dark evil looking mushrooms growing on the trunks of fallen trees. They look poisonous enough, but they could never be mistaken for the ordinary edible ones.

She doesn't find any more interesting specimens, so decides that she will go home and do some research. In the meanwhile, she decides to practice with these pretty red ones to see if she can combine them into bread or a pastry.

She pedals back to the village which is much easier than the outward trip, because it is nearly all downhill. Marie is almost euphoric when she arrives back at the bakery, and it crosses her mind that cycling could be an enjoyable way to spend some afternoons.

Then she quashes the thought.

Riding bicycles is for fitness fanatics.

She opens her knotted scarf containing the mushrooms and lays them out on the kitchen table. They look so innocuous lying here; it is difficult to believe that they are capable of harming anyone. Anyway, as far as Marie knows, these ones are harmless. All she is going to do is to experiment with them, for the taste and the texture.

She takes a carving knife and slices at the head of one of the mushrooms. It is easy to cut and slightly firm, rather like cutting a hard boiled egg. She wonders if she should include the red coloured skin in the recipe. Why not, as it is only an experiment. She cuts the pieces into smaller and smaller cubes until they are the size of matchstick heads. Then she selects two chocolate croissants from the morning's bake and starts to carefully insert the pieces of mushroom into the folds of the patisserie. The chocolate on the croissants should disguise the taste of the mushroom.

She takes the two croissants through to the shop and places them on her counter surface. She stares though the display window.

There she sees, cycling along the side of the road, the mushroom picker, Marc Chazelle.

What a chance!

Marie steps out of the shop to intercept him.

She can use him as a guinea pig and at the same time try to get information from him about where he does his mushroom picking.

"Bonjour, Marc!" she calls brightly…..

Marc Deux Chazelle and Claude Monet

Marc Chazelle is the twelfth child of the twenty one children that Madame Chazelle has brought into the world. He was the second 'Marc' of the family because when he was born his mother didn't think that he would live for long, so she gave him the same name as his eldest brother. She reckoned that both of them had been conceived when their father had been under the influence of Marc. In fact, most of her children had been conceived while their father was drunk, which may have had something to do with the fact that several of them grew up to be alcoholics.

Because there were two Marcs in the family, the younger one started off life his being called 'Marc Deux'. He achieved a certain importance because, as the twelfth child, he qualified his mother for a gold medal from the Government for 'Services to France'. Normally it is the eighth child that qualifies a mother for the Gold Medal for large families in France, but the Mayor of the village at the time of her eighth child did not approve of the Chazelle family, so he had not submitted Madame Chazelle's name for consideration. In fact Marc Deux was the thirteenth child as one of his older sisters had died when she was two years old, but the family was superstitious, so he was known as the twelfth and his next younger brother, who followed him into the world, was known as the fourteenth.

Whether this unfortunate number had anything to do with luck is not certain, but it did not change the fact that when he was born the umbilical cord was twisted around his neck. He suffered a shortage of oxygen for those few vital minutes during and after birth. He was lucky that the long term effect of this was not more severe, but as it was, it did reduce his ability to learn and understand. However, in spite of this drawback, in his teenage years he developed an uncanny ability to move around the village in a way that was as unobtrusive as a weasel.

He never managed to qualify for a driving licence and so it was a grave mistake when he was given a job driving a tractor, with a mower attachment, to cut the verges of roads near the village. The 'Département' was responsible for this error and had to bear the responsibility when he crashed into a parked car, while looking at the cutter blades, rather than where he was going. It was the only official job that he was ever been given.

After an investigation into the circumstances of the accident, Marc Deux was given a monetary allowance from the State and was left alone, to be taken care of by his family. This meant minimal supervision of the young man, because his mother was occupied in producing her ever increasing family.

Madame Chazelle was not only famous for her large family, but also gained notoriety when the caretaker of the Japanese owner of the Chateau in the village had a problem.

Mr Yoko Sukianni had taken over the chateau from Monsieur de Gouvier after the ceramic factory went out of business. There was talk that the reason for the closure was because a large amount of cash went missing, and could not be accounted for. It was all to do with salaries and pension contributions that were apparently stolen from the Chateau. It was the final incident during a period of declining demand for ceramic ware that precipitated the end of the factory.

The new Japanese owner only came to the village once a year. Each time he arrived in his helicopter, which touched down in the enclosed courtyard, he secluded himself out of sight for a month. Nobody knew what he did during this period as he was rarely seen, and the caretaker had been instructed to say nothing about his employer. However he did once let slip that his employer was keen on breeding Racehorses.

These few, but special, animals were kept in stables within the courtyard and were allowed to graze occasionally on the fields surrounding the chateau during spring, when the new grass is at its best.

The emergency at the chateau occurred while the owner was not there.

One of the mares died during the delivery of her foal. That was catastrophic enough but the sire of this valuable foal, by expensive artificial insemination, was a prominent Irish stallion. The foal was born in July which was a problem because there were no cows with newborn calves at that time of the year. The caretaker knew that he needed to give the foal a first drink of colostrum from an animal that had just given birth, in order that the valuable young horse could acquire the antibodies and strength that it needed.

Madame Chazelle had just given birth to her eighteenth child at home that same evening. The news of both events travelled on the 'grapevine' through the village which, because of the later time in the day, was via the village bar rather than via the bakery.

Madame Chazelle heard the news, fed her new baby, tucked him into the well used family cot and then walked down the driveway to the gates of the chateau.

The caretaker was horrified at her suggestion, but acquiesced when she explained to him that, "Mother's milk is mother's milk, and I have lots to spare!"

The foal took to her with no problem and she saved the small animal's life. She became known as the 'Nourrice de Cheval Médaille d'Or' (Gold Medal Horse Nurse) as a result.

She is the most recent Nourrice of a long tradition of Wet Nurses from the peasants of the Bourgogne and Morvan, who had found work feeding the children of wealthy Parisians, ever since the seventeenth century. In those days it was a valuable source of revenue for these poor families, who sent their women to feed the children of the wealthy mothers of Paris. In this way they made money for their families, while the Parisian Ladies kept their slender figures and their buoyant breasts. Beautiful breasts were very important assets in those days as they were more on display, due to fashions and see-through dresses of the time, than at any other period of history.

Marc Deux was ignored by his family and left to his own devices which led to him cycling around the village and the adjoining countryside. He had a loose routine, which involved doing a circuit of the houses where villagers had vegetable plots. He knew from his patrols when people went shopping and what routines they followed when going to work. In this way he was able to filch tomatoes and fruit and sneak them into his handlebar pannier. He sold these ill-gotten gains to fruit and vegetable shops and private individuals in Seurre. In this way he acquired pocket money for booze. He was only following the example of his father, who was well known for supplying wild mushrooms.

It didn't take long before the local suppliers of cannabis started to use Marc Deux for distributing their merchandise.

The main family involved in the cannabis trade lives in Labergement les Seurre. They believe that they are carrying on a tradition of supplying the local market with its needs that had started in the time of the Phoenicians. They are only supplying a demand and so therefore, they think that they should be considered as honourable traders. The two sons of the family have a black BMW with which they patrol the villages. They have a series of stopping places where they wait for their clients. They use Marc Deux for the distribution of small amounts of cannabis, which he hides in a small abandoned hunting cabin near the river.

Marc Deux is a liability however, because he uses the drug himself occasionally. Then he stops at the village bar until he gets thrown out by the landlord for being a nuisance. The Police know about these low level activities and they threaten Marc Deux from time to time, but with limited success. Villagers complain to the Mayor but she won't 'section' him to an institution, because that would mean alienating the Chazelle family, and that could cost her far *far* too many votes.

So the community continues with this veiled tolerance, waiting for a defining moment when some sort of action can be taken against Marc Deux.

Marc Deux is blamed for many things.

Whenever a gardener can not find his rake, or a housewife can't find a towel that she has washed 'just yesterday', which she is sure she 'has put on the line to dry', then the villagers declare that the village idiot has struck again.

He is blamed for pigeons missing from the dovecotes, for missing hubcaps and even for the otherwise inexplicable loss of heating oil from locked tanks. All the while, however, he circles the village on his bicycle, not quite understanding the hostile glances that are thrown at him over walls, through windows and in the street.

For this reason he nearly falls off his bicycle with surprise when Marie Peron calls to him from the Baker's shop as he cycles past.

She had never done that before.

He squeals his brakes to a halt and eyes her with curiosity and suspicion.

She is actually smiling.

"Bonjour Marc," she calls brightly.

"Good morning, Madame," he answers cautiously.

"Isn't it a lovely day?" she asks.

"Yes."

"Are you well?"

"Yes, not bad."

"How are the family? And your mother?"

"They are all going well."

"Will you pass on my greetings to her?" asks Marie.

This is too much for Marc Deux. He knows that he isn't the brightest person in the village, but even *he* knows that something is wrong if Marie Peron is being *this* pleasant to him. He fingers the handlebar and the bell on his bicycle. He fidgets with the brake levers.

"What is it? What do you want?" he asks finally.

"Nothing Marc, except maybe you would like to try this?"

Marie proffers to him a warm fresh chocolate croissant that she has been holding in the folds of her dress.

Marc Deux looks at it with suspicion. He knows that, for the price of this croissant, he could get two or three cheap beers at the supermarket.

"Go on, take it. It's a gift. Free!"

He takes the treat and then doesn't know what to do with it. Should he stuff it into his mouth here in the street or take it with him?

Marie Peron is looking at him to gauge his reaction.

"Would you like another one?" she asks.

'This is obviously a trap,' thinks Marc.

She proffers another that she has been holding in her other hand. Marc Deux is tempted to grab it, jump onto his bicycle and ride away. He knows that, in his large family, two of anything gets shared whether you want to share or not. He hesitates and then takes the small gift.

"Thank you." he says.

"That's alright." Marie smiles, "Why not come around tomorrow and I'll give you a jam beigne."

Marc Deux reacts by stepping back, but then realises that she means a jam doughnut, not a slap. The two words are the same in French.

Marie sees his confusion, and reminds herself to proceed slowly, because although this young man is sly, he isn't very bright.

Marc Deux nods to Marie.

"Thank you, Madame" he says, as he mounts his bicycle and rides away, before she changes her mind.

Marie wipes her hands on her apron as an automatic response, turns and re-enters her shop. Marc Deux rides down to the river where he leans his bicycle against a tree and examines his croissants.

They look alright, and they smell alright.

He tastes the end of one.

It is perfect.

The layers of pastry melt in his mouth. He tears pieces from the body of the pastry and there he tastes the nodules of chocolate that have melted and reset in the cooking process. There is something special that happens to good chocolate, when it resets after cooking in good pastry.

Marc Deux savours it to the full.

When he has finished both of the croissants he sits and stares into the waters of the river. This place is tranquil for him and there are times that he can just stare at the water and think of nothing in particular, for the whole afternoon.

Mistily he wonders why Madame Peron should want to give him these presents.

Nobody does that in this village.

This is strange.

He knows that he shouldn't tell anyone, especially anyone in his family, because they will all want what he has got. There won't be enough for them all. He wonders how he can remind himself to go to the bakery in the morning.

He takes his bottle of Pastis from the basket of his bicycle and examines it. It is only about a third full, so he goes to the edge of the river and carefully fills it with water. The contents turn milky and the aroma of liquorice rises from the neck of the bottle as he sniffs it.

He settles down by the water's edge and sips at his bottle and wonders if anybody will come today to buy some cannabis. It is comfortable lying here on the grass with the water flowing past.

'It is Thursday,' he thinks, 'so this is the right place scheduled for Thursday for those regulars from Bagnot. They are turning into good customers.'

He sips at his bottle until, all too soon, it is empty so then he relaxes and falls asleep on the grass, in the sunshine.

The swan must be at least five metres high and all of its feathers are sparkling, as though there are currents of static electricity coursing between them. It is beautiful as it stares down at the young man on the grass. It blinks its long eyelashes over achingly blue eyes and clears its throat.

"Come along now Marc, why are you sleeping away the day? We have things to do!"

Marc opens his eyes and looks at the gorgeous head silhouetted against the green sky. The beak is smiling at him. He rubs his eyes and sees that his hands have changed into flippers. He can see his pointy nose so he pushes his whiskers full forward with his flippers, which is what seals do when they are curious.

"What?..... What things..... do we have to do?"

The trees, who are dabbling with their roots in the water, giggle to each other. One nudges her neighbour and whispers, "Silly boy, he's forgotten already!"

The reeds nearby, who are always rustling secrets to each other, start pouting.

"It'ss sso ssilly to whisper ssecretss!" claims one.

"Yess!" lisp the others.

"You promised that you would be ready," says the swan, "to come flying with me today."

Marc looks at his flippers and wonders just how he will be able to fly with them. He flaps them and finds that, as he is lying on his back, he can smack them together as though he is applauding. Each time he slaps them they grow. He starts creating gusts of wind with them that jostle the branches of the trees.

"Here! Stop pushing us about!" complains one of the trees. "We've got children here."

Marc can see that the wind he is creating with his flippers is tumbling some of the little bushes. They are playing near the bank of the river.

"Well, you should have taught them to swim." he retorts crossly. "It's all your fault."

"So are you ready now?" asks the swan.

"Yes. Where shall we go?" replies Marc.

"As far as the sun and back and then we'll stop on the moon for some cheese and wine."

Marc doesn't think he can stand up so he rolls and wriggles towards the water. The grass is so soft and the pebbles are squishy, like creamy éclairs, and they taste almost as good. He wriggles into the water and starts to flap his flippers that are now longer than his body.

He feels so graceful and powerful as he surges forward. Everything is so effortless. His wonderful flippers are flexing as he powers through the water. He knows he must be leaving a wake of froth behind him, like a racing powerboat.

Why hasn't he done this before?

He is leaving the swan behind.

The water is warm and thick, like melted chocolate.

It tastes so good.

And it smells even better.

He breathes the water and flaps his wings and feels ecstatic. He is happier than he has ever been, in his confused life.

He wonders briefly why the sky is becoming dark.

Curious... but it doesn't really matter.

Patrice Mortier declared at the inquest that he had seen Marc Chazelle enter the river.

"I saw him from where I was fishing across the river. He came down from the village on his bicycle and then sat on the grass. Later he seemed to fall asleep. I thought he was drunk again. Anyway, he didn't make any noise so he was not disturbing the fish. The next thing I saw was that he was rolling around on the grass flailing his arms. There was a swan on the water nearby and I thought that maybe he was trying to catch it, because he rolled into the river and started to flap about."

"Did he shout for help?" asked the coroner.

"He was shouting something, but it wasn't for help. It sounded like 'I can fly, I can fly', but I am not sure. He was over two hundred metres away."

"What happened next?"

"Well, he flopped about for about half a minute, and then just lay in the water. The current took him away towards the south."

"Was there anybody else in the vicinity?"

"I didn't see anyone. Then a car came along on my side of the river, so I stopped the driver and asked him to call the emergency volunteers in Seurre. He said he would. By that time the body was out of sight on the other side of the island. When the pompiers came they didn't believe me at first. It was the downstream lock keeper who found him three days later, floating near the lock."

Doctor Melun confirmed that substantial traces of alcohol had been found in Marc Chazelle's blood and that the autopsy results declared that he had severe cirrhosis of his liver. The cause of death was drowning.

The Police testimony listed the number of times that they had received reports and complaints about Marc's drink related behaviour. They told the inquest how they had dragged the river for the body and had sent divers down to search in the holes that had been left from the old sand dredging operations. They declined to say that their efforts were not as sustained as when one of the gendarmes from Chalon had fallen into the river. On that occasion the off duty policeman had fallen off the back of one of the pleasure powerboats, and his drinking companions didn't notice his absence for several minutes. On that occasion the SAMU helicopters had been called to aid in the search, but Marc Chazelle did not rate such expenditure.

The owner of the village bar confirmed that Marc had been banned from drinking there, but declined to add that it was the Police who forced this restriction, rather than him.

The final verdict was 'death by misadventure' and the inquest was closed.

Marie Peron is disappointed as usual.

Her 'guinea pig' had gone and drowned himself, so she still doesn't know if the mushrooms tasted alright and if they are poisonous or not. She decides that she will try them out on an animal instead and then see what happens.

She goes into the tabac next door to her bakery in order to buy a tin of dog food. It is more expensive here than in the supermarkets, but it does save her the trouble of going to Seurre. If she was to ask PP to buy dog food, with his weekly shopping, he would want to know why.

She has never bought dog food before, as she has never owned a pet of any kind. She is impressed that the tin opens with a quick release lid. She pulls the top off the container and smells the contents.

Not bad.

The aroma of the dog food will undoubtedly cover the smell of the mushrooms, even with a dog's smelling capability. She empties the contents into a bowl and stirs the mixture with a spoon. There are all sorts of lumps in it, and there are even a few peas. Lumps of mushroom in the gravy will be perfectly concealed.

She takes a single mushroom from the plastic container that she uses to hide them in the fridge, so that PP will not find them. She slices the whole fungus into pieces and mixes them into the food, until all traces of the red cubes are covered with the slimy gravy.

'It might be suspicious if I leave the bowl outside the shop, especially as it is now late,' she thinks. 'So I'll put it near the bar where the patrons tie their dogs. Then I can watch from a distance to see what happens.'

She has a look outside the shop to see if there is anybody in sight. There are two bicycles leaning on the wall near the bar on the other side of the tabac. That means that there are some people already in the bar, but there are no dogs tied up outside. She knows that 'walking the dog' is an excuse that several local husbands use for getting out of the house and away from their wives. Those customers will be along soon.

Walking the dog is a euphemism for having a Pastis. That is among the barflies. Some of the husbands 'walk the dog' by making it run behind the car down along the riverside road, which gains them sufficient 'time' for a couple of snifters on the way home.

She walks nonchalantly past the tabac and puts the bowl of dog food behind the bicycle rack outside the bar. The dogs should be able to reach it from there and yet it is not easy to see in the dusk. Marie returns to the bakery and then takes her broom and starts to sweep outside the shop as an excuse, to see what happens next.

Within fifteen minutes there are two dogs tied up and she can see that they are slurping at the food. All she has to do is to wait. Then a striped cat that lives across the road comes over to investigate. Marie has seen that this cat sometimes hunts for mice in the fields near the chateau. It helps itself to the food in the bowl as well. It seems as though the dogs don't mind the cat being there, as they are both sitting patiently and staring into the distance.

Nothing is happening so Marie decides to go inside and make a cup of coffee. PP has settled himself in front of the television prior to having an early night, so Marie drinks her coffee and watches a bit of the programme that PP likes.

'What does he find so interesting about it?' she wonders.

The programme concerns people with imaginary lives. It seems that they live in a city somewhere, where they do no work and yet have money and time to sit about in a café discussing their personal problems. She doesn't find real people interesting, so why should she spend her time looking at people who don't exist.

It doesn't make sense.

Then, over the noise of babbling voices on the television, Marie hears the sound of dogs howling.

She goes through to the shop and looks through the glass display window, where there is a gap in the curtain. There is a commotion going on outside the bar.

She opens the door and sees that several people are standing in a group. Two of them have their dogs on leashes. The animals are sitting in the centre of the gathering of men and they are howling. One is a spaniel of sorts and the other is a terrier of dubious parentage. One could be forgiven for thinking, from the noise, that they were wolves.

The two dogs seem to be trying to outdo each other by baying long yodelling notes, as though they are trying to sing an opera. Neither of the dogs seems to notice the men who are looking befuddled by this extraordinary behaviour.

The cat is on top of the low wall next to the bar and it is also yowling with passion. Some of the men seem amused while the two dog owners are understandably concerned.

How are they going to explain this to their wives?

A car, approaching from Seurre, slows up because some of the men are standing in the road causing an obstruction. The driver dips his headlights and that seems to trigger a reaction in the cat. It flies off the wall and attacks the car. It jumps onto the bonnet and attacks the windscreen, snarling and spitting. The driver gets such a shock that he brakes and swerves and collides with the raised flowerbeds along the side of the road. Men jump out of the way and dogs howl as the cat slips off the bonnet of the car.

It falls under the front left wheel.

The car stops with the cat under the wheel. The dogs go berserk and start leaping about like trout caught on a fishing line. They try to run up the men as if to sit on their shoulders and then start snapping at everyone including their owners.

The bar proprietor calls the gendarmerie to report the accident, because he wants to get his word in first, in case the accident is blamed on him and his bar. He knows that the first to make a report is the one who is usually believed, and he doesn't want a repeat of the fracas that had occurred six months before.

It wasn't his fault that those two women started fighting during the Remembrance Parade over the husband of Madame Souviene. Certainly, they had both been in his bar beforehand, but he was not responsible for the fact that Monsieur Souviene was not a faithful husband, and that his wife didn't care that he slept around. The police had blamed him because the two women were drunk.

"It is always unfair that they always blame the barman. I'm only in business just like everybody else!"

Anyway, that fight in the street had been a 'spectacle' for the village, and it had given the men in the bar something to guffaw about, which is always good for business. It was like that other time when the husband of Régine Pipot had tried to murder his wife. Pierre Pipot had been in the bar all afternoon complaining that his wife had taken up to going to Discos in Beaune, and that "Now," he said, "I have had enough!"

He was going to demand his conjugal rights that night. He had thumped the bar counter with determination in between bolstering his resolve with pastis. The finale was that when she came home she had refused him, and so he had chased her into the street with his rifle. Fortunately he called the police to tell them they should come to stop him, because he was going to shoot his wife. They arrived and he surrendered his weapon, after a lot of shouting and swearing outside the bar. The magistrate made Pierre go on a 'drying out' programme, rather than sending him to jail, because his rifle wasn't loaded at the time and also there is certain sympathy, in France, for husbands who get emotionally unbalanced, for good reason.

The whole incident had cost the bar a good customer, but the subsequent 'post mortems' and lively re-enactments of the night in question had bolstered trade. The barman had been blamed by the magistrate for not limiting his customers' consumption, which is why he was going to make sure that this time, his version of the accident outside the bar was going to absolve him of any blame.

The gendarmes arrive with their blue light flashing and their siren warbling, all the way from Seurre. The pompiers come soon afterwards but there is nothing for them to do, except to move the crashed car, which was now an obstruction in the road. The driver is unhurt physically, but is complaining about mad cats, and how is he going to explain this accident to his father, whose car he has borrowed. One of the pompiers picks up the flattened cat by the tail and drops it into the rubbish bin, next to the door of the bar.

Then one man complains that one of the dogs has bitten him, so he is escorted to the ambulance to be taken to hospital and checked for rabies.

The others, who have not been bitten, start to tell each other lurid stories about how they know of someone who had heard of a person who might have had rabies. All quite untrue, of course, but when had that ever been a restriction on bar stories? The stories had been embellished and exaggerated over the years, and although they all know this, it doesn't do a lot to calm the patient in the ambulance.

Eventually peace is restored and the patrons return to the bar to exaggerate to each other about what had happened. The two dog owners take their delusional dogs home, to then try and explain to their wives what has been going on, and that it is ***not*** **at all** drink related.

Marie stares down at the scene of confusion from her bedroom window and smiles to herself.

She isn't sure what the mushrooms have done to the dogs, but what ever it is, it will be good to see Claude Monet standing in the street and howling at the moon.

****

Claude Monet in fact didn't howl at the moon, but he did suffer the most frightening nightmare about a month after the cat and the car incident.

The nightmare started soon after he came home from an evening when he attended a Communist Party political meeting in Dijon.

His wife greeted him at the door in her négligē.

"Hello Darlink!" she says in an accent which she hopes sounds a bit like Russian, and which possibly might excite him.

Claude Monet has his mind on other things, and certainly is not interested in his wife's impression of a middle-aged Red Russian Tart.

"I have made, for you, my Comrade, a special Ivan soup with high vitamin bread from the baker. It is guaranteed to blow your mind! You will be like a Cossack Stallion!"

'Oh Brother,' he thinks, 'this I can do without!'

More to keep her quiet, than because he is hungry, Claude Monet eats the bread and soup and then makes an excuse to retire. His wife climbs up the stairs with him to the bedroom, making little whinnying noises.

'She must have been at the Cognac again,' he thinks.

She has lighted candles and doused the pillows with scent.

He really isn't in the mood, but he does his best. He is distracted, but he knows that she will get sulky for a week if he does not put up a pretence of enjoyment.

In the end it isn't all that bad, but he is grateful to roll over and fall asleep.

He awakes two hours later with the room reeling as though he is on a ship in a gale.

He struggles uphill towards the door and has a conversation with the doorknob before it will open the door and allow him through.

He tumbles down the carpeted stairs and bangs his head on the wall. The lounge furniture is moving around the room laughing at him, and strange shapes are flitting across the ceiling.

He battles to the front door to escape being smothered by the carpet, which for some reason has become luminous.

In the road, it seems to him that the streetlights are brighter than several suns, and that the road itself is like a conveyer belt that is taking him past the village shops towards the church. He thinks that he is shouting patriotic slogans as he goes along, but in fact he is unintelligible.

At the church he knows what he has to do.

The Dijon chapter of the Communist Party had rejected him the evening before, from the committee, because he had failed to win the position of Mayor in the village. What he has to do is to announce that he is going to take the position anyway, in a private 'coup d'état'.

He bashes the door of the church open and staggers inside to shout to God and the congregation that, "Now I am in charge".

There is nobody in the church to acknowledge him, but he knows what he has to do.

He has to summon them all, every one of them, to hear his announcement. They have to come and pay homage to him.

He finds the bell rope and starts to pull on it and in his mind he can hear clarions ringing out across the land. Multitudes are coming from everywhere to give him the recognition he deserves.

He is rising above them all and is looking down at the crowds at his feet. He knows, for a fleeting moment, how it must feel to be Lenin at a May Day Parade, with the crowds adulating his accomplishments.

He has, at last, found true power.

With the strength that is born in madness he hauls himself up the bell rope, while it clangs and bangs at the bell in the belfry. Finally he reaches the top where the rope goes though a hole in the apex of the ceiling. He knows that he doesn't need the rope anymore... because the masses have come.

The people are united below him.

He winds the rope around himself in the way an Emperor winds a cloak, by swirling it over his shoulder.

That is when he releases the rope and gravity, which up until then had not seemed to have any effect on him, takes charge.

He drops about four metres before the slack snaps tight around his neck.

The rope twangs tight as the bell gives one last great clang and Claude Monet's head and body separate. His body falls in a heap into the centre of the aisle and twitches there for a few seconds, before lying still.

His head hits one of the pews with a sickening crunch, which he thinks he can feel......before it rolls... making him dizzy... but only for a moment...

Monsieur Pierre Tichet, conducting one of his early morning village patrols with his dog, sees that somebody has left the door of the church ajar. When he investigates, he sees that the door locking mechanism is damaged. He pushes the door fully open and discovers a headless body, lying in a pool of blood.

He vomits his morning 'baguette and coffee' onto the threshold of the church, before running back to his house to call the Gendarmerie. He forgets to call his dog, which sniffs at his master's breakfast before bounding after him, in this exciting new game of 'catch'.

"There's a b-body in the church," he stammers into the telephone. "A dead one!"

"Ah!" said the gendarme in Seurre, as he rubs the sleep from his eyes. He had been on Saturday all night duty and had only just come off duty and fallen asleep.

"Which church... yes... and you found the body... yes... and how do you know this person is dead? ... Blood... No head ... NO HEAD? ... NAKED? ... Do you know who this person is? ... No sir, I am not trying to imply that... No, sir, I realise that you can't recognise... With no head... No sir, I was not trying to imply that you would know who is... was... from... Yes, alright.... Yes, I will be there... Yes, as soon as possible."

Although many people heard the bell during the night, nobody questioned the reason for the noise. Everyone thought that the reason for the ringing bell was nothing to do with them.

There was no chance of it being an air raid, and if it was a fire, then the emergency services would deal with it.

That is the best part of closing all the window shutters in the evening and keeping them closed all night.

It shuts the whole world out, with all of its problems.

At the inquest Claude Monet's wife couldn't explain why he had got up in the middle of the night, to then run down the road with no clothes on.

The cause of death, from the post mortem, was one of the easiest diagnoses that the pathologist had ever had to investigate. He had run routine tests on alcohol levels in what remained of the blood and the results showed insignificant percentages for a normal Saturday night of revelry.

There were no witnesses who came forward to give evidence about how Monsieur Monet got to the church with no clothes. Monsieur Bonnadot, the postmaster, who had known the deceased since his schooldays, gave evidence that he had identified the head of Monsieur Monet, in order to save his wife the trauma of seeing her husband's decapitated body.

The coroner's verdict on the death of Claude Monet was 'depression followed by suicide', following the unfortunate man's rejection from his political position on the committee of the Communist Party in Dijon.

Only Marie Peron knows otherwise.

Monsieur Le Duc on patrol

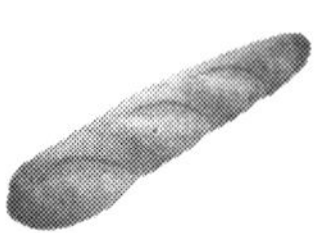

Le Duc opens his eyes and stares at the world in order to remember where he is, and then he yawns with his jaws as wide as a deep-sea clam. As he closes his mouth, he has to be careful to arrange his teeth to slot into their scabbards. It doesn't do to clamp your mouth shut, when you have a tender tongue and a couple of dozen needle sharp teeth to sheath.

Then he stretches his front paws, with claws extended, into his blanket, which he grips as he slowly elongates his front legs and then power ripples the muscles along his back. The whole luxurious enjoyment of becoming awake flows down his body and into each of his rear legs in turn, as he flexes his muscles and tests his sinews. Now he is tuned for action.

Outside the night is still dark with a sliver of moon. The stars are painting the rest of the sky with a pattern of lights that turns the dark into day for a cat.

Le Duc jumps down from his basket, which is in an elevated position in Monsieur Fabien Lafarge's conservatory. The retired headmaster's house has large glass panels that allow a view over the surrounding country. Le Duc pauses to check the cat-food bowl where he sniffs at the same boring cat biscuits that have been flavoured with additives and tastes, which appeal to humans rather than to cats.

Who ever heard of a hunting cat wanting Salmon flavoured dry biscuits!

Why not mouse flavoured?

It is just not natural to eat fish. He knows this because he had tried sniffing at those slimy catfish that the fishermen discard down by the river. They smell peculiar and that goes for the fishermen as well! He had also found that the slime on the fish was difficult to get off his whiskers.

Le Duc pushes the cat-flap open and smells the morning air. The heady scent of Colza from the nearby fields almost swamps his senses. In the starlight he can see the fields of yellow flowers extending to the south. They are almost dazzlingly luminous to him. Among the roots of the crop he knows that there are colonies of mice, but they are too easy to catch for a cat that likes a challenge, so he turns towards the village to start his early morning prowl.

The next house is locked up with shutters closed against the night air, as though there is a poison miasma that threatens to overcome the inmates. This is a most uninteresting house to investigate, as it is surrounded by gravel and has a concrete drive that leads to a locked garage.

Le Duc passes through this plot and then jumps onto the boundary wall at the rear of the property. The top of this wall provides Le Duc with a safe route behind all the houses in this street, all the way down to the small village roundabout. The last house in this row has a locked chicken coop inside a barn which Le Duc knows had got a nest of rats under it. The rats live below the chicken's cages because from there they have easy access to the sacks of chicken feed that are stored in the barn. Le Duc also knows dormice hibernate in winter in the recesses at the top of the stone walls of the barn, where the huge oak beams lie. The dormice, although they are sometimes fun to catch, they stink and so, as far as Le Duc is concerned, are inedible and therefore not worth the effort of the chase.

At the roundabout Le Duc can smell the combination odours of manure from the cowsheds, mixed with the stench from the drains that flow under the road towards the sewerage treatment tanks. Cows live within the confines of these yards and barns adjacent to the houses, in this part of the village. Some of these houses, where the livestock used to be kept below the living quarters for heating in winter, had been converted to provide more accommodation for the humans. The horses that used to have their stables adjoining the houses had now been replaced by tractors. Le Duc can smell the combination of centuries of dung, which has been compacted into the ground, along with the stink of spilt diesel fuel.

It seems that the humans insist on conveying their own droppings away on their water borne drainage system, while permitting the cows and dogs to leave their dung lying about in the streets and sheds. Le Duc is fastidious about not taking a route that leads across these yards of manure. He would never leave his droppings lying about in this manner, because all the other cats would know where he had been and what he had being eating.

These are private matters for a cat.

Not to be shared!

He prowls towards the main road that passes through the centre of the village by walking down the side street from the small roundabout. He knows that the main road is a dangerous and exciting place for a cat, because he has had a couple of narrow escapes there, from the traffic. One house on the right side of the street has pheromones wafting from it, so he pours himself through a gap in the garden gate and carries out an investigation.

There is, without question, a Queen on heat in here. He sniffs at the air gap under the front door. Yes, she is almost ready, but the humans have locked her up. He will have to pass by later in the day when they have opened up their lair and let her out.

That will be interesting!

Le Duc leaves his calling card by spraying a squeeze of urine at the centre of the door. He can vary the smell depending on the message he wants to convey. He has subjugated all the opposition males in this part of the village, so he has no reason to waste too much testosterone extract here.

The Queen will smell his message and she will know from the bouquet of scents that he will be back. She will deduce his tantalising promise of siring strong kittens that will grow up respecting their mother… Hah!

What a load of lies one can transmit with just a single piddle!

Now he has to cross the main road.

There is no traffic at all. He can see a light in one of the shops across the road is throwing a blinding pattern of luminosity over the pavement and adjacent flowerbeds. It is coming from the large window where the Baker's Wife displays her patisseries.

Le Duc ambles over to investigate.

He jumps onto the outside sill of the window and peers inside, with his pupils reduced to slits against the glare.

The Baker's Wife is at work, which is strange because Le Duc knows that, at this time of the morning, it is usually the man who lives with her who was busy. The man works in his bakery around the side of the building, where his large warm ovens are situated.

The woman is kneading bread on the counter and as Le Duc watches her, he sees that she is adding ingredients to the dough. She lays out packets of seeds, nuts and spices next to her breadboard and in an open jar on the work surface she has a quantity of chopped dried mushrooms. Le Duc can smell from the outside of the shop that these fungi have an odour of iodine.

Le Duc does not know what iodine is exactly, except that it has a definite poison smell that warns animals not to eat it. Rather in the same way that those dormice smell so noxious, so that cats know that they will be ill if they eat them. The Baker's Wife looks up from her labour and sees Le Duc.

"Scat you flea bitten ball bearing rattrap!" she screams.

Le Duc doesn't know the meaning of her words but her intention is clear enough. He doesn't feel in the mood to waste time with her so he drops to the ground. Then, on second thoughts, he turns his tail to the doorway next to the display window and squeezes a really pungent squirt of urine at the wooden support.

There! Now that will soak into the wood and the whiff should last a week or more.

That will warn all those dogs that came to be tied up outside here, while their masters are buying bread, that Le Duc is still King of the village.

What a miserable existence these dogs have.

They have to show affection and be subservient to their masters, while they get towed around on the end of a lead. Then they get left outside the shops and have to wait patiently. And then, the worst thing of all: they have to pretend to understand the garbling noises that humans make!

What a joy it is to be a cat rather than a dog!

Le Duc wanders to the rear of the baker's shop where he knows that there is a family that leaves top notch scraps outside their back door. These are off cuts from the butchery where these particular humans work. They believe that they are leaving these pieces of meat for their cats, because every morning the cat bowl is empty. They have the impression that their two cats need a bowlful of meat everyday, but in fact they are supporting a wide population of animals. What Le Duc does not eat, the hedgehog takes or the weasel steals, so that by morning the bowl is licked and clean and is waiting for the next instalment of largesse. Le Duc helps himself, ignoring the snuffling of the hedgehog that is rooting for worms in the grass.

Le Duc continues his patrol, crossing roads and trotting down alleys until he comes to the grounds of a familiar house. There is a forest near here where he knows owls live, but there are no dogs on this property so it is a safe place to sleep. He feels bloated after gorging on the meat so now he needs a catnap. The day is brightening as he jumps to the top of the woodpile under a special shelter that has been erected to keep the logs dry. This is a safe and comfortable place to clean up and sleep.

As the first rays of the sun touch the rooftops Le Duc lies on his side and licks at his bulging stomach. Then he licks his paw and wipes his face and whiskers.

He settles into a deep slumber.

Marie Peron completes her special loaf of bread. She has since given up using the red mushrooms because she has found another much better place for gathering mushrooms. These are, she is sure, the poisonous ones that Marc Chazelle found. They look similar to the creamy coloured Champignon de Paris mushrooms, but they have yellow stains on their heads and they are slightly slimy to touch. They grow in a dip in the ground that is hidden in the forest behind Montmain. In wet weather the vlei there is flooded, because the water does not sink underground, nor does it have anywhere to flow. During summer, even in a drought, there is enough moisture retained in the soil for the minute root fibres and spores of the mushrooms to survive. At first Marie thought that these mushrooms couldn't be poisonous, because she had seen snails eating them. She picked the snails and the mushrooms and taken them home. Then she repeated the experiment that she had tried with the dogs outside the public bar. This time, instead of using pieces of mushroom, she cooked the snails and put them into the dog food. She wanted to see if the snails could eat the poison, and not be affected by it, but still have enough toxins inside them to make a dog dizzy.

Now that she has got rid of Claude Monet, she has decided to take revenge on the rest of that schoolboy gang. The problem with Monet was that he had made a rather spectacular exit. The verdict concerning his death was suicide, however Marie is not sure that she will be that lucky with her next victim.

She had heard Monet, as he was cantering down the road towards the church that night he killed himself, shouting those peculiar slogans. She had seen him from her bedroom window as he passed, with everything 'hanging out'. The spectacle wasn't quite as good as the dogs, which had howled in the night outside the bar, but it wasn't bad. However, it had been very fortunate that he had gone mad at night, and not during the day, when people were up and about.

They might have restrained him and then a link to what he had eaten might have been discovered. As it was, his wife must have known that something odd had taken place, but she had packed up and left for Paris that same week, relieved to get away from this parochial little village.

Marie had since realised that those same red mushrooms, which she had fed to Marc Chazelle, were what made him go mad and drown himself. That experiment had worked, but she had been lucky again that there were no other suspicions concerning his death.

She had decided to try and find another way to take vengeance on the rest of the gang.

She enjoys savouring the anticipation of retribution, in the same way that she relished dreams about Claude Monet having an accident, when they were at school together. She decides to order a book about mushrooms from the mobile library.

The library tours the villages of the 'département' and arrives each couple of months, in the back of a bus. Marie has to wait, after ordering the book, for the next return of the bus to receive it. Now she has plenty of time to study the contents of the book before she has to return it. She finds a list of dangerous fungi listed in a special chapter at the back of the book. From the pictures and descriptions she identifies the variety of mushroom that the snails, which she fed to the dogs, had been eating.

Monsieur Cendanini has lived in the village for over thirty years. He is still called the 'Italian', because thirty years is not long enough for him to be considered a local. He had moved here with his wife from Milan in Northern Italy. He has brought with him a skill that is over two thousand years old. This is the skill and the art of laying Italian tiles.

The Romans first introduced the technique of laying mosaics and tiles on floors to the Burgundy region, when they came to grow wine. It is fitting therefore that another Italian should carry on this tradition. Fredo Cendanini lived with his attractive wife and their lovely daughter. He considered that life in France had been kind to them all because now he owned his own home and had his small and successful business.

Every morning Fredo Cendanini collects his baguette from the bakery, because he had adopted that habit from the French. He still ate his pasta for lunch, because he and his wife considered that eating pasta was a part of *their* tradition. It was also his tradition that he should go out in the evening and that his wife should stay at home, because 'that is the way that it has always been in Italy, for a married man' he insisted.

However, for Fredo Cendanini, the options were somewhat limited in the village. There was only the village bar or the small hotel to go to, and he chose the bar because the prices of the drinks were more reasonable. The bar was also a place that Fredo found some of his work contracts. It was here that he met men of the village who had news about who was coming and going.

They knew who had 'come into some money' recently, or who had achieved a promotion at work. This meant that they might be persuaded to replace their floor tiles. He also met with the local builders who were a good source of information about possible new clients.

Fredo's daughter left home to go back to Italy to get married and so Fredo bought a dog, so that he and his wife could have something to care for, as a replacement for their daughter.

Fredo's wife insisted on going to Milan at least twice a year in order to see her daughter. She needed to see that her daughter was looking after her new husband in true traditional Italian style. This meant, among other things, making sure that he put on weight. Her visits were not always without rancour, because a young girl brought up in France does not have the same tradition and view of life as an Italian girl.

Certain things they enjoyed doing together, such as evening promenades, which is when Italian families like to walk and display their fashionable clothes. They went window shopping arm in arm, comparing prices and discussing shoes. But they clashed over what freedom meant and how it had changed over the period of one generation. Fredo's wife thought that her duty as a wife revolved around being at home for her husband, but her daughter believed that she had a life of her own, and wanted to enjoy big city freedom. In was the young woman's reaction against being brought up in a rural village, in France.

It was on Fredo's wife's return from one of these trips to visit her daughter that disaster struck. She was travelling north through the Gotthard Tunnel, when two trucks ahead of her collided. One was loaded with tyres. The collision started a fire which was enhanced by spilled diesel fuel. The fire spread and ignited the tyres.

Black smoke billowed down the tunnel making it impossible to see. Cars and motorcycles collided and spilled fuel from these vehicles added to the conflagration. Extraction fans pulled smoke from the tunnel, but also sucked more oxygen towards the fires. The heat was intense and impossible to escape.

Part of the roof of the tunnel collapsed, imprisoning people in their cars. The final death toll was never certain, but in the inferno Fredo's wife was lost. Fredo Cendanini could not find closure because there were no traceable remains of his wife for him to bury and mourn over.

It was as though she vanished into a dream.

Fredo's dog then became the centre of his life.

After a year he tried to find a French woman to share his life with him, but none of them could put up with him and his 'Italianicities'. They all left after a month or so, complaining that he was excessively neat, and that he always wanted to know where they were every minute of the day.

"Who does he think I am, Madame?" complained one of his partners to Marie one morning in the bakery, shortly before she also left. "All the time he wants to know where the housekeeping money has gone. Doesn't he know that a woman needs to spend more on her appearance than on floor cleaning products? He is a tile fetishist. He even has tiles on his bedroom wall, with murals of naked women. He is impossible!"

Fredo's dog is a female Black Labrador.

She loves him in spite of all his drawbacks.

She loves the way that he combs her everyday, so that her hair does not collect on the floor and in the corners of the lounge. She loves the walks that they have together everyday along the river, where he throws sticks into the water for her, so that she can fulfil her natural instinct to retrieve them for him. She leaps into the water, whatever the temperature, while he calls encouragement to her. She realises that he is almost totally deaf, so she learns to make sure that he can see her before she displays what she wants, with her body language.

She wags her tail enthusiastically and learns to grin and jump on her back legs to show her delight. She watches him, waiting for him to turn around so that she can display her joy at his company.

She knows that she has to come and call him when the telephone rings, because he can't hear the bell. He then picks up the telephone and shouts, because Fredo always thinks that the person on the other end of the line is deaf as well.

All the while that Fredo shouts on the telephone, his dog wags her tail and stares at him with adoration.

They are in love with each other.

She is quite happy to wait for him when he goes to the bar for the company of other men, because she is not jealous.

When she sees the bowl of food that Marie has left behind the bicycle rack she has no suspicion that it would be harmful. She has no concept that anyone would ever want to hurt her, so the slight odour of iodine does not put her off. She eats most of the food in the bowl while she waits for her master.

Marie watches the dog eat the food from her bedroom window, which is on the floor above the bakery. From here she can see the pavement in front of the shops and the bar. This will be a better experiment than the others because Fredo Cendanini comes to the boulangerie every day to buy his baguette, so Marie will be able to follow the progress of his dog's health.

The next morning Fredo Cendanini walks to the bakery for his customary baguette. He arrives without his dog. He tells Marie that he has been up all night, tending to her.

"The vet from Seurre has come to examine her and he said that she has swallowed some poison." he says to Marie. "Where can she find poison? How can this happen?"

Marie, as usual, says nothing.

The next day the dog's condition is worse and then almost miraculously, she seems to recover. Fredo does not know if it is as a result of the treatment from the vet, or if the poison has been purged from his dog's system naturally.

The third day after his dog fell ill, when he comes to buy his bread, he is wreathed in smiles.

"She is better," he announces. "She is still weak, but she wagged her tail this morning, and she licked my hand. I gave her some milk and I think she is going to be alright."

Marie wipes her counter top. She takes his money for the bread. She knows that it was useless to say anything to Fredo because, unless she shouts, he won't hear anything.

It seems to her that the snails had indeed been poisonous from eating the mushrooms, but that the poison was only strong enough to make a person, or a dog, ill.

Two nights later Fredo's dog dies in agony.

The little bald Italian is devastated by the loss of his friend. What hurts him the most is that that the vets are unable to trace the source of the poison.

He blames himself.

'She must have found some rat poison,' he thinks.

He goes into a depression, with the cumulative effects of losing his wife and his dog. His daughter comes to visit to try to help her father through these dark days. He pleads with her to think about having a child, so that at least he can have a grandchild to love and live for. She knows that this will curtail her freedom and so promises nothing.

Fredo Cendaninni drowns his sorrows in the village bar. His work becomes shoddy, he is late for appointments and the word spreads that he is no longer the person to have, to lay tiles. His drinking companions share his misery, for as long as he has the money to pay for his share of the drinks.

He is no longer tidy.

Michel Bonnadot says to his friends, "It won't be long now, before he ends it."

Marie is delighted with the effectiveness of her experiment.

But she knows that she has a problem, because the effects of the poisoning are rather too obvious. If she uses these mushrooms or snails in the bread, then there is every chance that the doctors will raise the alarm. Maybe they will call for an autopsy and then they might discover the source of the poison.

She goes to her book to study again what sort of mushroom she might be able to find, which does not give these same obvious symptoms.

There are some that are poisonous when raw, but when they are cooked they became edible.

'They wouldn't do at all,' she thinks, 'because when they are baked in the bread, it will be the same as cooking them.'

Some of them are so dangerous that only a single mushroom can kill a man, but they all take a while to work.

All of the poisonous ones make the person very ill, with vomiting and diarrhoea, before destroying their livers and killing them.

She wants a type of mushroom that just kills them, and in such a way that it won't be obvious that they havc eaten something poisonous.

'What I need to do,' she decides, "is to feed them small doses over a period of time, so that they get ill progressively. All I have to do is to find a mushroom that meets the requirements laid down in the book. Then ensure that my victims eat the mushrooms. Then later, when they are suffering with induced ill health, I can administer the 'coup de grace' with one of the really poisonous ones and nobody will be suspicious.'

This bread that she has prepared this morning is one such loaf.

She has supplied her present victim, Augustin Février, for a year with her special bread and now that he is really ill, it is time for her to finish him off.

This bread is similar to the others that she has sold him for the last eighteen months, except that today the type of mushrooms in the recipe is different. Occasionally she has slipped in a piece of red mushroom, to give him some bad dreams. Nightmares even! The trouble is that he has eaten the bread in the mornings, and has experienced his nightmares during the day!

Well, as far as Marie is concerned, that made up for the nightmares that he and Claude Monet had given her at school.

Her bread is ready.

She sniffs it and is disappointed that the whiff of iodine is still there, but it is not strong. She had hoped that the odour was part of the more volatile properties of the mushroom, and that it would vanish with the baking.

She places it under the counter in the bakery so that it will be ready to hand, when Madame Février comes in later.

Madame Février is always very reliable.

She is always on time.

******

Le Duc is stirring again on the woodpile having slept for three hours. The sun is well up in the sky and from his vantage point he can see a woman opening and closing the garden gate. She is back from the baker and Le Duc can smell that same tang in the air that he had detected earlier that morning.

He is very disinclined to move as he is comfortable. He has absolutely no conscience about being late for anything or needing to be anywhere, except that he has to meet up with that female cat on heat. But that can wait, because he knows it will still be a couple of days before she will be ready. He can afford to let the other cats gather and caterwaul, before he arrives to chase them away.

He knows that 'timing is everything'.

He is still lying on the woodpile when he hears the first retching sound from inside the house. He is there when he hears the woman shout urgently into her telephone. That is a curious thing that humans do. His human at the top of the hill does that as well: shouting into that instrument in a one sided conversation with himself.

Humans are strange that way.

He watches as the doctor's car arrives. Le Duc doesn't know that this is a doctor, but he can smell the strange bouquet of aromas that wafts from the man's medical bag.

They are the same sort of smells that the female cat near his home once smelled like. She was away for a day and when she came back she had a bald patch on her side.

After that she never came on heat again.

And she got *so **fat***!

He is bored with watching so he drifts off, back to sleep. There are still strange gagging sounds emanating from the house.

He is still asleep three hours later when the sounds stop. The doctor comes outside. He doesn't hear the advice that the doctor gives to the woman and he wouldn't have cared anyway.

This house is a boring place now.

It used to be better when the man had rabbits.

Then there used to be rats here because of the food the man stored for the rabbits. Rats raised on rabbit food make good eating. And, every now and again, he got the chance to scoop a baby rabbit from one of the cages.

"That was fun, because that is what we cats think we do best…

Killing, that is."

How wrong they are.

Augustin Février

The bell in the village church seldom tolls these days.

In the past, before the days of wristwatches for common people, it used to ring out each hour so that the villagers could get to work on time, and also to know when to go home in the evenings. When the farmers who worked in the fields surrounding the village heard the midday chime, they would lay down their tools for that most important meal of the day: The Frenchman's Lunch.

They would break out their bread and cheese, uncork a bottle of wine and take a couple of hours off in order to celebrate life, food and companionship. Even the horses pulling the ploughs and the milk cows grazing along the riverside knew what the bell meant.

The bell was a heartbeat.

Village life was governed by the bell.

Now it tolls only for death.

It is tolling this morning and Marlene and I know it is for the funeral of Augustin Février. Its mournful sound had started pealing with a certain amount of enthusiasm, chiming with a regular beat and then the sound had deteriorated into a series of tired clangs, after which it petered into silence. It seems to be a sombre representation of the life of Monsieur Février. He must have started out with the optimism of youth some sixty five years ago only to run out of energy in later life until finally succumbing to the inevitability of death. The vanishing meaning for his existence and the fading sound of the bell seem to characterize each other. We had only met him when Marlene helped him burn his old rabbit hutches, but we thought that we should attend his funeral anyway in order to show that, in this small community, we have an interest in 'village affaires'.

As we walk up to the church I can see from a distance that a crowd is gathering. The bell in the small central steeple is now silent. The building is unpretentious compared to some of the grand edifices in neighbouring towns, but seems adequate for this rural village. Of course, when the village was in its heyday, its population was double that of today and the church was able to accommodate everyone then. The church seems neglected and forlorn as though it is in mourning for its more important past.

Our Priest, Father Dedicus, is a rotund little man who had earned the nickname of 'Pére Petit Tonneau' (the little barrel), which is a throwback to his childhood days when he was remembered as being a tubby boy. He had only managed to tug at the bell rope for a few minutes before he was out of breath. This physical exertion, it seems, is rather too much for him.

He had told me a month ago, "I have asked the Mayoress to approve the replacement of this old bell by one of the new electronic ones. Then all I would have to do is press a button. We could have the sound of impressive peals of bells, like the church in Seurre. This single old bell is not striking enough."

He may have meant that he wasn't striking it hard enough, or that he was going on strike. Perhaps I misunderstood.

Apparently he needs something to blame for his dwindling congregation.

He claimed, "This bell only manages to upset the family of bats that live in the belfry. They have probably gone deaf and nobody else seems to listen! If she sells the bell then the bronze will pay for the installation of the new system."

The bats had taken up residence after a large nearby barn, where they used to live, had been dismantled. This communal 400 year old storage place had been condemned because of sagging beams and wood rot but the church has survived centuries of war and weather because it was built with granite from the Jura Mountains.

Jacques told me, "These bats in the church are a good luck sign for the village."

This seems to be a rather pagan thought to me.

He went on, "It proves that there is no pollution!"

I suppose that made sense if the insects that the bats ate had not been poisoned by insecticides.

Père Dedicus looks at us, his assembled congregation, with a look of disappointment. Perhaps he was expecting more of a turnout for this funeral. As we gather near the oak door of the church I see that each new arrival makes a circuit to greet every other villager, in a ritual that we have learned is so extremely important here in France.

Marlene and I circle around and shake hands and wish a "Bonjour" to most, and a "Salut" to closer friends. I wonder, while I am doing this, how the villagers, who do not want to be seen talking to each other, cope with this formal procedure of greetings.

A couple of months ago, after we had replaced the roof on our main house, we had tried to have a "crémaillère", or house warming. We ran into the problem that everybody we invited wanted to know who else from the village was coming. Each one said that they wouldn't attend if "so and so" was going to be there. As new arrivals, we had no idea of the history of these past disputes and family spats.

Annette for example, who lives near the church, had told us that she wouldn't go anywhere near her sister.

When we asked why, she said, "Oh, I don't know now, but it has always been like that. We don't speak any more!"

When we asked where her sister lived, she said, "Oh, far away! Up there by the Post Office."

Our small crowd outside the church is beginning to feel uncomfortable, anticipating the funeral, perhaps.

Nobody wants to go inside the church as though we don't want to be alone with the coffin of Monsieur Février, in case he is contagious.

It may be, also, that the old-timers are delaying any interruption to this small social event. Some of them seem to live permanently inside their houses and the only sign that there is life in the house is that the shutters open in the morning and close every evening. It is not easy to winkle them out of their houses into the open. Some of them seem to suffer from a strange form of rural agoraphobia.

Madame Février is standing near the entrance of the church. She is dressed in black, as expected, but she looks as though she is always dressed in black. I find it difficult to imagine her in any other colour.

Each person greets her with a "Bonjour Madame" and a handshake, or a "Salut Marie" with a 'kiss into space' while touching each cheek to cheek, depending on their relationship.

I confine myself to a handshake and a respectful nod, because I am a newcomer in the village and have not met Madame Février before.

Marlene is not nearly so constrained by the fabric of imaginary behavioural taboos as I am. She takes both of Madame Février's hands and stares into her eyes and says, "I am so sorry for your loss Madame. I hope you can find peace now that your husband has found rest from his suffering."

That is what she means to say.

That was what she had rehearsed, with reference to the large English/French Dictionary that we had at home. This large volume has expressions and phrases for most events and circumstances, but as you will know, the written French and the spoken French are as far apart as two languages can ever be.

The resulting message of condolence that Marlene gives to Madame Février is understood by her as "I am drunk so much for your forgetfulness Madame. I think that you will be tranquil now that your husband is sleeping after his hangover."

The words dessoûlé and désole sound the same to an English ear, but in French mean 'drunk' or 'sorry' respectively.

Marlene's smile is broad, encouraging and sympathetic, and quite at odds with what she has said, so Madame Février is nonplussed for a response.

The physical contrast between these two figures is as marked as their lack of comprehension of each other.

Marlene is exuberant in spite of the funeral, as though her whole being is a celebration of life, because she could see no reason for not enjoying everyday, even if the occasion is to mark the demise of one of the long standing members of the village. She is a woman of generous proportions in both stature and generosity. She has dressed in black, but has offset the effect with a white scarf, white belt, handbag and shoes.

After all, we didn't know Monsieur Février *that* well!

Madame Février on the other hand is a dumpy person and is about the same height as her late husband. She has large hands and an unhappy expression with frown creases. She looks as though she has never enjoyed life. The proof of this lies in the fact that she had remained unhappily married to her husband for close on fifty years.

Annette had told us, after the announcement of Monsieur Février's death, that Madame Février hadn't loved or even liked her husband when they got married, and that situation hadn't varied much for their entire existence together.

"When she was young," Annette went on, "she thought that Augustin would be a 'provider', but she was wrong. She thought that to marry a husband was far more important than some fickle sentiment of love. They fell out with each other about fifteen years ago, although they carried on living in the same house. She tried to poison him, did you know? She tried rat poison, but he never ate it! When that failed she used to poison his cabbages. She didn't like cabbages, so she used to pour bleach onto their roots. Everybody in the village knew about it, except him."

Madame Février stares at Marlene as though she is looking at a creature from outer space, which is an entirely correct assessment. Madame Février has never travelled further than fifty kilometres from her home in the village. She had only travelled at all because she had been compelled to go to Dijon with her husband when he had been sent there by the doctor to consult a specialist. Marlene, by contrast has travelled, worked and lived with me in various countries and has learned the languages that these countries use. Although her normal French is 'up to speed' she still stumbles over local patois phrases, but has no reservations about engaging anyone in conversation, even if the resultant miscomprehensions lead to her being laughed at by the locals.

She is quite confident enough with herself, and with life, to join in and laugh with them.

Unlike me!

I see a veil of incomprehension clouding in Madame Février's eyes. I try to alleviate the situation by saying to Marlene in English,

"Shall we go inside now?"

Madame Février realises who we are, perhaps from the description that her husband must have given her about 'the English' who had bought the old 'Haunted House Down by the River'. We are released as she turns to acknowledge the Post Master's wife, whom she has known from her schooldays over half a century ago.

We enter the church and take up a position on the left hand side fairly near the back. This is in accordance with our lowly position in the ranking of mourners. Marlene reminds me about who is who in the community as the congregation enter the church.

I say that she reminds me, because she insists that she has told me before who they all are, but I never seem to remember. Perhaps this is because I spend time away at work and by the time I get home, my memory of who is who in the local community has slipped. Also, with the renovations that we are doing on the house, I don't have much time for socializing.

She finds all this exasperating because she has the ability to remember people and faces from the distant past. She can see a child and identify who the parents are, even if she meets them for the first time months later.

She will say to them, "Oh yes, I remember seeing your son playing with his friends by the tennis court. He was wearing a blue T-shirt and was riding a red bicycle. I recognise you from the way he moves and the way he smiles! He is just like you."

I won't remember anything of the occasion with the children, except perhaps that there were some short people making a noise.

I need Marlene to be my memory and my reference of people and events.

"That's the retired Gendarme, Monsieur Corbier." Marlene whispers in my ear.

"You remember him? He's the one who was part of the President's Cavalcade. He rode a motorbike and had to stop the traffic in Paris for the President to pass, until one day he fell off and they found him smashed in more ways than one! He still managed to get a Heavy Duty Licence after that though! He has retired from truck driving now and he has come back to live here, where he was born."

I look at the man with a corrugated face that seems to have weathered many a storm in a bottle. His nose is the shape of a rare root vegetable and it seems to be held together with a network of veins. It must have been a distinguished 'wine smelling' nose once, but now it is like a pockmarked battlefield. In spite of this he does not have a good colour to his face. There is pallor and a seeming translucence to his skin which is obvious to me; however

I am not the medical member of the family. Marlene, with her nursing background is usually quick to spot health deficiencies in people, but she is already looking at the next couple walking up the aisle, in order to brief me about who they are.

Monsieur Corbier shuffles with his wife to a pew near the front of the church; which is a position that seems in keeping with their long relationship to the late Monsieur Février.

"That's the Post Master and his wife," Mary whispers. "You must remember him from the Post Office?"

"Yes of course," I murmur back, "He's that rude character that seems out of his depth with just the simplest transaction. I saw him shouting and swearing a month ago because he had run out of some denominations of stamps. I'm sure that it was his fault, simply because he had forgotten to order replacements. I wonder how his wife puts up with him. He looks like a large bombastic twit to me!"

I watch him as he walks, preceded by a vast liver, to a position near the front of the church. His trouser belt sags down in the front and his belly flops over the top of it to form a flap of flab. I muse that he has to be a strong man to carry all that excess weight.

"Yes, his wife stays at home hiding most of the time. She hangs up his seven enormous underpants and pairs of socks all in a row every Wednesday on the washing line, in full view of everyone going past. You know where they live, in their little house attached to the back of the Post Office building?"

"I know the one. What's his name?"

"He is Michel and she is Michelle. Very confusing! I don't know their family name. I must have a look at their post box by their gate and see if they have put their name on it."

"Probably he hasn't written it there, because he knows who he is and where he lives. He doesn't need his own name on his mailbox to deliver mail to himself!"

"Oh, Ha Ha! Well, I'll have a look next time I go up there. This is Sandrine coming in now, you remember her surely! She came around for tea last month before you went off on your last trip."

"Of course I do!"

Sandrine sees us, smiles and gives a little wave and then sidles along the pew to sit next to Marlene. Sandrine has been widowed for several years and is rather lonely because her remaining son and daughter have both moved away from the area. Marlene somehow notices lonely people and so has gathered a few of them into a loose circle of acquaintances whom she invites for tea and a chat in our garden. They have learned that Marlene never divulges the subject of these conversations to anyone else, so as a result they have learned to trust her as a new friend. They can share their private thoughts with her that they would have found difficult to disclose to their families, or their so called friends whom they have known all their lives.

Sandrine is a gentle soul who, like her late husband, has also lived her whole life in the village. In those strange ways in which villagers know all about each other but never make close friends with those nearby, Sandrine leads a private life. She doesn't drive a car so she uses a practical style of bicycle with a basket on the back to do her shopping. This means that sometimes she has to brave the elements of rain and sleet to cycle three kilometres to Seurre to do her shopping. The exercise and the lack of luxuries in her life have given her a healthy complexion in spite of her age.

She greets us both and then starts a murmured conversation with Marlene about health, the weather and the family. My instruction from my wife, about who is who in the church today, comes to an end.

There is a flurry of late arrivals into the church most of whom I do not recognise but I do see the Baker's Wife, Madame Peron. She is wearing a hat with flowers as though today is a carnival rather than a funeral. I recognise her from an occasion when I had to buy croissants from her shop for some visitors who were staying with us. I want to nudge Marlene to say that I have actually identified someone, but she is still whispering to Sandrine.

Jacques comes down the aisle towards us. He is looking quite strange in a suit rather than his habitual working blue denim overalls. This makes two people I have recognised! He gives us a wave and a smile and takes a position with his wife in the pew in front of us.

"Salut Christophér!" he whispers, as we shake hands.

"Ca va?" I ask.

"Ah, oui!" and as he answers he holds his hand out, palm down, and waggles it slightly to indicate that life is okay, but not too good or too bad.

The Lady Mayor, Madame Beringer, is also putting in an appearance and of course I recognise her too. I *am* doing well! She is a very neat woman with an abbreviated hairstyle designed for minimum maintenance. She has retired now, so she is devoting her energies to the post of Mayor without other distractions. She is a lady who has a shrewd knowledge of when and where to be seen, because she is very well acquainted with the politics of the community. She knows exactly who is a friend or an enemy of whom in the village and she knows, to the last electoral vote, which group to support or oppose with each situation that arises and about which she had to make a decision.

"This is why," I had been told by one elderly disgruntled couple, "the numerically superior families with their collective votes are able to get away with house extensions and constructions that are **'impossible'** for us lesser mortals with only two votes."

The Mayor nods an acknowledgement to us and then takes a seat in the left front pew of the church.

Madame Février enters the church with somebody who looks like her brother and together they take their positions in the front pew next to the aisle.

When everybody is settled, Père Dedicus starts the service.

I am able to understand some of the service with my fractured French. I find that the Lord's Prayer is easy enough to follow because of my ingrained memory of it from my boarding school days. There is no organ, organist or even a piano, so everybody sings the hymns with Father Dedicus leading the congregation with his strong baritone. The reverberation of his voice seems to be the result of his barrel-like body shape. I ponder why this village has only a single bell, whereas Seurre, in spite of its violent history, has a full church organ and a complete clarion of bells. In the past Seurre must have been far more important that this little village.

Most of the people here attend the church only for the extremely rare weddings and rather more frequent funerals. There seems to be a diminishing interest in religious observances, except by the very elderly. Mass is only held once every month or so.

Consequently Père Dedicus has three churches in nearby villages in which he conducts a rotating Sunday Service. His congregations have to rotate with him in order to partake regularly in their dedications.

Possibly this tends to create links between these communities which would have otherwise remained isolated, in keeping with the tradition of French rural life. Even the different village hunting syndicates take their members from only a single community, which perpetuates this isolationism. Only the week before the funeral in Seurre, I heard a motorist ask a pedestrian for directions.

The response was, “Ah! Monsieur, I have no idea where this place is, that you want because, you see, I am also a foreigner. I am from St Jean de Losne!”

St Jean de Losne is only 12 kilometres distant from Seurre, so is far enough away to be a foreign land or ‘autre pays’!

Sandrine has also complained to Marlene that her children have scattered far and wide.

“My son is in the distant town of Chalon, which as you know is a whole 35 kilometres away, and my daughter is now living in Paris which is in a remote and far-away country!”

The funeral service is approaching the end, and this is the time when people can stand up near the coffin and say a few words about the deceased. There is nobody with anything to say about Monsieur Augustin Février, least of all Madame Février.

Father Dedicus leads us into the final hymn and as I stand there silent not knowing the words I remind myself how my mother used to mime singing in church. She knew that she did not have a ‘voice’, so rather than sing off tune she would silently mouth the words. She was rather annoyed with me when I teased her about it, but here I can not follow her example as I do not even have a hymnbook.

There are no pallbearers for the coffin so the undertakers have mounted the ‘casquette’ on a gurney bedecked in black, which they wheel out to the waiting hearse. The hearse is a retired and repainted ancient ambulance from the local taxi firm owned by the son of Roger du Bois, who started the company before the War. This company supplies taxis, an ambulance and a hearse. They undertake, if that is the right word, to ferry expectant mothers to hospital for the birth of their children, to taxi their children throughout their lives and then be available for this, their final journey to the cemetery. Once when I ordered a taxi at the railway station in Seurre I was picked up by the ambulance instead.

Occasionally the hearse is also used as a taxi. It has a seat for only one passenger beside the driver, but there is lots of room for baggage in the back.

The mourners with closer ties to the Févriers than us make preparations to go to the cemetery at the top of the hill at the rear of the village. Some are going to walk there and others drive. We consider that we have paid our respects, so we sidle away from the crowd and walk down the road back to our house by the river.

Sandrine joins us pushing her bicycle. Marlene has invited her to 'pop in for tea' which will give us a chance to catch up on the latest news of the goings-on in the village.

It takes only two minutes to reach our gate which accesses the courtyard. A mood of Peace descends on us now, which is in marked contrast to the vaguely unreceptive feel that the property had when we bought it. It is beginning to look as though we have made some progress. The roof of the main house is now completely replaced and we have painted the shutters a light sky-blue.

This caused consternation in the village when we did it, because we should have known that the colour of shutters in the Bourgogne was either Burgundy red or 'Crème' or occasionally a ghastly green.

Everybody knows that. It is a recognised fact.

"Who are you to break the tradition of centuries?" they asked.

'C'est un scandale!"

"Do you have permission?"

The villagers finally accepted that, because we were not people of the Bourgogne, perhaps we should be pitied for our ignorance.

We have no 'History' so how could we be expected to understand these complicated matters?

"What can you expect from foreigners?"

So, with a shake of the head and a shrug we have been left to be what we obviously are, which is '*Différent*'.

This is a delightful word in French which covers everything from an aberration in behaviour, to a comment on the taste of food that is not French. It is emphatic but at the same time not too insulting. It implies that we should have known better but the indiscretion would be tolerated, for now.

When we first arrived in France, Marlene had adopted this word 'différent' as a tactful one to use when asked for an opinion. Whenever she was asked what she thought of the taste of food, or her opinion about some facet of French life she would answer, after a pause for thought: "Oui, c'est différent!"

She said this, pronouncing it 'Wee sey dee-fran', correctly keeping the final 't' silent, but forgetting to stress the 'ér' in the middle of the word.

Because the 'x' sometimes becomes silent in Dix or Ten, this came out as "Dix Francs!" or "Ten Francs", so she became known as 'Marlene Ten Francs' by our friends in the Alsace. They would ask her for her opinion whenever they could, and then giggle with internal glee when she lived up to her nickname, but it was all humour with affection.

The rest of France, of course, does not consider that the Alsacians have a sense of humour at all, which is unfair.

Soon this idea of having different colours for shutters spread, and home owners in the area began to paint their shutters blue as well. This coincided with a change in the law that decreed that the tax payable on the valuation of a house was not only to include its exterior appearance, but was also to include the valuations of facilities, such as balconies, central heating, patios and a pool. As a result, it is no longer necessary to keep the exterior of a house looking like a relic from the Roman occupation.

We pass through the archway from the courtyard into the front garden. This is where the lawn slopes away from the house down towards the river, which gives an impression of space across to the far bank. I keep the grass trim which gives our neighbours a confirmation of that expression "Pelouse Anglaise". This is translated as 'English Lawn', because the French perceive the 'English' to be enamoured with closely mown lawns.

We try to live up to this expectation.

It is here in the riverside garden that we settle with Sandrine to review the events of the day. We have time to discuss who came to the funeral and who didn't, and how it was that Monsieur Février came to meet his end. Marlene knows how important it is for elderly people to talk about their neighbours, because they have so little other news of their own. She listens and nods as Sandrine speaks.

"I have known Monsieur Février all my life," she says, "but we have lived at opposite ends of the village. I have seen him occasionally at the 'vides greniers' (attic clearance sales) but otherwise I have had nothing to do with him. My husband worked for the EDF so he was always out and about, but old man Février never seemed to go anywhere or do anything. I call him 'old' although he was about twenty years younger than me. He never seemed to have much interest in life and what is more, he didn't even have a dog!"

This seems to be a condemnation of the highest order, because not to have a dog indicates an almost complete lack of participation in living. In the countryside a dog is either a recognised 'chien de chasse' (hunting dog), or a guard dog. The hunting dogs can come in a variety of guises and forms from long legged crossbreeds to wirehaired terrier type varieties, all of which are forgiven their lack of beauty by being recognised as courageous hunters.

"Il est un Chien de Chasse formidable !" claim the owners.

Even a poodle, when out for a walk with a man, comes into this category of "chasseur extraordinaire". Before you can pat a Frenchman's dog, or as in Marlene's case, make googly noises at it, you need the permission of the owner. If you insult somebody's dog it is the same as a personal insult of the owner. We found that the easiest way around this complication was to eye the animal from a discreet distance, and then say to the owner with a tone of appreciation,

"He looks like a rare and fearless hunting dog!"

The owner normally glows with pride and says, "Ah yes, she is a fine hunter, but with very good manners. She is very gentle!"

As he says this he hauls on the choke chain of his snarling companion. This is the cue for the dog to give an impression of wanting to taste your leg.

If it is a guard dog he might say, "He is very fierce and he is prepared to die in order to protect the house!"

The hunters with the genuine hunting dogs profess to care for them but they will abandon them on a hunt if the dogs get lost, to find their own way home. These are regarded as working dogs and not objects for love and affection. 'Home' for most hunting dogs is a cage with a kennel in it, or a length of chain attached to a tree without shelter. The French equivalent of the RSPCA seems to have different parameters of what care or cruelty means.

It appears from what Sandrine tells us that, "Country people have a pride in their dogs, but do not love their dogs."

"So," she explains, "For Monsieur Février not to own a dog indicates that he was neither interested in hunting, nor did he have anything in his house worth guarding!"

"I would have thought that he should have lived forever," I say to Sandrine. "He had no stress, a bit of physical exercise from his gardening and fresh vegetables to eat. Maybe he ate fish from the river. With such a good diet and red wine every day, he should have lived to be a hundred, like some of those people up in the cemetery!"

"Well," Sandrine answers, "He always seemed to be healthy whenever I saw him, but suddenly about a year ago he started to deteriorate. It took a while before his wife could convince him to go to a doctor. They found that he had intestinal cancer so the doctors did an operation, but it seems that the cancer had spread and there was nothing anyone could do for him."

"It is strange that the cancer should present so suddenly and spread so fast." Marlene joins in. "Normally at Monsieur Ferrier's age it grows slowly and there is time to catch it before it develops too far. There seems to be quite a bit of cancer around here. I believe that Monsieur Vincent who lives up near the main road has been diagnosed with a problem of some sort and he has had to have a course of chemotherapy."

"I have heard about that," said Sandrine. "He is another one of this generation of people who are about the same age and who are having this problem, whereas us older ones are remaining healthy and living longer. Myself, I blame the water! Ever since they started messing about with that new pipeline from the waterworks in Broin we have been getting dirty water. I think they are putting something into it. I don't trust them! That is why I always get bottled water delivered to me at home. I have to have it delivered because the bottles are a bit too heavy for me to carry on my bicycle from the shops."

"You should tell me if you want anything like that from Seurre," says Marlene. "You can always come with me in the car, when I go shopping."

Sandrine smiles, and answers, "You know, Marlene, I really prefer to go by myself because I always get impatient when I go with somebody else. And anyway, my son comes past once a week to see me, so he brings me some of the heavier things that I need."

I have to admire this gentle elderly lady and the way she protects her independence.

Our conversation pauses as we watch a pair of swans, in close formation, fly past us up the river.

Their wings stroke the air in unison and the sound of whistling flutes follows their passage.

I shake myself back from daydreaming about swans to the present company to find that Marlene and Sandrine are discussing Monsieur Corbier. Both of them had noticed that he was not looking well in the church. Sandrine continues to tell us about him.

"He was fine when he came back to the village and bought that house from his cousin. I think he had a part share in the house already, so he had to pay out only part of its value to the rest of his family. He had all sorts of plans at first, because when he stops drinking he is actually a very nice man. But then he lost his vitality. I think he had problems staying awake at the wheel when he was driving those big trucks. Now he just stays at home. He even has to pay somebody to come and cut the grass for him because he hasn't got the energy any more. It really is a shame to see what is happening to him."

"Well, I must be getting back," Sandrine announces. "I am expecting a telephone call from my daughter, so I must get home for that. Thank you for the tea."

Sandrine had been converted to Marlene's little band of friends who now accept and enjoy 'English Tea' and scones, rather than the lukewarm perfumed tisanes of the French tradition.

Marlene walks with her to the gate, still chatting about those last minute things for which there is never enough time. I collect the tray and return our special tea crockery to the kitchen.

We only use this special set for visitors, as normally we are too busy with renovation projects to do anything more sophisticated than grab a chipped mug of tea on the run.

Sandrine's French is so good for our growing knowledge of the language, because she speaks clearly and is happy to explain to us those words that we stumble over.

Like many French people, she is delighted to find that we have difficulty in learning this language, with which she had been competent since childhood.

She agrees with us that French is 'très compliqué'.

Monsieur Vincent

Monsieur Vincent was born in the village but has not lived here for all of his life, because at the age of seventeen, back in the mid nineteen fifties, he had left his parent's home to take up an apprenticeship at an engineering works in Chalon.

The buildings in Chalon, which this enterprise took over, were originally built by the Germans during the Second World War for the construction of U-boats. The site is on the banks of the Sâone River, which gave the finished U-boats access to the Mediterranean via the Rhone to the south. The main buildings above ground level had to be repaired and even replaced in some instances because of the damage sustained by the Allied bombing raids in 1943 and 1944. However the heavily reinforced underground pens for the U-boats had not been affected significantly, so these areas were adapted to the maintenance and reconstruction of barges, for the commercial traffic on the waterways of France.

Monsieur Vincent had fallen in love with one of the young secretaries in the main office administration block. Together they had shared their evenings walking and holding hands along the banks of the Sâone River, where it passes along the eastern flank of the town. It was some years before he developed sufficient courage, and funds, to ask the young lady to marry him. She agreed and they set the date, and arranged to have the wedding ceremony and reception back in his home village. There they could have all their friends from work, and his schooldays, join in the celebration.

His fiancée's father had been shot by the Germans when she was just a baby, on suspicion of being involved with the Underground during the war. He had been carrying messages between Partisan groups and the SAS parachutists in the Morvan Forest. It was a risky thing that he had done, because the war time sympathies in the Chalon area were firmly on the side of the Germans. It was a sensitive area because it was on the demarcation line of Vichy France and Occupied France.

This wartime sentiment had continued after the war in the Chalon area, even infiltrating itself into the structure of everyday life. The Challonaise are sometimes called 'Les Allemands' by the people who now live in what was Occupied France. These divisions are still felt keenly by country people. The Police during and after the war, in the town, were regarded as being similar to the Gestapo. The Vichy France police were called the Milice. Their sentiments live on.

"The Chalon traffic police," our villagers say, "are 'formidable'!"

This is not a complement.

This is another polite word like 'différent', but is used to express their mixture of fear and revulsion.

For these reasons the bride-to-be was happy to have her wedding day away from Chalon. Monsieur Vincent's village is only 35 kilometres away, but the atmosphere and outlook is a world apart.

Their wedding took place in the promising month of May of 1966, when the flowers were in profusion and the young cherries had already set. The apples were beginning to form on the branches in the orchards. The fields of Houblon around the village were already green, with the vines twinning their way to the tops of the webs of supports, which hold the plants up to the sun.

Monsieur Vincent's father was one of the Houblonnières engaged in erecting these structures. The work involved protecting the young shoots against frost, and then the spraying several times during the growing season against mildew. Then they had to hand pick the flowers and dry them, to remove the sticky aromatic extract for beer production.

It was an extremely labour intensive crop and the harvesting was an event that employed all the members of the family. The year that the Vincents were married was the last year that hops was grown on a commercial scale near the village.

It was also the last year that the three fêtes held in July, August and September to celebrate the growing, flowering and reaping of the hops were celebrated.

All this fecundity of this last season was to bless the new Vincent family, and over the following six years they produced two sons and a daughter. This was considered to be the correct number of children for the family of an Engineer.

Monsieur Vincent himself was one of ten children, which at the time was also considered a correct number of children for the family of a farm worker.

Monsieur Vincent did well with his professional career, as he had inherited a strong work ethic from his father. As a result of this he could afford to send his children for further education. Upon his retirement he returned to the village of his birth, as so many French people like to do. He and his wife were looking forward to a life of ease and fulfilment in their comfortable large house near the old centre of the village. Because of his financial planning, their long term future seemed secure and enviable.

It was only a couple of years after he had settled back in the village that his health took a turn for the worse. He was shocked one day to find blood in his faeces. As an engineer he knew that he had to seek immediate professional help, which he did. After a consultation with Dr Melun in Seurre he was referred to a specialist in Dijon, who was experienced in intestinal abnormalities.

The X-rays were not encouraging, so with some trepidation Monsieur Vincent was committed for surgery two days later. The devastation that the surgeon found was as though Monsieur Vincent had been subjected to severe trauma of some sort. The subsequent damage and consequent repair malfunctions to his body had caused the onset of cancerous growths in all of his organs.

The surgeon, when he was in initial consultation with Monsieur Vincent and his wife, was also concerned that Madame Vincent was not looking well. She had a pallor which he thought was not only due to the shock of the circumstances of her husband. He tactfully recommended her to have some blood tests.

The results of the blood tests arrived the same day that Monsieur Vincent had his initial surgery.

The results were not good. They indicated that Madame Vincent was suffering from Leukaemia and that her red and white blood cell counts were approaching emergency levels. An immediate blood transfusion was prescribed, followed by, like Monsieur Vincent, a series of sessions of chemotherapy.

A double blow like this seemed to be beyond the laws of chance, in the opinion of the consultant. He decided to start an investigation as to why two people, who had enjoyed normal good health all their lives, should suddenly be struck down with these virulent cancers. Was it something to do with retirement? He questioned his two patients about their life styles, their eating and exercise habits. After recording and analysing all the information, he was no nearer to finding the reason for this double disaster.

The Vincent's children were summoned and between them they worked out a plan so that they could take care of their parents in relays. This way the courses of chemotherapy could be administered at home by the village nurse, who ran a small clinic from her house. Their eldest daughter, Sabine, was going to take the first shift and then her brothers would take over and do their share.

The news of this disaster did not leak into the village news grapevine immediately, because the Vincents had not built up a local circle of close friends. Certainly Monsieur Vincent knew some of the people who had been at school with him in the village, but since then he had gained the status of a professional. He did not feel that he needed to renew associations with school acquaintances who had worked for printers, spent their lives driving trucks or storing boxes at the ceramic factory.

In any event, his old school friends would have rejected him, because "Who does he think he is? Better than us? Engineer? Zut Alors!"

He also had not felt the urge to have any contact with his old headmaster Monsieur Lafarge, who was living the life of a recluse on the edge of town.

Monsieur Lafarge was still disliked by all his old pupils, because of his cruelty in the classroom back in the fifties. The sexagenarians of the village still reminded each other occasionally about how the headmaster used to twist their ears during classes.

We only become fully aware of the plight of Monsieur Vincent and his wife when, one day, their daughter comes walking down the road past our house, towards the river, with tears in her eyes.

Marlene is tending to her multicoloured irises in the flower bed near our main gate, when she sees this forty year old woman in distress.

Marlene is never a person to look the other way when someone needs help.

"Excuse me," she says, "do you think that I should move these plants here over to this position, so that they can get more sunshine?"

The woman stops in her tracks and stares at Marlene with total incomprehension. She is so lost in her misery that she has not noticed, though her tearful eyes, that there is somebody weeding the flowerbeds at the side of the road.

"Quoi?"

"I am wondering if I should move these plants now, or if I should wait until they have finished flowering. What do you think?"

The lady is stumped for an answer. After living in Paris for the last twenty years she has become unaccustomed to the French rural practice of greeting strangers, for no other reason than that they are passing in the street.

"I don't know."

"Well, come with me and give me your opinion. I was thinking of putting them in the flowerbed on the other side of the house, but I need somebody to help me make the decision."

Marlene takes the woman by the arm and walks with her across the courtyard and through the arch into the riverside garden, as though they are old friends.

"There," she says pointing, "that's where I was thinking of putting them, or perhaps over there under the cherry tree?"

"I don't know. I am from Paris and I don't have a garden... only an apartment in the Sixth Arrondissement so I know nothing about flowers and gardens. But..." she looks around, "This is very beautiful here!"

"Take a seat," says Marlene, "And let me get you a cup of tea?"

"You're not from around here, are you?" asks the woman.

"Ah! You can tell from my accent?"

"No... It is just that the act of asking a passer-by into your home off the street, for a tisane, is not normal."

"Maybe," answers Marlene, "But then I have never been restricted by what people call normal. I am making tea and I would like you to share it with me."

The visitor is still overcome by her grief and is disorientated with this approach by Marlene. She takes a seat. With a few words of encouragement and a warm smile from

Marlene, she starts to pour her heart out. Marlene listens with empathy and understanding as she has done with others, so many times before. Perhaps, because we have lost a child to leukaemia, we are able to share and understand the grief of others, who are experiencing this kind of anguish for the first time.

After an hour of listening to her visitor, Marlene knows that her visitor's immediate distress and sorrow have been alleviated a little. Only then do they introduce themselves to each other. Sabine Vincent is shocked that she has talked so long to a complete stranger, without the formality of an introduction. It is a measure of her grief. She had only wanted to have a walk by the river to calm her thoughts, and here she has found someone who is able to take on board all her worries. At the same time she has this feeling that she can trust Marlene emphatically.

This is, of course, true.

However sadly five days after this first meeting with Sabine, we are again walking up the road towards the church. Father Dedicus is tolling the bell of the church, to call the friends of Monsieur Vincent to come and pay their last respects.

Sabine and her two brothers are already seated in the church by the time we arrive. I imagine that, because they hardly know anybody in the village, they want to avoid the awkwardness of meeting them outside for the first time, in these circumstances.

Père Dedicus is seated to one side of the altar surreptitiously wiping his face and neck with a handkerchief. He is again showing the strain of exercise from pulling at the bell rope. His rotundity seems not suited to these exertions. I wonder to myself if he had considered getting the services of a village lad to do this duty for him.

Monsieur Vincent's coffin has been put in place near the altar. I can see from our position in the church that it is an expensive looking model, lavishly decorated with bouquets of flowers. There is also a portable organ on the opposite side of the church from where Father Dedicus is sitting, and it is providing sombre music. It must have been brought in to make up for the lack of musical facilities in the church. I can not see anybody who looks as if she could be Madame Vincent, so I assume that she is having treatment at home and is too ill to be here.

There are less people attending this funeral than that for Monsieur Février, which I assume is because the Vincents have lived away from the village for many years. I see some well dressed visitors in the front pews who are possibly the drivers of the expensive cars parked outside the church. I had seen, before we entered the church, that the registrations on the cars are from the departments of 75, 39 and a 52 among others, which were the codes from Paris, Chalon and Toulouse respectively. Perhaps these strangers are work colleagues from Monsieur Vincent's professional past.

I notice that the Lady Mayor has not come to this funeral. The Baker's Wife, Madame Peron is in attendance again, with the same flowery hat as before. She must know almost everybody in the village, because they all must be customers of her bakery. The hearse outside the church is a much more upmarket model than the local ex-ambulance vehicle, and it looks as though it may have come from Dijon with its '21' registration.

Père Dedicus's sermon is about trying to understand the complexities of the working of God's intentions, when people are summoned to his side with so little forewarning. It seems to be a sermon that is more suited for the funeral of an accident victim. In a certain way, I surmise, the speed at which Monsieur Vincent's condition deteriorated, it amounts to almost the same thing.

After the final hymn Monsieur Vincent's coffin is carried away by his sons and some other young men whom I presume to be friends of theirs. Sabine follows the cortège looking distraught behind the veil that she is wearing. I see that Marlene wants to follow them to the cemetery, if only to give some moral support to Sabine and the family who are, after all, among strangers here.

We walk up the road to the cemetery passing on the way the Mayoral Offices, the Post Office and the village shops, all of which were closed with an extended lunch break.

Whether this closure of facilities is as a mark of respect for the Vincent family or due summer lethargy I am not quite sure.

Our route takes us past the turreted Chateau with its long straight driveway lined with trees. We pass Jacques's cousin's house which now has shutters painted purple! This is a bold leap forward in this traditional area. It seems that the breakaway from traditional shutter colours is spreading.

Jacques, who lives in the next house to his cousin, is working in his blue denim overalls outside his house. Once again he is repairing somebody's lawnmower, while another 'friend's' powerboat engine waits for attention. He is almost always occupied with mending the broken equipment of his circle of friends. This circle expands by the word of mouth of those whom he had helped before. He is such an amenable fellow that everybody takes advantage of him. He has a waiting list of people hoping to get a cheap repair for their domestic appliances and paraphernalia.

We have to stop for a few moments to commiserate with him, about how there are not enough hours in the day to get everything done. Jacques is a very sociable person, which is why he is so willing to help others. His return compensation for this is that he loves to chatter. The result is that the 'few moments' turn into twenty minutes, before we can drag ourselves away.

By the time we get to the cemetery we find that the coffin is already at the new graveside. Father Dedicus has gone into the final stages of the service, with only a small group of attendees.

I am not sure if this is supposed to be a family only affair, so we stand at a respectful distance.

"Sabine is taking this hard," Marlene says to me.

I can see Sabine standing apart from her brothers. Suddenly I have the feeling that Sabine is anticipating that this occasion is a rehearsal for the imminent funeral of her mother. Marlene has always had the ability to understand people's feeling far better than I, from only a glance. I have asked her how she does it and she has told me that it is from their stance, but I think that it is more than that.

"Wait here." she says to me.

She walks quietly towards the group and when she gets beside Sabine she takes her arm so that they stand silently together, as the coffin is lowered into the ground.

Rather than stand at a distance by myself I withdraw and then start to wander among the gravestones, looking at the names and calculating the ages of the occupants below.

I am struck by the difference between this cemetery and its equivalent in England. Here the graves, for the most part, are well tended and have evidence of care. There are recent messages of never-ending love and flowers on most of them.

I find Augustin Février's grave which has a simple slab of granite and a single dried bouquet. I wonder if this floral offering is from his wife.

At one end of the cemetery is a row of graves with small signs declaring that these people have died for their country.

"Pour la Patrie," is printed on each metal peg.

I consider for a moment the number of names of those killed in the First World War, on the War Memorial in the village, compared that to the population of the village. I realise that the loss is five percent and that most of them had never been found, to be brought back and buried here.

It was not as catastrophic as the town of Oradour sur Glane in the south of France, where the entire community of 642 was murdered by the German SS, in a reprisal for an attempted assassination of a senior German Officer. Although some people thought that it was a propaganda coup by the Communists, who were said to have stored explosives in the church. When it blew up and killed everyone, they blamed the Germans. Would we ever know the truth?

It comes as a shock to me to realise that this figure is almost the same as the present day population tally of our village.

There are three graves here of young men killed for their part in the Resistance in 1944. I wonder for a while how their lives would have been spent had they not been murdered. I remember Jacques telling me that when he was a boy, he and his friends used to play on the site of an old German gun emplacement, which had been built during the war. Apparently, during the liberation, an American tank had trundled down the main road from Paris and caught the battery unawares, and with a single shot had hit the pile of ammunition situated near the gun. The explosion had blasted the gun, its mounting, the crew and all the shells and other ammunition over a wide area.

"What fun the children had back then," Jacques had told me, "finding and playing with all the live ammunition that had been buried everywhere."

My reverie is broken when I realise that the funeral rites are ended. People are filtering back to the entrance of the cemetery, and their cars. I see that Marlene is in deep conversation with Sabine, so I keep my distance as this is obviously an important and personal conversation.

I follow them to the cars where, after a few minutes, Sabine gets into her car and drives away.

Marlene looks for me, waves and with a smile says, "Right, let's go home."

It takes us ten minutes to walk back through the village which gives us an opportunity to see the gardens along the way, and to compare changes that people had made since the previous year. Some of them had no interest in gardens, while others had been stimulated into a sense of competition. The competitiveness had been encouraged by small prizes that the Mayor presents to the best gardeners, each year.

On the way, just when Marlene thought that the time was right, she casually mentions to me,

"I am going to help Sabine with her mother. She has been telling me that she is having a hard time coping. It doesn't look as though her Mum is responding to the chemotherapy very well, and the distress caused by her husband's death hasn't helped. It will just be for a few days while Sabine visits her family back in Paris. Did you know that she is part of the High Speed Train design team? She doesn't know anybody here so I volunteered to help her."

"I am sure that you know what you are doing."

"She tells me that her brothers don't know how to handle the situation, and that she has to get back to organise her children, and also to get compassionate leave from work, in order to be able to spend more time with her mother."

"Did she say if they have any idea what has caused this illness?"

"No, they don't seem to have any idea. There doesn't seem to be any history of cancer in the family that they know about. Both of her mother's parents have had good health all their lives. Sabine's mother does not know much about her biological father's history, as he was killed in the war when she was very young. Sabine says that her mother doesn't like to talk about him. Her father's parents were farming people here in the village, but all her father's brothers and sisters have moved away years ago. She doesn't know much about what has happened to them all. This whole thing has come about so suddenly that they haven't yet managed to contact all of the family. Isn't it strange! Here in the village there is the Chazelle family who have hung around without moving, doing odd jobs and with several of them living on Social Benefit whereas Sabine's Uncles and Aunts have all left to find work elsewhere. I think Sandrine told me that there were originally twenty one children in the Chazelle family and the old lady Chazelle even got a letter from the President's Office congratulating her on her patriotism for contributing to 'Les Enfants de la France'. Apparently you get a medal from the State if you have a lot of children."

"Ouch! That must be a full time job, bringing up twenty one kids!"

"Oh, I think that they brought each other up! Their mother was too busy getting pregnant."

"It's almost like Africa!"

"Only here, the majority of the children survive!"

We turn into our gateway and walk through to the river garden.

"I think a cup of tea is in order, don't you?" I ask.

"What a good idea… Are you making it?"

"Sure!"

Marlene starts taking care of Madame Vincent at her home. Her patient is in between chemotherapy sessions. She is very weak and the distressing thing is that there is very little that Marlene can do for her, except to make her comfortable.

Three days later Sabine returns from Paris to be with her mother, just in time for Madame Vincent's return to hospital.

We never see Sabine or her mother again.

Madame Vincent's request was to be cremated which was carried out in Dijon with only her family present.

"What are the chances," I ask Marlene, "of two people dying of almost the same thing at the same time, unless there is a common cause?"

"I don't know," she answered. "I would have thought that something must have caused it. There are no nuclear power stations near here, no microwave towers and no large power cables. It doesn't make sense. A plague, or infection, a virus or a disease would have affected other people as well. I wonder if they could have been injected with some radioactive substance. But why?"

"Perhaps we should get ourselves a Geiger counter?"

"Oh wonderful! That will be another thing to lie about the place. I think we have enough junk here already, don't you?"

"Oh, I don't know." I answer, "I could store it with my metal detector and all those spare electrical motors that I am hoping to use…sometime!"

The Ratman

The Ratman has never worked in his life.

That is to say, he has never been employed in a way that is considered acceptable in modern polite society.

He has created for himself, however, 'un travail' that is his overriding passion.

It is a vocation that is as strong as any other extreme occupation, in a world filled with people who have religious or professional careers, which they follow with commitment and zeal to their graves.

In another life he might have been an explorer like Columbus, or van Riebeck.

Perhaps he might have been a voyager like Cook, or a wandering Bushman or a migratory moose.

He is afflicted by the same syndrome that has diseased all of them, which is simply the unquenchable urge to be somewhere else from where he is.

Some of these travellers had sponsors, like Queen Issabella or a greedy Government to urge them on to make discoveries. The Ratman has had support from a social system which has been designed to give sustenance to those unable to take care of themselves.

The Ratman has no qualifications.

But he does have a single ability, and that is to ride a bicycle.

And so this is what he does, all day every day.

He rides from his hovel in the village to Seurre, to buy a bottle of water, and then he rides home. Within the hour he is riding back again with an empty plastic bottle. He returns with a full one. But this is not a hobby, which he does to pass the time on a pleasant sunny afternoon. This is an occupation to which he has to dedicate all his waking hours, with the same commitment as a devoted priest.

He rides in blizzards.

He rides in heat waves.

He rides in the early mornings, when the new frost on the road crackles under the wheels of his bicycle.

He rides in the rain, when the great eighteen wheel trucks splash sheets of water, from the puddles in the road, into his face.

He may be soaked, frozen, sweating or exhausted, but he keeps to his schedule.

He is as dedicated to his cause as any Don Quixote searching for terrifying giants, with their four whirling arms.

His problem is that, although he travels, he doesn't know what the goal of his search is. He has an indefinable quest that not even he understands, except for his search for food. When his mother was still alive, she was living at the hospital in Seurre. The staff used to give the Ratman lunch everyday. After his mother died, the tradition continued. Somebody said, in jest on his behalf, that as he had been fed by the hospital for more than thirty years, he had a 'right' to be fed as a form of usufruct.

In his youth he was known, occasionally, to steal panties and bras from washing lines. But this was considered to be neither a theft for personal gain, nor for some deviant sexual fantasy, but simply as a result of the confusion that exists in his mind.

His plight was considered at the village council meetings and the consensus was that he was harmless, and that to confine him in an institution would be a death penalty for him.

In Seurre there is a delightful man who runs a small business in the main road. He has dedicated all of his life to this business. Monsieur Gerard Thon is the sole proprietor of a repair shop. He mends lawnmowers and motorcycles, bicycles and prams. He fixes punctures and restores brakes.

The wonderful thing about Gerard Thon is that he is one of those rare service providers who charge a price that is related to the work that he does, rather than charge a price that you would have to pay for a new replacement part.

Of course, the Ratman is his best customer.

But the Ratman can't pay for all the brakes he uses or the tyres he wears out.

The Ratman has become a charity case for Gerard Thon.

Gerard keeps a selection of old tyres from unwanted bicycles that have come from the sons of rich customers. These are the bicycles that are "last year's colour", or "don't have the latest speedo". Normally they would be discarded in the town dump, but they are collected by Gerard who then adapts the parts for the Ratman's bicycle.

I am not sure that the Ratman appreciates this or if he thanks Gerard for this service, because he hardly ever communicates with anyone, except for the village Postmaster.

The village post office is where the Ratman has to go to collect his social security money. Each week he has to stand and get shouted at by Michel Bonnadot the Postmaster, because he can't fill out his monthly application form. The Ratman has never been able to read or write. Michel does not select the Ratman especially for this abuse; he tries to abuse everybody who comes into his little post office. He is particularly adept at pretending to not understand tourists.

When a foreigner comes into the post office, with a post card in hand and asks for a stamp, Michel takes delight in pretending to not comprehend what the visitor wants.

Hesitantly : "Bon Jour Monsieur, je voudrais un timbre, si vous plait?"

Michel, aggressively : "Quoi?"

Apologetically: "Un timbre? Un tumbre? Un tombre?"

Michel: "I don't know what you are talking about!"

One day Marlene interrupted this pathetic little game by saying to Michel, "For Christ's sake, Michel: What do you think this person wants? She has got a post card in her hand, some money in the other hand and she is not from here. Don't you think that she wants a stamp to post the post card?"

Michel went into a fat sulk, like a small boy who has had his frog taken way by a schoolteacher. We have never been friends since.

It would be logical for the Ratman to buy his bread from Marie Peron's bakery next door, after getting his money. But no, he climbs onto his bicycle and heads off to Seurre, whatever the weather.

It would seem that the Ratman will never amount to anything or own anything precious, but he does have one hidden asset. His bicycle must have covered a greater distance than any other bicycle in France. And this is in a country that reveres the bicycle, to the extent that cycling has become a National Sport. Although the Ratman does not achieve the speed of the racers in the Tour de France, he has been peddling on his bicycle for over fifty years. His bicycle must have enormous value as a collector's item.

There is a reason that the Ratman does not buy his bread from Marie Peron.

It was she who instigated his arrest when he stole her underwear from her washing line, by leaning over the fence at the rear of the bakery.

Although that had happened forty years ago, after Marie had become the proprietor of the bakery, neither of them has forgotten the incident.

They would have continued their mutual non recognition of each other forever, had not a small event occurred, which brought them into contact again.

It was when the Ratman fell off his bicycle outside the bakery.

It wasn't his fault…

He is cycling past, crouched over his handlebars as though he is studying the way his front wheel goes round, and round, and round… and round.

He always rides this way because he is suffering from a crooked back. One of the patrons of the bakery parks her car and then opens the door without looking. The Ratman collides with the door, then falls onto the road and bumps his head. He is fortunate that there is no other vehicle passing at that moment.

The driver calls to Marie to help her move the Ratman to the side of the road, so that he will be safe from any passing traffic.

Marie wants to ignore this call for help because, as far as she is concerned, anything that happens outside her shop is nothing to do with her.

However she does do something.

She calls PP.

"PP! Old André Thomassin has fallen off his bike. Will you help Régine move him? I can't leave the shop! PP, did you hear me?"

PP pokes his head through the doorway leading to the baking room with the ovens.

"Yes Marie, I did. Where is he?"

"Where do you think? Really! In the road of course! Where else would he be?"

PP looks through the glass door of the shop where he sees Régine Pipot trying to help the Ratman to the side of the road.

"Wait!" he calls, as he opens the door. "Here, let me help you!"

He checks for traffic and then trots across the road.

The Ratman is groggy.

He is sitting up now and his jaw is moving as though he is trying to say something. PP puts his arms around the Ratman's slender frame, from the back, and lifts him easily to his feet. Then he carries the small man across the road; so that he can sit on the raised concrete flowerbed in front of the bakery.

Marie stands behind the counter, staring through the glass display window of the shop, at the scene outside. As she watches, she polishes her countertop with her cloth in a reflex action that is similar to the way a cat licks itself for reassurance.

Rather than concern herself with thoughts about how the old man is, she thinks how she can ensure that she can't be blamed for anything.

'The best thing,' she decides, 'will be to telephone the pompiers. It isn't a real accident, but it will cover me if the old man has concussed himself, or broken something. I'm not happy that PP has heaved him off the road as though he was a sack of flour. PP, and I, could be blamed if something goes wrong with the old man's health. The old devil is as close to death as it is, without any help from us!'

Marie goes through to the rear kitchen where she has her telephone.

PP, meanwhile, is extremely concerned about old André Thomassin's condition.

But the Ratman is a tough old chap, who can remember what it is that he wanted to get, and that was to go to Seurre to get his bread.

"Croissant!" he says, "Baguette!"

"Of course!" says PP, "I'll get you some. Straightaway!"

He leaves the old man in the care of Réginé Pipot, and goes into the bakery. Marie is nowhere to be seen. He takes a fresh baguette from the basket next to the till and below the counter he sees a croissant with a white icing topping. He snatches that, wraps them both in tissue, goes outside and gives them to the Ratman.

The Ratman is standing now and is more concerned about his bicycle than anything else. It is propped against Régine Pipot's car, where she had put it for safety. He takes the bread from PP in an absentminded fashion, murmurs something to himself and totters across the road without looking for cars.

PP and Régine watch him as he puts the bread into the wooden box that he has tied behind his saddle. He mounts up and rides off towards Seurre, as though nothing has happened. He is weaving slightly, but then he does that most of the time, these days.

PP and Régine go into the shop just as Marie emerges from the rear kitchen.

"I've called the pompiers," she announces.

"Eh Bien!" says PP, "but he has flown! Gone! Disappeared!"

"Merde!" declares Marie. "I'll have to call them back! But, maybe…? If I let them come, then at least if he falls off again somewhere down the road, then we will be covered. We will be seen to have done the right thing!"

Marie is living true to form, in her world, where Marie comes first and everybody else comes a distant forty fourth.

She serves Régine Pipot without saying another word. PP resumes his work with the ovens. Marie polishes her countertop. The pompiers arrive with panache and flair, with their new red emergency vehicle, which has impressive blue flashing lights. The "bee-bar bee-bar" of their siren can be heard all the way from Seurre. They leap from the truck, ready for action with their shiny helmets gleaming in the sun. Between them they have a fine selection of moustaches, all at 'attention'.

Everybody emerges from the boulangerie, the coiffure, the tabac and the post office.

There is a conference in the street.

Traffic stops.

Hands are shaken.

Greetings are shared.

Friendships are renewed.

It seems that the accident has disappeared.

The pompiers say that they saw André Thomassin on the road towards Seurre, and that he looked alright.

"Which is not all that good at the best of times," one of them added.

"We'll stop and have a look at him on the way back."

They all shake hands and wish each other a 'good appetite' and an 'enjoyable afternoon'. The pompiers climb back into their truck and debate whether they can justify sounding the siren on the way back to Seurre, just for the hell of it… Better not!

It is an hour later that Marie realises that the croissant with the icing topping is missing. She had been experimenting with her red mushrooms and a sweet croissant rather than a chocolate one. She wanted to see if the smell of the red mushroom was hidden by the sickly sweet smell of the icing.

Where is it?

It hasn't fallen down below the counter onto the floor.

It isn't anywhere.

After pondering for a few minutes she asks PP.

He remembers and tells her what he has done.

"I gave it to Monsieur Thomassin!"

He doesn't know why Marie's eyes go wide.

She doesn't say anything.

The Ratman cycles to Seurre staring at his front wheel. It is beginning to drizzle. He slits his eyes against the weather and pedals on. He decides to deploy his all-weather gear, which consists of a summer parasol, which he uses as a shield against snow and hail. He keeps his pace, true to his mission, true to his schedule that he has to pursue, whatever the weather, whatever the time.

Onward and onward.

He passes over the bridge as he has done thousands of times and freewheels to the roundabout. He pedals again past parked cars, without a qualm, as though he has already forgotten that a car had caused him to fall off his bicycle only minutes ago.

At the supermarket he parks his bicycle outside the bakery section. He pushes the front wheel into his own personal slot on the rack, the one that he always uses. He sees that he already has a baguette and a croissant in the box on his carrier.

He pauses and stares.

How did they get there?

Where did they come from?

He stands and deliberates for a while and then thinks that he must have already been into the shop, or that perhaps that he had forgotten to take them out of the box after his last trip.

No matter.

He has got bread.

It is time to return home.

But first, he must stop and eat his croissant.

He mounts his bike and pedals to the rear of the supermarket where it backs onto the river. He has his personal rock here which he uses as a seat. It is away from people and he can see up the river from here. It is habitual for him to use this rock, because these days he can not focus all the way up the river. He can not see that far any more. But he doesn't mind, because he knows the view well. He has been looking at it for over half a century.

Whatever the weather.

Whatever the time.

For fifty years.

The croissant tastes different to normal.

He doesn't buy these ones with the icing on.

He wonders why he has got one today.

The girl in the bakery always gives him the same thing, whenever he comes to the shop. He doesn't have to ask. It is always the same.

Whatever the weather.

He munches on his croissant and then licks the sticky residue from his fingers.

It's time to go. He mustn't be late.

He mounts up and pedals off along the river towards the bridge, and his way home.

Perhaps it is because he is lean as a whippet and that he has a blood circulation as efficient as a high-speed hydraulic system, that the hallucinogenic properties of the mushroom circulate so quickly through his blood and brain. Five minutes later, as he enters the edge of the village, he is convinced that he is riding a motorcycle.

He has never ridden a motorcycle before.

The engine is silent, which is strange but he is not curious about it.

He is never really curious about anything.

He finds it odd that he is going so fast. The world seems to be flashing past him. His pedals are whirring as though of their own accord. He tries weaving and leaning as he careers along. There is a car somewhere behind him, hooting and hooting.

No matter.

He knows that he can just zoom across the road and swerve back again, just in front of that great big articulated truck coming the other way, without any danger whatsoever!

If he wants to.

He can do anything.

He can sweep across the jaws of death.

He can tilt at windmills and slay dragons.

Nothing is impossible.

The exhaust roar of the truck is like the roar of a dragon. The driver changes gear as a precaution, then slams on his emergency brakes. To the Ratman, the squeal of brakes and shriek of pneumatics is like a shriek of fear from the beast.

The smoke from skidding tyres is its fiery breath.

But the dragon can't catch him. Nothing can.

He will never feel the clamp of its jaws.

He does feel something.

As the front grill of the truck propels him through a garden wall he does feel his bones breaking, but there is no pain. The legs and wings and wheels and scales of the juggernaut dragon crush him to death.

He knows in that final moment that he is in the grip of a mighty monster.

He sees colours that he has never dreamed could exist.

He is physically shaken and pummelled as though by an enormous sexual experience. His mission is accomplished.

He has found what he has been searching for.

He finds exhilaration at last.

He has found peace.

He does not die alone.

As the truck sandwiches him into oblivion, against the garden wall, it collapses and falls onto a cockerel.

This cockerel is a free-range bird that controls his harem of hens in the garden of the village nurse. He is supposed to be confined to a shed because of the panicky regulations concerning the bird-flu virus, but the nurse has told the village council that the regulations are rubbish.

She is not going to comply.

The council had considered the matter and had come to the conclusion that to alienate the nurse, who would one day be called to each of them in turn, for some future emergency, would not be wise.

So they decide to look the other way.

They pretend that they don't know. They must make sure that they have no official notification of this transgression of the rules, so that they can not be blamed, if something should go wrong at some stage in the future.

So it is with a sense of satisfaction that they learn of the cockerel's demise.

Even if the cockerel is the National emblem of France, its death does resolve the problem of complaints about the noise of his crowing, for the committee.

And as for old Monsieur André Thomassin?
Well, he is no longer a traffic hazard.

And Marie Peron?
Once again she has escaped discovery.

Monsieur Corbier

Alan Corbier was Claude Monet's close friend and confidant, when they were at school together. He had been at Claude Monet's side when the bully had forced his personality and desires on the other school children. But Alan had never been a bully himself. He was simply a fellow who liked to go along through life in the wake of a shark, rather in the way that a remora sticks to its host and feeds on the scraps that comes its way. In this fashion, Alan Corbier had been able to benefit from the packets of sweets that Claude Monet always seemed to have. He had always had first choice of the lunchboxes of the other children, by virtue of his position.

He benefited from his status of being part of the group of the village bully.

When the boys left school, it was almost inevitable that Alan Corbier would go forth to find a replacement figure, for the one he had lost from his schooldays.

The replacement figure turned out to be the Gendarmerie.

The Police Force took Alan Corbier into its folds and gave him security, status and a sense of importance. These were the same things that he had enjoyed in the shadow of Claude Monet.

Alan Corbier was a sociable boy and he grew up to be an obliging and pleasant man. This characteristic of course would ensure that he never was to achieve a high rank in the Gendarmerie, because he was never forceful enough in his own right. He was not charismatic in any way, but he was a team player, in that he would never let the side down. He was a reliable friend and a good companion.

The Force was perfect for him.

As the years went by it became apparent that Alan Corbier was not going to become a sergeant, nor that he would aspire to joining one of the specialist branches that required passes in examinations and successes in the field. For this reason be became attached to the Presidential Convoy team. This involved riding a motorcycle around Paris, or wherever the President was going to be travelling by car.

He and the others had to swoop, with authority and panache, in front of the traffic to halt all the plebeians in their tracks, while the convoy of the President passed without so much as a minor application of brakes.

It was a wonderful life.

He had authority without responsibility.

With a scowl, which was not his usual expression, he could cower motorists to stop, and then with a regal wave of dismissal, he would zoom off to the next intersection, passing the Presidential car with a roaring gear change, to stop the traffic again, up ahead of the convoy.

This progress through the streets of Paris, when viewed from the air, looked rather like the progress of a Queen Bee through a hive. There was activity on all sides, with a few privileged workers accompanying the Queen on her never-ending duties for the State.

After duty hours were, for Alan Corbier, the best.

This was when the corps of motorcyclists and drivers could get together in a bar or Bistro, and relive their day, with tales of derring-do and bravado. They recounted their ventures and disputes with the traffic in rather the same way that golfers discuss matches, by embellishing the daring episodes and ignoring the blunders.

They drank together.

They drank too much together.

But they could do it!

They were like Gods.

Life was perfect and would go on forever.

One day he got a letter from his school friend Claude Monet. It seemed that his friend was now working for a printing works in Paris, and that he wanted to organise a gathering of school friends back in their old home village. The reason for this was that Claude Monet was getting married, and he did not want to have the reception after his marriage in Paris, but wanted to have it at his old home in order to impress his old school friends. It seemed a good excuse for a get-together and so Alan Corbier said that he would be delighted to attend.

He asked for, and got permission, to take his official motorcycle home with him. That promised to be the best thing of all. He would be able to ride through the streets of the village on his shiny late model BMW, where he did not, as a child, have the money for a bicycle.

Yes, this would prove that he had ***arrived!***

The date set for the reception was the third of May 1986.

Of course, Claude Monet was a communist, and as such was not going to have any form of religious ceremony to mar his wedding. The official declaration and signing of papers would take place in the town hall in Seurre, and then the reception would take place in the village hall.

Everything was arranged.

Phillip Vincent, who was now an engineer in Chalon had agreed to come. He sounded a bit superior on the telephone, as though he was a bit too important these days, but he did say that he would be there with his wife. Augustin Février would have to be invited, because he was one of the gang in the old days, although it seemed that had done nothing with his life, except work in the village factory. Of course, they would have to include Michel, the Postmaster, and Monsieur Lafarge the old headmaster, but the latter probably wouldn't come.

That would be the old gang back together, if only for a brief moment.

Claude Monet's wife-to-be was not at all happy about going off to this little village in the Bourgogne for her wedding. However it did mean that they would be able to host the reception for a fraction of the cost of hiring a hall in Paris, and Claude promised her that with the money he saved, that they could spend it on themselves. He was going to a Party Conference in Italy after the wedding, so they would be able to travel there in style, and have a honeymoon to remember for ever!

The formalities took place in the office of Monsieur Fromage, the Mayor of Seurre in the mid eighties, (who was known behind his back as the 'Big Cheese') with only Claude Monet, his wife and Alan Corbier in attendance. Monsieur Fromage's secretary and Alan Corbier were the witnesses who signed the documents for Claude Monet and his new wife.

Then they went to the hall in the village that had been prepared for them by the village Traiteur who still operated his catering business from home.

It was a couple of days before this wedding party that the terrible news of the nuclear accident at Chernobyl was announced.

The meltdown of the Power Station caused a radioactive cloud of material to rise up into the Stratosphere, where it swept down across Europe and split apart to spread its deadly polonium and heavy metals across the countryside.

Russian helicopter pilots tried to limit the dreadful effects of the accident by flying over the gaping crater and dropping loads of concrete into this maw of hell. They knew that they were going to expose themselves to lethal doses of radiation and that they would die agonising deaths as a result. Their flying was one of the most gallant and heroic actions of self sacrifice of the entire 20th century, even including all of the incredible achievements of the two world wars. The lives that they saved by sacrificing their own must rank as one of the highest acts of courage ever attained by human beings, and at the same time, be one of the least rewarded and recognised.

But for their actions, thousands, maybe millions could have died.

As it was, some did and some would.

And of these, some would be in a little village in France, where they had gathered to celebrate the wedding of one of their school friends. They did not know at the time that they had been subjected to a freak fall of polonium, and that the lethal doses of Alfa Gamma rays that they received would not be apparent, for something like twenty years. The little shower of rain that fell on the forest of Montmain seemed so inconsequential at the time. The polonium fell where the mushrooms grew, in a small vlei which didn't drain well. By fate, the mushrooms were collected and used by the village Traiteur when he prepared the snacks for the reception of the new Monsieur and Madame Monet. The radiation from the polonium would not have affected them, had they just been exposed to it, as their skin would have been sufficient protection. But they ate it, and so set in motion a slow destruction of their internal organs that only needed a further small additional insult to upset their natural repair mechanism, and cause their organs, years later, to become cancerous.

In fact, it is possible that they may have achieved a reasonable old age and suffered ill health only later in life, had they not been subjected to more lethal doses of radiation.

These later doses, however, were not accidental.

These were administered with evil intention and malice aforethought.

They were administered to them in doses in their daily bread, prepared for them by the village baker's wife. She knew what she was doing, because she had read in a little book about mushrooms, that fungi tends to absorb radiation from the ground, and that it stores radiation in the mushrooms that it creates above ground. The minute tendrils that creep like a mould for extreme distances underground tend to carry these dangerous elements back to the mother plant, where they are concentrated in the fruit that is the mushroom.

The combination of the radiation insult at the time of the Chernobyl accident, the addition of radiated mushrooms administered over a period of months, followed by a poisonous 'coup de grace' of toxic fungi would kill them as quickly and as surely as a bullet in the brain.

And this is how Alan Corbier died, after an illness that caused him to deteriorate over the period of nearly eighteen months. Dr Melun did not call for an autopsy, as he had no suspicions concerning Alan Corbier's health. His patient had simply developed cancer and had quietly wasted away.

All he had to mark his life was his few memories of being an important motorcycle rider in Paris, in the days when the President depended on him.

That was until the day that he fell off on the cobblestones in front of the Palace of Versailles.

It wasn't really his fault. The cobblestones were wet from a recent shower, and they were polished as smooth as glass from wheels over the last two hundred years.

It could have happened to anybody.

It was just unfortunate that when he slipped and fell off his motorcycle, the top pannier bag behind his seat popped open.

And his half empty bottle of Pastis fell out.

Along with an apple.

His emergency rations!

They skidded across the cobbles.

They smashed against the steps.

Where the President was standing.

To receive Princess Diana.

It could have happened to anyone.

Of course, they had to have an enquiry, which was chaired by an ex Commandant of the Presidential Convoy Detachment.

He was not about to admit that off duty drinking was out of control among the drivers and riders, or that surreptitious drinking on duty was tolerated, because of the long hours that the men had to wait, at the whim of the President.

After all, how is a man supposed to ride a motorcycle along a winding road, without a little reinforcement to straighten the road?

This is an accepted fact in the countryside, where only the Roman roads are straight. All the others, which weave with gentle curves through the countryside all started as tracks around farmer's fields. These roads which seem to weave in the morning are known to be much straighter and smoother after lunch, with a little wine reinforcement.

And in cities too, it is known that a little wine reduces the stress of traffic delays and anxiety.

Everybody knows this, but it couldn't be recognised as being tolerated. So poor Alan Corbier was stripped of his position in the corps of riders, and given early retirement.

He wasn't charged for being over the limit, for the simple reason that he was not given a blood test. They knew what the result would be, and then they would have to investigate the entire department. Such an indiscretion must not be allowed to occur, so Alan Corbier was patted on the back and sent on his way.

He didn't really mind, because he is a team player. And team players understand that they must sacrifice themselves for the good of others. And anyway, he would make more money as a truck driver. Especially with the travel allowances and the money that he could save by claiming cash for the toll roads and then using, instead, the minor roads through small villages.

Yes, there were lots of ways to benefit from early retirement from the Gendarmerie. And the risk of being caught with the tachometers, which record how many hours driving you have done, is less than other drivers because of the 'code'.

The 'code' is that retired Gendarmes, who are truck drivers, don't get stopped at traffic check road blocks, because of the 'sign'.

The 'sign' varies.

Sometimes it is a little clown puppet hanging from the rear-view mirror. Sometimes it is a small bunch of plastic flowers on the dashboard. Sometimes it is a peaked hat with that month's special insignia.

Only the select inner circle knows what the 'sign' is for that month.

Alan Corbier would have continued truck driving well past his official retirement age, because the money was good, if it hadn't been that he moved back to the village of his youth. It was after that, when he started to have fatigue attacks, and nightmares in the daytime. He found he couldn't keep awake at nights on the long haul trips on the boring National Roads. He was running out of energy.

Eventually he went to see Doctor Melun.

It was after that when he decided to retire.

It wasn't too bad, because he still got companionship at the village bar. There he was able to swap the same old boring stories with Augustin Février and Michel the Postmaster. They sat and bemoaned the state of the world as they knew it, which concerned the price of water; the way that the supermarkets were still making profits out of the conversion from Francs to Euros; why the potatoes these days went mouldy so quickly; why the children didn't say 'Bonjour' politely any more; why the Mayor was planning the building of the new Mayoral Offices and 'Salle des Fetes', when she should have been making a proper 'Piste de Pétanque'; why the Mayor of Seurre was planning a one-way road system in the town, when the present system worked perfectly well.

No! There was not a lot to approve of in the world.

"Oh sure, the National Football team does alright occasionally in the World Cup, but they don't play with enough Art."

"Our Rugby team does okay, but they are ***so*** inconsistent."

"Yes, the train system works well, but they pay the staff too much. More than us, anyway and that's not fair!"

"The summer is good, but now it is too dry."

And "Did you hear that the President is going to have all the disability pensions reviewed to take away our benefits? Does he know how hard we have worked for these, Hein? We have dedicated all our lives to the State, and this is how we are rewarded!"

"It's disgusting!"

"All of our lives wasted!"

"Well, part of our lives, perhaps."

"Well perhaps, not so much, but ***some*** of our lives."

"Well a ***bit***!"

"Anyway… they ***owe*** us!"

"It's our Right!"

Moving

The time has come for us to make yet another move from the house in Seurre to our ‘new’ house in the village.

I have taken eighteen months to finish the Seurre house and to make the riverside one habitable.

I have installed an electrical system to which I can add more circuits and plugs as time goes by. The huge metal bath, which has enough material in it to armour a tank, is now in the garden, replaced by a bathroom suite. The kitchen is now an improvement on the single wooden fired stove that Madame Trolly used. This was an antique device with a leaking hot water jacket around the fire insert. We tried to use it but it seems that we lacked the necessary skills to manipulate the various dampeners and vents. All we managed to do was to fill the kitchen with smoke and to annoy a colony of wasps that had taken up residence in the chimney pot, high above the apex of the roof.

Some of the French villagers still think that we were mad to have made the purchase of the house.

“You can’t eat the view!”

“You should have taken a bulldozer and flattened the Forge!”

“And have you considered the flooding and the humidity from the river? What about the trees falling on the house?”

“What about the mosquitoes?”

“And do you know about the Ghost of old Madame Trolley? She is known,” said one neighbour darkly, “to bang the shattered shutters in the wind and look out from the upper windows, if people stop in the road and stare at the house. Sometimes she makes gestures to you that you must go away!”

In fact, all her ghost seems to do to us is to open the attic door from time to time. We blame each other and the wind, to try and explain the phenomenon.

Marc Deux Chazelle, who had fallen into the river and drowned, had even tried to shoot her ghost with a pellet gun, during the time that the house was abandoned. This was why the window panes were broken when we first bought the property. I could only repair these windows after the Redstarts who, after returning from their migration, had hatched their eggs, raised their brood and moved out. They were using the broken panes as an entrance to the protection of the interior of the house.

I found one of their nests on a mantelpiece. When I approached it the little chicks opened their mouths for food. Later, after they had received instructions from their mother, they hid themselves by tucking their heads down under each other. However they forgot to tuck their tails in, which stuck up in the air, so that the nest looked like a feathered pincushion with tiny quills stuck into it at odd angles. I placed bird nesting boxes in all protected niches around the outside of the house and the Redstarts have taken to them now with minimum fuss, except for one family that gained access to the Forge. Now I have to be sure to leave one door open for them, for as long as they insist on nesting here.

Our house in Seurre was bought by the first person that looked at it, which was what we hoped for, by pricing it very realistically. The garden was at its best when we put it on the market and the interior beams and woodwork looked as though they had been in position for ages, but with modern fittings, plumbing and wiring. We needed to move during the summer school holidays, so that the whole family could be involved with the transfer.

Of course our children are still grumpy about the move.

I understand how they feel because my parents had also moved me from one farm to another, when I was their age in Africa. The new house back in my youth was also by a river, but after only one holiday with a raft on the river, paddling past the hippos and avoiding the young crocodiles, had convinced me that the move was a good one.

For similar reasons I hope that our children will accept the move. Of course there are no crocodiles to examine in the Bourgogne, but there are other activities that can be enjoyed on the water. We now have an assortment of floating paraphernalia which includes a tatty canoe, several kayaks, enormous old sailboards and an inflated tractor tyre.

Now we can watch our family learning the rudiments of wind surfing while we sip tea on the front lawn. The wind is fluky as it sweeps past trees and gusts through gaps, but the advantage is that these difficult conditions speed up our young trainees reaction times. The swans regard these activities with tolerance, as though we are retarded. They keep their distance from the shouting and noise, but deign to inspect pieces of baguette that we throw for them. Occasionally they stare at us as if to indicate that dabbling at bread is a bit below their dignity.

At last the moment of truth arrives when I decide that it is time to bring our trusty wooden boat to her new anchorage at the village.

I had brought her across the English Channel, overnight, from England when I first moved the family to France.

We arrived at Calais in a misty gloomy dawn.

I motored into the harbour and moored to a buoy.

Then I had to clear customs (before all the borders were as 'open' as they are now), and find some way to unstep the mast. This is a massive operation as the mast is a huge heavy wooden one that was originally part of a Gaff Rig, and weighs several hundred kilos with all the rigging. For this I had to get a ship's crane, as the little one in the Calais marina was not strong enough to do the job.

This was my first introduction to negotiations at a grass roots level in France. I had, in the past, many contacts at airports and hotels in France, with all my travels, but I had never had to negotiate 'on the black' before. This is a term that covers an alternative economy, which has grown out of the necessity to avoid the crippling taxes that hamper almost every form of enthusiastic endeavour in France.

In short, I had to find a crane operator who would do 'something' during the lunch break for 'a consideration'. Calais used to be an important port, but now is almost exclusively a 'roll-on/roll-off' ferry port. However, I found an office filled with crane operators who looked as though they had not ventured outside for months. The atmosphere in the office was fogged with smoke from the Galloises cigarettes that were glued to each man's lower lip, like a sort of uniform gesture of contempt for the world.

"Is there someone," I stumbled in French, "who could help me lift the mast out of my boat?"

I received the universal blank stare that is reserved for all visitors to France. This is a stare that is taught at school, I think, because everybody is adept at it. It consists of a widening of the eyes, a slight jaw drop and a holding of the open hands in a manner similar to a rugby player about to receive a pass that never comes.

What I didn't know was that, before I started out with what I wanted, I should have greeted everybody individually, shaken everybody's hand and discussed the weather and the difficulties of Life. My personal difficulties should be something left to be discussed later, when all the other important issues had been dealt with.

However, with England only a few miles away across the Channel, they had obviously met my type before, so they acquiesced and, with the slipping of a few hundred francs into blue overalls pockets, they condescended to help me out. They were excellent operators, and in a few minutes I had the mast laid horizontally along the length of the boat. Now we all shook hands and wished each other a good appetite for dinner, as they all departed in a variety of rusty vans and wobbly bicycles to their homes.

We now had to negotiate with the lock keeper to let us into the canal system.

The canal system is a network of manmade channels carved the length and breadth of France. With incredible foresight these canals and lock systems were designed to transport large barges between river systems, which were also modified and tamed. The depth and width of these canals varies depending on the assessments that were made on the probable needs of the future. However, these days, the railways have taken over a large amount of the freight and so some of the canals are underutilised. However, with great prescience, the system has been kept fully functional and serviceable. It was with this system that I intended to get as near to Bâle as I could, which is where I was working at that time.

In the morning of the next day the lock keeper opened the lock for us to enter. I motored in and we tied up. The sea level outside is higher than the level of water in the canal, so we descended to the internal level before he opened the lock gate on the inland side. We untied and I applied power in order to motor into the waiting pen for barges.

Nothing happened.

We were stuck.

My keel was immersed into the mud that had accumulated over decades on the bottom. Evidently this lock had been considered sufficient for the few yachts that entered here each year, and none of them had the depth of keel that we had. Probably there were a few bicycles, perhaps a few washing machines immersed in the mud and hopefully ***not*** any unexploded bombs from the Second World War.

I started selecting forward and then reverse thrust, with the rudder in different positions and after ten minutes we detected a small movement. I persisted as slowly I managed to get the bow of the boat to turn a couple of degrees. Slowly, by ramming back and forth, I created a little bit of movement until eventually we slid and gouged our way into the holding pen.

We tied up at the side of the pen and had a cup of tea, to sit and assess the situation. It had taken me more than an hour to do the first fifty metres. I had only another five hundred kilometres to go. On this rate of progress, it should take me five years, motoring for eight hours a day to get to my destination. That is if I did not get permanently stuck somewhere along the route.

I asked the skipper of the only other yacht in the basin what he thought; as he had just travelled the system inbound to Calais.

"Give it a go!" he advised. "There is hardly any traffic, and if you find it too difficult, you can work your way back."

So with misgivings we started the voyage.

Technically the canal was deep enough for us, because the depth was a few centimetres deeper than our keel, but the approved maximum draft for boats is somewhat less. When I asked the lock keeper about it, I got the Gaelic Shrug number 19: "I don't care; it's not my problem; do what you want!"

And so we puttered off down the canal.

It was like going through the looking glass into the breathtaking world of Alice in Wonderland. We left behind us the town of Calais, with its bars, Bistros, cars, people, busses, trains, ships and noise.

We entered a space that was like a quiet silver road, lined with overhanging trees and populated by birds and butterflies and squirrels. Perhaps the contrast was more extreme for us, as we were used to the open ocean. The difference between huge grey North Atlantic swells with froth cascading down their leeward slopes to this smooth magical carpet ride past fields and grazing cows was almost too much to comprehend. Dolphins were replaced by herds of sheep. Raucous Black-Backed Gulls were supplanted by thrushes hopping though the undergrowth next to the towpath.

I puttered along at a brisk walking pace, while the family sat on chairs on the deck to watch France unfolding in slow motion before us. We came across an elderly fisherman, who retrieved his lines from the canal. I was expecting him to be upset with this intrusion into his private space. He noticed our red ensign hanging from the post at the stern of the boat.

"Viv e Angletere!" he called, "Viv e Winston Churchill, Viv e de Gaule!"

We paused to chat to him.

"Oh yes," he said, "I remember the war. We had lots of activity here."

We chatted for a while about the Liberation and what it meant to France, and then we puttered on down the canal.

I am still bemused by the fact that at sea, a lee shore over the horizon is still too close in a gale, and yet here we are, with the sides of the canal only a yard away and yet I felt quite safe. We tied up for the night and the children had the chance to run along the side of the canal and climb trees.

This travel by canal in France seemed to me to be one of the best kept secrets in the world.

The next day everything changed.

We joined the main shipping lane, which is a river busy with barges and ships that seem as big as a city block. They were all going much faster than we could go.

Wind, waves and wash from propellers pummelled the waters and churned the surface into a maelstrom of activity.

It was like joining a motorway after travelling with the tranquillity of a footpath through a forest. I couldn't wait to get off this superhighway of steel and urgency.

We found another canal that would take us longer to get to our destination, but was infinitely preferable to this bedlam of boats. With gratitude we sank back into the peace of rural France, with only the lowing of cows and the birdsong to disturb us.

The days merged as we motored south. We bought vegetables from men with canal side allotments. We bumped along steel aqueducts over rivers, as the boat's keel knelled like a bell at the bottom of the structure. We motored into tunnels thousands of metres long, which were as dark as the insides of an elephant.

Each one of the three hundred locks that we had to negotiate had a place about a hundred metres before it where the barges engage reverse in order to slow up. At each of these places a hole in the bottom has been scoured by the wash of their giant propellers, and consequently there is a ridge of residue that is slightly shallower than the rest of the canal, next to it. We got stuck on each one of these ridges. The other traffic does not have the same draft as we have and so it is only us who was affected by these shallow spots. Which is why, of course, there are the depth restrictions, so I had only myself to blame. I was concerned that if I got really stuck, I would have to pay for a crane to come and lift us out of the canal, in which case I would have the boat stuck in a farmer's field for perpetuity.

However, each time we managed to get free.

Once I had to ask for help from a farmer with his tractor. I had to attach a web of lines to all the strong points on the boat which I attached to a huge towing rope that I had stored on board. He reversed down the slope at the side of the canal and disappeared from view, as all the lines went 'twang' tight. It worked.

Most often we were able to attach lines to trees and then we could winch ourselves off mudbanks as though we were pulling up the anchor.

At last we found the Sâone River, which meant that now we were in the system of rivers connected to the Mediterranean and the south. The river seemed unbelievably wide after the confines of the canals. What a joy, to have this deep wide river… and then we got stuck again! Fortunately, with the swell of the bow wave of a passing barge I was able to slide back in reverse, and free the keel.

I had to go to work then and the children had to start school, so we had to abandon the boat. We left her tied to a pontoon with promises to return soon.

We did, and in so doing we became attached to where she was.

So it was ***she*** who anchored ***us*** in the Bourgogne, rather than the other way around.

The part of the river that passes the village is no longer used as part of the navigation system of France. The river has not been cleared since the sand barges ceased dredging gravel and sand from the bottom, for the construction industry. The consequence is that there are deep holes where the sand has been scooped out and shallow spots where tributaries have deposited mud from the floods.

Of course, I find all the shallow spots with my keel as I work my way up the river, on the last part of my voyage.

At last I arrive in the front of the house where the water is over seven metres deep (four fathoms for the purists) where I intend to secure the boat. I rattle out the anchor chain and let the boat drift back in the current to lay the scope.

I see a movement upstream.

There is a flying formation of swans that stretches from riverbank to riverbank.

They are low over the water in the distance, and from where I am watching, their wingtips overlap, so that the display is like a continuous horizontal fluctuating line of white.

They get closer until I can see individual birds, each with its own rhythm of flight. Yet they all contribute to the 'oneness' of the formation.

Whistles of energy from their wing beats fill the air around me, with an excitement that is as intense as a naked first love in a field of young wet wheat.

For a moment I believe that I can comprehend their communication, their love of what they are doing, and their pride at doing it well.

My body prickles with anticipation for what they will do next. I try, for a moment, to count them, but the sight is too beautiful to analyse and enumerate.

And then magically, as though by a coordinated command, they flare… and glide… and ski… and settle.

All at once the formation breaks and the individuals are like pupil pilots after their first successful formation landing. It seems that they are slapping each other on the back and saying how clever they are.

The only difference is that pupil pilots land in pairs.

These twenty one swans have touched down in a huge coordinated formation that is normal for them, but impossible for us.

They collect around the boat.

I take a turn around the Sampson post with the anchor chain, and then I am on my hands and knees to get closer to them, in the same way that I used to talk to the dolphins at sea.

They are all around me now and I am so happy and so grateful.

Their outlines become wavy as tears blur my vision.

I just don't think I have seen anything so beautiful, synchronized and natural as these birds sharing a few seconds of their lives to show me what flying really means.

I have watched Fish Eagles fight for thermals and fishing rights in the Zambezi Valley.

I have watched, from a cockpit, a formation of Geese manoeuvring through the clouds ten thousand feet over Athens.

I have watched Quellea and Starlings loop and whorl in the sky, in formations of thousands, like huge living organisms with but a single mind.

I have seen the Frigate Birds off St Helena dive and pirate food from pelicans.

I have watched a solitary Albatross circle our boat for days in the South Atlantic, as he touches the surface of the swells with a wingtip to frighten the flying fish into the air, so he can catch them. But the sight of these airborne ballerinas coming to share a few moments with me is like a present more valuable than any material possession in the world.

How I would like to believe that they are a welcoming committee.

How I would like to think that they are doing this for an ulterior motive that involves me.

But I can't.

There is no way that I can ever be that important.

But I know, now, that I can come and sit by this river at any time, to make this tentative contact with Nature. It will only take me a few paces to get to this window to another world.

Vendange

My oldest son Craig, who has been working at the Royal Shakespeare Company as a deputy director, comes to visit us in France. He arrives, curious as to what has induced us to settle here. He is working on his third novel, adapting various books into screenplays and rewriting Shakespeare plays for use in schools.

He thinks that he will find us in a rural retreat where he can contemplate the classics.

How romantic for him: a sojourn in France to recharge his batteries. Perhaps he will have time to write, or to re-examine the meaning of life and to mull over the relationship between the academia and modern man.

How wrong he is!

It is not his fault that he got trapped

We talked him into it.

And as a result, I got trapped too!

I convinced him, and myself, that to really understand France we must engage with it. We must become a part of it, at a grass roots level.

"We need to participate in activities that have been going on for two thousand years." I tell him, "We need to get our hands in the soil."

I enlisted both of us to pick grapes during the 'vendange', or harvest.

This is a simple activity which disguises an exquisite form of torture in France.

It takes place 100 days after the flowering of the vines.

The vines in the Bourgogne spread like a great carpet over the hills south of Dijon. The slopes capture the sunlight where the roots dig deep into the limestone substrata. This carpet undulates with the folds in the countryside, and it changes colour with the seasons. The spring rain brings delicate green shoots from the gnarled plants, where only a small twig remains after severe pruning. The shoots grow, turning the hillsides from grey to lime green. As the season progresses the leaves darken with the primeval responsibility of combining energy, water and soil into fruit. Vignerons stride through the lines with hope or foreboding, depending on their character.

Ancient adages concerning ratios of sunlit days to rain compete with Science. The old men quote sayings learned from their grandparents while the youngsters consult formulae on computers. All are concerned with sucricity, acid and the likely taste and percentages of alcohol that the grapes will produce.

Regardless of all the apprehension and cautious optimism, the grapes do what they have done for aeons, without the interference of man. They create millions of globules of magical elixir, which they surrender, only for the privilege of being allowed to exist on this prime piece of real estate.

When bunches of ripe grapes are hanging like over endowed mameries below these twisted vines, just waiting to give nourishment and joy to the world, the agony for us amateurs starts.

The torture begins at 5am when the alarm bell rings. It continues as we stumble about trying to remember where we put our working clothes. Then Marlene insists that we have to wolf down a plate of porridge for energy, "Because you know that the French people will only have a coffee and baguette for breakfast. It's not enough. You need to have *fuel* with which to work."

We take a brisk walk through the crisp dark predawn air to the bus stop.

We exchange gruff 'bonjours' and hand shakes with all the other sadomasochists. They are huddled in groups, standing like rugby supporters with hands in pockets, watching a dull game in the rain.

The bus arrives and we clamber aboard. A young couple rush towards us rubbing sleep from their eyes.

The old men nod knowingly and smile.

They used to be late when they were young, and for the same reason!

The bus transports us through the twisted streets of Beaune, to the fields of Chateau la Tour. There we stand like conscripts in the army, but we are not issued rifles. We are each given a bucket and a pair of secateurs. We are herded into rusty vans for a bumpy ride up to the steep slopes of *Charlemagne Grand Cru.*

"Débarquez, Allez vite!"

There, in the dawn light, are lines of vines stretching up a hill. We stand at our allocated positions like swimmers about to take the plunge in a cold marathon race.

"Allez!"

I bend to take the first bunch in my hand.

It feels cool.

It feels good.

I cut my finger.

"Baissez la tete!"; "Coup!"

"Get your head down! Cut!"

It is like the first day of basic training in the Army.

I can still remember Colour Sergeant Galvin screeching "Halt!" "Quick March!" "About Turn!" as he crashed the heels of his boots into the tarmac, as though trying to piledrive a hole into the hard surface. I was an involuntary conscript back then; this time I am a volunteer.

What the hell am I doing here?

I hear muttered curses from other vendangers in Spanish, Dutch and Polish, as well as French. There is also the odd "Bugger!" in English. It is interesting how a swearword anesthetises pain or anguish.

I am not the only one wondering why I signed up for this.

Already my back is protesting from bending over the vines and heaving a bucket of grapes up the hill. One of the supervisors comes to examine our lines to see that we haven't missed a single grape. It is easy enough to do, as these white grapes disguise themselves shyly in amongst the leaves. It seems that they are less brazen than their red cousins, who hang like testicles under a bull.

Proud and full of sperm.

But here we come, the 'elite vendangers', to emasculate these hundred year old vines and to take away their vital juices, to supplement our own. We search and snip every stalk. Sometimes bunches grow together so there are two or three stalks hidden in the foliage and twisted canes.

"Casse Croûte!"

It is ten o' clock, and it is time to stop for bread and wine. It is time to "Break the Crust! (of the bread)."

We stand around the back of the van to get our rations and now that it light enough to see each other properly, we examine our fellow workers with curiosity.

Who are these other crazy people who have embarked on this course of self flagellation?

Multilingual introductions take place.

There are people from all over Europe. All ages. All nationalities. Some have done this before. So why didn't they know better? Why do this, when you have experienced what is involved? It must be a Lemming Syndrome!

There is a young man from Holland with plasters on his fingers; a girl from Paris who is an operatic singer; a couple from Lyon who are here to make and save some money towards buying a flat; a group of French women who all know each other: they are the regulars. They are built like proper vendangers. They are stocky with strong hands, scarves around their heads and have gentle distain for us amateurs.

It is time to start again.

My back protests before I can even bend over. It knows what is going to happen this time and it wants to go on strike. Heaving tiles up to a roof and heaving buckets of concrete to lay slabs has not prepared me for this special form of torment.

Away we go.

The French vendangers are off, like tractors, up the hill. The snipping of their secateurs is like machinegun fire. They speed ahead of the rest of us. I find that the early morning wine is helping to alleviate the pain.

Perhaps this is really is not so bad, after all.

I search through the leaves to find the cool bunches of grapes. I am beginning to find the hidden stalks more easily now. I am learning to keep my fingers out of the way of my cutter's snapping jaws. The morning settles into a pattern of snip, catch, chuck, push-kick the bucket, snip, catch, chuck, push-kick the bucket…

We get to the end of the line at last. We have a moment to stretch and click our vertebra back into place. We have a few stragglers in the lines. The young men, Craig included, quickly assess which stragglers are attractive young girls, and they start cutting back down the lines to help them.

I gaze across the vineyards.

The fields stretch into the distance. They spread up the slopes, where the underlying limestone has been found, as far as the fringe of trees that cap the hills. Below us is the road that connects Beaune to Dijon.

It is crammed with vehicles.

There are tractors pulling trailers which are loaded with multicoloured plastic boxes loaded with grapes. There are vans, busses, lorries and trucks scattered along the tracks though the vines. Everywhere there are groups of vendangers, just like us, bobbing through the lines. Heads pop up as each one moves to the next plant and then they duck down again.

It reminds me of a sea of dolphins bobbing up to breathe.

There are thousands of them.

Back to work.

Another line; another hill; another hundred buckets.

It is getting warm now and everybody is shedding their waterproof clothing. The early dew has dried off from the leaves and the sky is a perfect blue.

News helicopters clatter overhead as the photographers capture this most important moment in the Bourgogne calendar. The entire region's hopes are riding on the quality and the quantity of the harvest. Tourists stand on mounds with cameras to record the activity.

I hear one remark to his companion, in English, probably thinking that we won't understand.

"Where do all these people come from?" Then answering himself in a public school accent: "Morocco probably! Brought in for the harvest, don't you know!"

I have to answer.

"Actually," I say, mimicking him with a similar accent, "some of us come from London! My son over there is a Theatre Director. I am an Airline Pilot. That chap over there is doing his final year of medicine at Manchester University! That Polish fellow over there is a solicitor from Oxford."

Pompous Ass!

Back to the vines…

At last the sirens wail. The church bells ring out. It is midday. Time for lunch. We are ravenous. Work stops. The French vendangers stop on the dot.

They will not do a single snip after twelve o' clock.

They will not be exploited.

That was what the Revolution was all about!

It is time for 'repas'.

We file back down through the vines to the vans that will take us back to the chateau and the hall where the vendangers are fed.

The vines are kept to a very uniform height in each part of France and here, in the Bourgogne, that is decreed to be at elbow height. In the Alsace the vines are strung out much higher above the ground. This uniformity gives a tidy aspect to the slopes, as they undulate away into the distance. Variations in the colours of the leaves expose where the underground soil varies, and consequently, from where the subtle variations in taste are derived. One field of grapes on one side of a road may be a 'Grand Ordinaire', the other side a 'Premier Cru', and above that a 'Grand Cru'.

I can see that all the people in the other fields are wending down the slopes towards their vehicles. Busses start up and tractors drag their loads back to the villages and domains where the vats are stored. The roads are temporarily crammed with vehicles of all sorts, including some World War 2 Army Trucks that are only brought out of storage for these occasions. Some of these contraptions are barely serviceable but the Gendarmes are believed to cast a blind eye to these indiscretions. Perhaps!

Within a few minutes the vines are deserted as the two hour celebration of food and wine is enjoyed.

The vignerons produce some wine 'on the side', which is kept specially to give to the pickers during the harvest. The quality of this wine is variable, and the producers that share good quality wine with their teams are the ones who have waiting lists of applicants for the harvest.

The mean vignerons, with the poor wine, have to recruit aggressively to find workers.

This information spreads by word of mouth though the underground of vendangers, and is openly discussed at the table. As is the quality and the quantity of the food.

The lunch is provided in a large hall where the tables are arranged in lines, conforming to French tradition. I see that Craig, who is a good looking young man, has gravitated towards a youthful group who are all making assessments of each other, in what seems to me to be a slightly primeval way. I settle with an older group that has men who have been doing the vendange for many years.

Conversation is easy because the standard subject is food.

This preoccupation with food and wine surprised me when I first came to France. That was the time that the first President Bush was squaring up with the international community against Iraq, to rescue the Kuwaiti oil fields for the West. At that time we received TV channels from Germany, Switzerland, Britain and the USA. All of them were comparing the relative numbers of the tanks and aircraft that they had sold to Iraq, compared to the numbers available to the coalition forces.

Strategic Experts from obscure Universities were propounding theories that they had learned from books.

Generals were preaching the threats that existed to the world from Iraq, which had to be eliminated by force, before it could do any damage.

It was a feeding frenzy for the news media.

But in France they missed the opportunity. The TV channels were filled with methods of how to prepare the best Vichyssoise, or the best way to prepare Ratatouille with the available vegetables of that year. Perhaps France has been invaded by, and has invaded, so many countries in the past that this latest euphoric exercise in violence had not caught on.

So here we are again, reaping the harvest of grapes in the same way that has been going on for two thousand years, on the same slopes that the Romans trod, to have the same pleasures that have been enjoyed for centuries.

Somehow, I begin to understand the timelessness of History and to discover how individual Presidents, Dictators and politicians all pass into oblivion. But that fruit from the soil lasts forever, if we take care of it.

I look at my mealtime companions who have come from all walks of life. They are the present day standard bearers of generations who have worked the vines. Today we are dressed in t-shirts, shorts and gumboots. In the past they sported long dresses, traditional hats and wooden clogs. These thoughts seem to worry nobody else.

I decide to stick to the subject of food.

It is as safe as discussing the weather with an Englishman.

Agreement exists in both cases.

Food in France is a subject of optimism and hope, of enjoyment and satisfaction.

English weather, with the exception of brief tempting interludes, is almost always universally dull.

After lunch, replete with wine and bonhomie, Craig and I settle on the grass for a brief nap. Voices murmur around us, birds in the branches overhead coo contentedly in the sunshine, muscles relax in the aftermath of work.

Clang…Clang!

It is two o' clock.

Back to work.

Muscles scream in protest. Backs seize up. Fingers cower in fear of desiccation. Toes compare blisters. Contentment vanishes. Pain is back. The torture starts again.

After what seems like several hours of work, the church bell strikes 'Three'.

Oh God, what am I doing here?

Another fortnight of bending, aching, heaving buckets… and the bell strikes 'Four'.

More wine… Oh blesséd anaesthetic… Salami on bread, then back to work.

A month of snipping, stripping and searching for grapes… and the bell strikes 'Five'.

When will it end?

The bell strikes "Six'.

Oh what a relief. It is time to stop picking.

My back refuses to interlink vertebra, tendons, muscles and joints.

It is very unsatisfied with me. It knows it earns its living sitting in a high altitude seat, with a backrest, jetting from one destination to another. Climbing into the back of a van with no springs and bouncing down a track to a chateau in France is not a part of its work description.

I look at Craig and he looks shattered as well.

This is not a part of the father/son relationship that he had in mind when he came to visit. I am pleased that my agony is not just age related. Everybody is moaning and contorting. It seems that Craig's back is also objecting to this change of pace, from a Director's Chair.

We hand in our buckets and clippers and pull our wretched bodies onto the bus. We weave back through the streets of Beaune, back to our village. There we totter back to the house and a good hot bath. Marlene greets us with food, a back massage and yet another glass of wine.

I go to my workshop to construct a seat for myself.

I have decided that I need a sort of 'milking stool' with a single peg-leg, so that I can sit occasionally while I untangle the tendrils and stalks of the vines. I pad the seat with dense foam and experiment with tying it on with elastic, so that when I sit, the leg automatically drops vertically into position. It seems to work.

The torture starts again, with the alarm bell at 5am. Porridge, that is good. A walk into the dawn is refreshing. We shake hands with our companions from yesterday.

"How is the back?"

"Oh fine!" I lie.

We are all lying about how we are not suffering. Our backs have forgotten the pain. Forgotten that is, until we see the slopes again. Then they remember and try to seize up in protest.

Oh no you don't!

And so we bend, and bob and snip and drop bunches of grapes into the bucket. But now I can sit on my padded seat.

What luxury! 'Quel Joie.'

When we get to the end of the line my back has accepted that my thighs are going to take the strain now, and has stopped its protest. My thighs will handle the work better, because they have been trained with years of horse riding and dinghy sailing to accept this repetitious type of exertion.

Of course my 'seat' causes hilarity among the throng of vendangers. They acknowledge that it is not a bad idea, but they wouldn't be seen wearing such a contraption, under any circumstances.

We grind through the day.

My body loves the injection of morning wine.

It enjoys the pleasure of wine at lunch.

The afternoon "tincture" adds a rosy glow to the day.

My back-pain has receded as though my back has resigned itself to the fact that this work is necessary to survival, and so it has to accept its frequent dose of endorphins, to drug it into acceptance.

Craig and I totter home at the end of the day.

The subject of resignation from the vendange is on our minds, but neither of us wants to broach the subject. It must be a sort of macho father/son competitive thing, where neither wants to be the one to chicken out first.

The third day is slightly better and by the fourth day we are actually looking forward to it.

Craig has found a gorgeous young lady from Lyon, who has cascading hair and amber eyes. He is now a 'porter' which means that he collects the grapes from the pickers in a large bin that he straps onto his back. This device enables the porters to empty it by leaning over the trailers so that the grapes cascade into the carriers. It also enables him to hover, between discharges, in the vicinity of Céline, which is the first step in the complex dance of the waltz of love.

I have time to see how the blush of the leaves in the vines is changing, in only the short time that we have been amongst them. Beautiful russets are spreading though the variegated greens of each leaf and the combination of these shades, on the slopes, blends together to form a harmony of colour. Dotted through the lines are the vendangers, wearing bright clothes and looking like musical notes strung out on a page of written music.

The days merge into one another.

We make friendships with other vendangers, with the combination of working, drinking and eating together. We discover, in that wonderful hazy reality, that all our problems are the same, wherever we come from, and that all our troubles can be improved or solved with the judicious imbibing of wine.

At last the vendange is over.

We have a final lunch where we throw bread at each other, instead of unripe bunches of grapes.

We get paid, which is why we are here, and the company gives us a bottle of wine each to take home, to savour or save.

We part from the other vendangers with promises to meet again the following year.

"Like hell." Craig and I say to each other in unison.

They won't see us again.

I haven't forgotten the pain of the first days.

But I forget my resolve during the months that follow.

My good recollections of the vendange are enhanced by that most important quality of memory, which is... of course... forgetfulness.

The next year we are approached by Steve. He is a vigneron in Pommard and runs a family business which has been in existence for as long as records can be traced. He was involved with wine in England before coming to France.

It is a rare occurrence for a family of vignerons to take an outsider into the fold, because the inheritance and ownership of vines is closely guarded. The value of the 'parcels' is difficult to assess here, because they very rarely come onto the open market. In this case the family were doubly fortunate, as they found Steve is a dedicated worker and a father for their next generation.

I am keen to 'vendange' again, because I have always gravitated to small companies and work forces. I have grave suspicions about large enterprises, particularly in aviation, where the sharks are to be found. Great Whites tend follow large shoals and ignore small fry, and that suits me fine.

It also seems that Steve's team are not regimented like a forced labour camp.

I also find out that Steve's wine is one of the best in the Bourgogne. Marlene and I both sign up. Craig has got the good sense to be busy this year, with a tour around England, presenting Hamlet.

Like many of the smaller family run wine businesses, when the harvest comes, everybody is involved. Three generations of the same family gather together to reap. Cousins, sisters and aunts join in. Long standing friends are invited. Some of Steve's team are veterans of over twenty five years of picking together. They, of course, take an almost proprietal interest in the vines and the quality of the crop. This is where I start to learn more about selection for quality.

Each bunch is trimmed to exclude any grape that is not perfect. After careful selection by the pickers Steve oversees each pannier to check again for quality. Then the grapes are fed into a 'de-stalker' after which the juice is pumped into vats for that magical transformation to take place, from juice to wine. As I watch the care that he takes with each stage of the process, I give thanks that the standards in the wine industry have been set by people who care about quality, rather than the mass produced, machine picked chemically impregnated products that have been designed to be the cheapest selection on a supermarket shelf.

But the best part of Steve's vendange is that Granddad, when he is happy with the team, produces a bottle or two of his special vintages.

These are to die for.

This is difficult to explain to someone who is educated on Supermarket 'special' offers.

These wines encapsulate all the reasons why slaves were made to pull barges up the Rhône, why the Romans came to overrun and control Gaul, why people have worked all their lives in the vines in spite of hail and gales and drought, why the Dukes of Bourgogne controlled the land with an iron fist and lived behind great walls to protect their wealth.

Armies have marched here for millennia.

Wars have been fought.

Lives have been lost and sacrifices made.

All this has been endured for the delicate flavours and aromas that issue forth from the fermented juice of the grape.

It seems that wine enhances life, in contrast to most other types of alcohol that are developed to sedate life into numbness and oblivion.

Granddad's speciality is a nut wine, which is made by putting green walnuts into quality wine. The nuttiness from the walnuts replaces the woody taste that is normally enhanced from the oak barrels, to make a special and different treat.

Of course the purists abhor these additions and they are not approved for sale, as representative of 'wines of France', but they are fun to enjoy during the vendange.

Now, when I walk the cobblestones of Beaune, past the Hospice in the town centre, surrounded by high intricately tiled roofs, I have a sense of communion with history. I have a connection with the past, because I have done exactly what the people who built this town have done, for two thousand years. I have picked and trod the grape, and more importantly, sipped and swallowed the wine that has made this place famous.

When you sip Bourgogne wine in Beaune, you can feel the spirits from the past, chuckling and nodding with approval.

Annette

Annette is our local French village information service, but she has never travelled. She tells us about the scandals, and warns us about who is who.

She tells us how one unhappy wife found a witch to cast a spell on her unfaithful husband, which backfired. The whole family, one by one, were afflicted by accident and illness, until just the wife was the sole survivor.

"The husband fell off a roof, the son died in a traffic accident when some logs fell off a truck and crushed him, and the daughter died of a tumour in the brain! That's because," Annette pronounced with certainty, "she didn't pay in full for the spell!"

"She should have got a magnetiser," she added. "They are much more successful, and they can sure anything! They can make you stop smoking, with no ill effects! My friend goes to one who cures her arthritis! It is True! She has no pain for months, and then she has to go for rejuvenation. There are more magnetisers and horologists than doctors and psychologists in France!"

Marlene is keen to get Annette to experience the pleasures of travel and the easiest first step is to go on a train trip.

Every time Marlene tries, Annette has an excuse. Sometimes she is ill, sometimes her mother is ill or her daughter is going to be telephoning her today. It seems that Annette doesn't want to use the village magnetiser for her own ailments.

Marlene starts by getting Annette to come for walks.

She introduces Annette to the sight of swans on the river and the way moonlight reflects across the water to make a silver pathway to the other side. She gets her to walk with her head up, to see the birds fly overhead, rather than staring at the ground at her feet. She starts a Tai-Chi class, which she conducts out of sight in the garden, in case her select group is spotted by a passer-by.

And then, after months of excuses, after all the reasons for delay have been exhausted, Marlene commits Annette to be free for five hours. For a surprise.

For a treat.

But she doesn't say where or what.

Marlene picks Annette up with the car and drives to Seurre.

There she buys a train ticket for the two of them to go to Dijon. Fawlty is relieved to have such a simple transaction to perform, so this leaves him free to complain about his latest cause.

"They are proposing a new one-way road system for Seurre," he declares. "Typical! It will be a catastrophe! A disaster! What do the Town Council think they are doing? It is idiotic! The businesses will collapse. The town will fail. All will be lost! And do they care? Phut! The Mayor is an idiot."

He gestures to the wall, where the timetable is displayed, with a series of shrugs that is the equivalent of shouting in body language. Perhaps he shouts at the wall when he is by himself.

Marlene doesn't want to get involved, and Annette doesn't care. She doesn't have a car, she doesn't drive and anyway it is nothing to do with her. They both live three kilometres away, which is far enough to be detached.

Fawlty waves his clip board in the air, with dramatic gestures that would have done any Shakespearean actor proud.

"I have a petition," he announces. "We will rise up and have a demonstration! We will gather together and …."

He is interrupted by a squeal of brakes as the train arrives at the platform outside.

Now he had to don his official SNCF cap, which means that he is on platform duty, and rush outside with his green flag.

Marlene and Annette clamber aboard, before Fawlty has a chance to remember that they haven't signed his petition.

Fawlty knows some of the passengers who are getting off the train, so he is distracted with hand shaking and greetings, until he remembers to blow his whistle, wave his flag and they are off.

For Marlene, the pleasure of seeing Annette, a sixty year old woman going on the train for the first time, is like reliving her experience of showing our children something new. Annette touches the fittings, sits on the edge of her seat and asks questions about everything.

They arrive in Dijon and Annette is confronted with an escalator. She has never seen one in her life before. Marlene has to hold her arm, and together they count, "Un, Deux, Trois", and they step together onto the bottom step. At the top, Marlene has to say "Marche!" as they both step off the moving staircase.

They leave the train station, arm in arm, and wander the streets of Dijon. Marlene points out interesting landmarks, the parks, statues and cathedrals.

The foreigner is showing the local person her own heritage.

They pass the Cathedral with its little owl carved into the stonework.

They wander the streets to see the old houses of colombage construction, which have somehow survived the ravages of fires, wars and wood eating beetles. The flowers of Dijon are famous, and they see why as they pass displays of hanging baskets and gardens of complex designs. Intricate wrought iron balconies overhang cobbled streets that are only wide enough for a horse drawn carriage. Modern stores stand adjacent to small traditional shops in a way that seems complimentary to both.

Annette is wide-eyed.

Then they go into a luxury hotel for ‘tea’.

Annette doesn’t want to go in, but Marlene insists.

“This is for the Bourgeoisie only,” Annette insists.

“Today, we are the Bourgeoisie!” answers Marlene.

Inside Marlene treats them to cakes and biscuits, with tea that is served from a gilded trolley by a uniformed waiter. It is one of the only places in Dijon that understands that tea has to be made with boiling water. Annette has already been introduced, by Marlene, to that ‘hideous’ (to the French) English practice of putting milk into tea.

When they return home, I ask Marlene, “How did it go?”

“I learned so much.” she says.

“I have learned again how to see the World through somebody else’s eyes. I have been reminded how lucky we are to have witnessed so much, and yet at the same time I have realised how innocent I must seem to some of the people that we have met. It has been an enlightening experience for both of us!”

Michel Bonnadot, the Postmaster

Alan Corbier was one of the member's of Claude Monet's gang at school, but he was a fairly benign member. He benefited from being part of the group, but Michel Bonnadot was the thug of the gang.

Michel Bonnadot would have been a leading bully himself, but for one thing.

He was dull.

He would have made a good anchor man in a tug of war team because what he lacked in mental capacity, he made up for with size. He might have been useful forward in the school rugby team, if only for his weight rather than his tactical ability. But the school had no rugby team, it had no playing field and there was no organised sport. Michel Bonnadot did not have the intellect to be able to control others with intimidation, he knew only how to beat them up, rather than threaten.

During school lessons Michel Bonnadot was subjected to the Headmaster's abuse. He had his ears twisted and his hair pulled by Monsieur Lafarge, who considered that this boy was only good for canon fodder. How the Headmaster wished he could have this boy at his mercy in the Army!

Monsieur Lafarge, during his lonely unhappy hours in his house on the hill, often contemplated how he would like to swap the lives of some of the fine men he lost during the war, for the useless bunch of children that he had to teach after it.

Michel Bonnadot relieved his own resentment with life and schoolwork by bullying the other children. Claude Monet learned to control Michel Bonnadot with sweets and with lunch treats from the horde they gathered from the smaller children. Claude Monet manipulated Michel Bonnadot

During the school term Michel Bonnadot managed to cheat his way through most of the tests, and he made other children complete his homework projects for him, so that in spite of poor grades in his Baccalauréat Exams, his average over the year just gained him enough points to achieve a pass.

This enabled him to get a job with the French Postal Service.

He started off delivering mail, which was more hard work than he bargained for, and in which he found he was not able to cheat as he had at school. Certainly there were times when he threw away some of the mail to save himself from the trouble of delivering it, but then there were repercussions. Agents from companies paying for advertising that was distributed by mail checked up on their distribution. Michel was found out for not delivering mail and fliers, and was disciplined.

His employment dossier was not impressive.

He had to attend courses as a part of his employment, and so slowly he advanced. Other more capable people above him in the service resigned and left to go to better paid jobs, and so by default, Michel rose in seniority.

Then an opportunity came his way.

There was a post advertised within the service for a postmaster's job at a small village that most people did not know anything about.

"Who wants to go there, to the back of beyond?" asked one employee.

"There is no advancement possible. It is a dead end job within the system." warned another.

"It is a well known fact that once you disappear into the countryside," the supervisor told them, "the good jobs and advancements pass you by."

"Thank you sir," Michel answered, "I understand that."

What he did understand very well was that this was the best opportunity he would get, and that if he did not snatch this one, there would not be another chance.

Michel was the only one who knew where this village was, because it was where he grew up.

He was the only applicant for this position. The job had a lower pay scale than the majority of other postmaster positions in the country, because of the small number of people in the catchment area. Also, as he would be the only person working at this branch, it was necessary for him to work longer hours than other postmasters. That reason alone was enough to put the other applicants off from applying. He was warned, as well, that there would be a problem finding a replacement whenever he was due for vacation, so he would have to take his holidays out of season.

So Michel Bonnadot got the job.

For him it was wonderful, because he did not have anybody to supervise him or give evidence against him. He was a one man band, and he was able to bully all his customers to his heart's content.

And he did.

Particularly, he enjoyed taunting those who were compelled to come to him for social benefits or pensions. He knew personal details about all of the more unfortunate people of the community, and felt quite at ease disseminating the details of their hardships to his drinking companions in the village pub.

Of course, he had to pass in front of Madame Peron's bakery to go from the post office to the bar, but he did this without once looking into the shop, or acknowledging her.

In some parts of the world it is quite acceptable to avoid a shop because of not wanting to trade there, but in France it implies an insult similar to ignoring someone in the street.

It is a snub.

Anyway, for Michel it was easy for him to ignore Marie Peron, as his wife bought the daily bread. PP bought the stamps that the bakery needed for their invoices, and so Michel did not have to deal with Marie Peron at all, in spite of the fact that they worked next door to each other.

PP was almost impossible to hate, even for Michel Bonnadot.

Michelle Bonnadot, the postmaster's wife, is one of those people who are destined to be a victim in life. She stayed indoors most of the time. She only ventured out to get bread in the mornings and to buy provisions from the mobile shops that came to the village each week. She bought the clothes that she needed from the haberdashery truck that came once every month, and collected her meat from the mobile butcher. Fresh fish came each week by lorry, all the way from Bretagne and she bought her vegetables 'on the black' from gardeners in the village. Her husband took care of all the official forms and documents, so she had no reason to go anywhere. She swept and dusted and polished the inside of her small house, which was attached to the rear of the post office. She neglected the minute garden, because that involved being outside, and that meant there was a risk that someone would see her and stop to talk. Her only excursion outside was to hang up her washing on a washing line that was across the road, next to the war memorial. She usually did that at lunchtime, when everybody else was indoors so there was no risk of being seen.

It was only after Marie Peron had started her successful elimination of the Monet gang that she began to entertain the idea that Michel Bonnadot should have been one of the first people she should have eradicated.

Perhaps it was because she had been in such close proximity for such a long time with him that she had not thought of it before. Rather the way that one accepts a deformity or a wart, which becomes so much a part of one's life that one learns to tolerate it, rather than to cure it.

But now, she had removed Monet and Corbier and Février, it made sense to her to eliminate Michel Bonnadot as well.

'It will be easy enough,' she thought, 'to use the same technique on him. That little mouse, Michelle, comes in for the bread everyday. I'll get at him through his wife, just like I did with Monet!'

Madame Michelle Bonnadot enters the bakery. She is a timid person whose inferiority has been exacerbated by her husband. She does not trade scandal. She has nothing to chat about.

She always buys the same thing, everyday, so there is no need to talk to Marie Peron. They don't even greet each other.

Nobody else seems to notice this lack of communication between the two of them, because Michelle Bonnadot times her visits to the bakery when she can see that there are no other customers.

There are no witnesses to their silent transactions.

She enters the bakery and places her coins in the ceramic bowl. Marie Peron wraps her standard order in tissue, and then slaps it onto the counter. They avoid each other's eyes, but it is not an uncomfortable transaction. They just do not see any reason to communicate with each other. Each of them lives in an isolated impenetrable bubble of self defence against the world.

So it is a shock for Michelle when Marie Peron says,

"Bonjour Michelle. I have a new type of bread for you to try. Here! It is a new recipe from the South. Try it for free and if you like it, I will make sure that you can have it regularly!"

Michele Bonnadot is so shocked by this unaccustomed generosity that she is stumped for words. She nods and proffers the money that she always pays, every morning, for three croissants and two baguettes.

Marie Peron places the items on the counter and turns to press the buttons on her cash register. She puts the coins into the correct slots, and by the time she slams the change drawer shut and turns back, her client has gone.

The front glass door of the shop sighs shut, with the new automatic device that PP had installed last winter. It works well, keeping the door shut so that the chilly winter weather does not enter the shop. It also stops that darned black cat running in and out when it feels like it.

Marie wipes the counter with her cloth and ponders her latest strategy.

The nut loaf that she gave to Michelle Bonnadot was the same as the ones she had started serving to all her victims. It was simply whole-wheat flour into which she added a few walnuts and pine nuts. She uses Olive Oil to give a rich texture and crispiness to the crust, because French people like to judge the freshness of their bread by this crispness. She has found that roasting the walnuts before she adds them to the bread gives a good nutty tang to the taste. She tried adding raisins soaked in wine, but that was too sweet and made the bread more like a cake. She didn't think that her victims would like that sort of concoction for breakfast.

She could see no reason why they shouldn't *enjoy* the meal that was going to kill them.

Now all she had to do was to wait and see if Michelle Bonnadot asked for more.

She did, and so Marie began the slow process of feeding the mushrooms into the bread, especially for the Bonnadots. Marie had collected enough mushrooms now to have a dried collection, so that she could keep using them all through the year.

It was during her 'softening' period, as she now called it, that Michel Bonnadot struck on the idea of boosting his retirement pension.

He had seen how relatively fit looking people collected a disability pension, when in fact they were able to ride a bicycle to the post office to collect their weekly allowance. However, although he was overweight and hardly exercised except for his daily forty paces to the pub and back, he had no reliable malady that he could claim as a disability. He complained to Doctor Melun that he had chest pains, but the Doctor could find no cause for this complaint, so suggested that Michel Bonnadot should start a 'regimen' to lose weight.

This didn't appeal to the lazy postmaster, so he decided to try another approach. He decided that back pain would be the best 'maladie' to adopt.

This is one of the most popular complaints in France for people approaching retirement.

It is difficult for medical examiners to refute.

He had to undergo a Radio Imaging Scan in Dijon, which was a frightening experience for him, as he was almost too large to fit inside the scanner. The scan was inconclusive.

He started to take days off work, which was very inconvenient for the villagers, who relied on the post office for their pension payments. He complained bitterly to everybody that he met so that everyone started to deviate from going anywhere near the Bonnadot house, in order to avoid his tales of woe.

"It is the Stress!" he shouts across the road to the Mayor, as she scuttles past on the other side of the road, hoping that she wouldn't be seen. "My blood pressure is high, my back is killing me, and I have ringing in my ears! I will endanger my life if I open the post office! Then where will everybody be? Hein?"

He carries on his act in the pub, demanding a special chair so that he can cope with the pain in his back. He is so convincing to others and to himself that he really does start to suffer back pain. While he continues with this 'theatre', nobody notices that his wife is ailing. When she starts vomiting in the morning, Michel shouts at her.

"What! Morning sickness! Are you pregnant? Who with? It sure as hell isn't me!"

It was after a week of his wife being ill that he condescended to call the village nurse.

When the nurse arrived and saw the pitiful state of Michelle Bonnadot, she immediately called Doctor Melun. The

Doctor summoned the ambulance and Michelle Bonnadot was whisked off to hospital.

Michel Bonnadot was put out that his wife had managed to get a 'maladie', when he was the one who was trying to attract one. But he was cowardly enough not to want her particular maladie for himself.

As it was, there was nothing that could be done for Michelle Bonnadot.

It was too late.

The cancer was well advanced. She was a little woman and the disease had caused her to lose even more weight.

Marie Peron was not dismayed by her near miss.

She reckoned that she would be able to continue supplying the postmaster with her special nut bread, and that he would succumb in due course. So she was more annoyed than usual when, the day after the ambulance took Michelle Bonnadot away, Michel came into the bakery and demanded two baguettes.

"Don't you mean the nut bread?" she enquired.

"No, my wife eats that stuff, not me! Anyway that bread is fattening, and the doctor told me to go on a diet, so I don't eat it. It's my back, you see! All day lugging heavy mailbags and parcels for people. It has taken its toll. Now I am suffering for dedicating my life to the public. I have slaved all my life for the common good, and now it is I who is in agony. Nobody appreciates how I have given my health for public service."

"How is your wife?" asks Marie.

"Who, Michelle? Not so good! I don't think she will be coming home soon, if ever."

Even Marie is astonished by his lack of concern.

The Tax Man

Monsieur Pierre Tichet has worked in the Beaune Tax Office all his life. He joined as a junior clerk after leaving school and he has known no other type of work. It suited him perfectly, because he was suspicious by nature and mean in temperament. He found a certain satisfaction in uncovering irregularities in tax returns, and he revelled in searching for individuals or companies that tried to evade the onerous tax levies that are a part of every transaction in France.

He specialised in tracking small companies and individuals who were responsible for collecting Value Added Tax. The time-consuming paperwork involved with this particular tax was often too complicated for sole traders and small enterprises to understand and complete.

It also gave him a sense of power, to be able to track down an evader.

He found that they were so easy to catch.

And if he didn't find them guilty of an infraction of the rules, at least he could intimidate them. The house painters and the pirate renovators were soft targets because, if they had a late model van, then they were certain to be guilty of not declaring all of their income. He found that the most common ruse they employed was to give a quote or a 'Devis' for a job, which then became the official document for the contract, but they would not include, in their tax declaration, all the other additions to the job that became necessary while the work progressed.

Whereas an English contractor might resort to sucking his teeth and clucking under his breath when confronted with giving a definite price for a job, a French cowboy contractor has a far wider range of expressions.

Perhaps French has less vocabulary than English but, not included in the standard dictionary are all the accents that are added to vocal conversations by means of body language. Even standing stock still, with a nose slightly raised, after giving a quote, can negate the contractor's responsibility for accuracy.

An English contractor might push his hands into his pockets, duck his head and look sideways and you ***know*** he is being dishonest.

A French cock-up artist would never let himself be so easily read.

Particularly when it comes to the calendar.

A French contractor's '*tomorrow*' means anything in the next month or so, a '*next week*' ***may*** mean before Christmas and '*soon*' means that he has got other work and this job doesn't interest him, but he is not exactly turning you ***down,*** because you look so anxious.

And he doesn't want to disappoint you!

That would be cruel.

The reason that Monsieur Pierre Tichet found it so easy to catch these pirates was that the people who contracted them were usually dissatisfied with the work that they had done. Thus they became willing witnesses, notwithstanding that they received a bounty of 10% of the tax and fines that the pirates had to pay.

The result of dedicating his life to the pursuit of villains, as he defined them, meant that he had no friends. This was not of great concern to him, as he regarded himself as a faithful public servant. He lived in an apartment in Beaune with his wife who worked for the vehicle registration department. It was this unofficial work connection that lead to many of his successes, as one of the first things that a Frenchman likes to do, when he has a windfall, or gains an inheritance, is to display his new status with a new car.

Whereas in the past a man might show off his horse with a fine saddle and bridle, or he might display his fine carriage pulled by a matched pair, now the sign of success is a new Renault, or a late model Citroen, or a shiny Peugeot.

The connection between declared income and new car registration, to a tax collector, is as obvious as feminine feline pheromones are to a tomcat.

Retirement for Monsieur Tichet almost coincided with the death of his mother in a little village on the banks of the Sâone. The house that his mother lived in was, at one time, a farmhouse. It was built in the seventeenth century with a framework of oak beams. The gaps between the beams were filled with sticks of willow and mud, which had deteriorated over the years.

Monsieur Tichet would never have considered moving into such a house in normal circumstances, but he and his wife had no friends in Beaune to keep them there. They had built up a nest egg so they decided to restore the house and then retire and live there.

Monsieur Tichet had numerous contacts within the 'renovation' underworld, but he was far too cautious to 'go on the black'.

However, that did not apply to the colour of the house.

The builders that he employed used fire bricks and cement to replace the 'willow and daub', with the result that the finished house ended up looking black. The combination of dark treated beams, gloomy grey cement and burnt bricks gave the house an appearance of an undertaker's funeral parlour.

The Tichets thought it was wonderful.

Part of the reason that Monsieur Tichet was reclusive and had no friends was that he had learned this characteristic from his mother. She had also been reclusive but for better reason. She did not want any of the locals to know about her background and what she had done during the Second World War.

She had lived in the Jura with her husband when the Germans invaded France. Unlike the majority of the population, who packed their belongings into wheelbarrows and hand carts and started fleeing somewhere, Monsieur Tichet's parents stayed put. They also had to consider 'Tosca', who was Madame Tichet Senior's sister.

Tosca had started life as a Dance Hall girl in Paris, and then following her success in the theatre, had gone to stay with her sister in the Jura town of Baume les Dames. From here Tosca commuted to her various engagements at theatres around the country.

This gave Pierre Tichet's parents a certain amount of notoriety in the community. Some of these rural people were not enamoured with the knowledge that there was an 'Actress and Theatre' girl in the community. It was in the days when actresses were regarded with suspicion by moralists. Perhaps that has not changed all that much, through the years. However, in this case their suspicions were well founded.

Tosca became the centre of attention of the German invaders. She was rather too important to be treated at a chattel however and anyway, her voice reminded them of their own Marlene Dietrich. She was seen wining and dining with the senior Germans.

She also turned informant.

Tosca started denouncing people who had stood in the way of her professional career. Directors, who had not given her those parts that she craved in the past, were whisked away, never to be seen again. Girls who had slighted her during her Dance Hall days were removed to 'troop entertainment centres'. These were buildings that housed women who were at the disposal of the invaders for carnal pleasures. The buildings were marked with yellow painted doors, so that even a drunk German soldier could find his way there.

People in France do not paint their doors yellow these days.

Monsieur Tichet Senior, Pierre's father, when he found out about the denouncements, plotted to kill Tosca, but unfortunately for him, his wife discovered his plan. For her, sisterly love was more important than her marriage, so she denounced her own husband to the Germans.

He was removed and executed.

When the liberation took place in late 1944 many of the local men joined the Free French battalions, who had worked their way across North Africa and up Italy with the Allies. They joined in the Allies' effort to rid the rest of France of Germans. Some of the men of the Jura were veterans of the First World War, and were considered too elderly to be allowed to join the Army, so they set about rounding up the French people who had collaborated with the Germans.

Tosca was one of many who were taken into the hills and shot. She was taken to an old abandoned farmhouse where the Gestapo used to execute their victims, which was where her brother in law, Monsieur Tichet Senior had been murdered.

Her body was left abandoned on the broken brickwork.

Other collaborators were shaved bald and hounded through the streets of Baume les Dames. Madame Tichet Senior escaped the fury of the mob, because nobody knew that she had reneged on her husband. She was thought of as just another victim of the war. Of course, many of the senior members of the Vichy Government retreated with the Germans, because they knew what lay in wait for them, after the Liberation, should they be caught.

Only Madame Tichet Senior knew what she had done, and the guilt over the years gnawed at her soul. She moved away from the Jura to the Bourgogne where she tried to start a new life. She was able to buy a neglected farmhouse in a small village where she was not known, with cash that had been paid to her sister, Tosca, by the Germans for services rendered. She knew that rural curiosity was dangerous, so she lived her life as a recluse, with only the company of her son Pierre. He grew up to become an employee of the Beaune Tax Department.

After her death of his mother, Pierre Tichet, renovated the house, but he did not develop the attic. He had a private suspicion that the spirit of his unhappy mother inhabited this space.

Pierre Tichet and his wife moved into the house when the renovations were completed to his satisfaction. There was nothing more to do. Everything inside the house was 'state of the art'. They knew nothing about gardening and they did not need to grow vegetables to supplement their income, because they both had good pensions. They played no sport, had no children, occupied themselves with no hobbies and had no interest in the standard retirement activity in France, which is fishing.

They bought a dog.

This was a Golden Retriever that lived up to its reputation and loved them both, in spite of their faults as perceived by other human beings. This dog gave them an excuse to 'go for walks' which is a euphemism for making sure that the dog left its shit on the roads of the village, away from their property. Their property was neat, featureless and unused, but they were not going to have it soiled with second hand dog's food.

The dog gave them a reason to walk the beat.

In their otherwise empty lives, they now had a reason to tour the village and peer into gardens, examine buildings, inspect campsites and re-enact the patrols of guards of the Third Reich.

And this is how I came to meet Monsieur Tichet.

I was a problem for him in many ways.

One of the first was that I was raising ducks.

The river in front of our house, which only comes alive with wildlife, is devoid of ducks. The reason for this goes back to the French Revolution.

Prior to that hunting was reserved only for the Bourgeoisies. The Kings and the Dukes of Bourgogne had large estates, which they used almost exclusively for hunting. They would career on horseback through the forests, with French Horns blaring, charging down sangliers with their lances. This was considered very sporting and the wild boar were kept exclusively for their use. Peasants were allowed into the forests only to pick up fallen firewood, which was permitted to make it easier for the sporting horsemen to gallop unimpeded.

After the Revolution, and the demise or expulsion of the nobles, the 'people' gained the right to hunt. And this they did, and still do, to the almost total extinction of game in some parts of France.

Of course, creatures like ducks have almost no chance.

Parties of hunters walk, drive and go by boat around any and every stretch of water, with repeating shotguns and hunting dogs.

We are used to pellets falling on our house from hunters across the river. Having lived though an eighteen year civil war in Africa, I have an instinct to retaliate in a violent way, but I have curbed my impulses by reporting the incidents to the Gendarmerie in Seurre. Of course the Gendarmes are hunters too, but stacked odds have never been detrimental to my passions before.

The Gendarmes contacted the hunting syndicates concerned to forward my compliants, so now I suffer the odd attacks with large squibs being thrown into my garden. These are usually late at night, and the perpetrators have usually made their getaway before I can get the gate open and pursue them. This is just as well, because we would probably have a confrontation that would become violent.

However, the end result of all this is that we still have no wild ducks on the river. So in spite of the warnings of our neighbours that the ducks will be shot, we raise ducks each year, to release on the river, in the hope that some of them may survive.

Monsieur Tichet took it upon himself to complain to the 'Mairie' that I was breeding birds on my property. This was a mistake, because the Mayoress also keeps poultry, and also this is a farming village in which all forms of livestock live adjacent to, and sometimes share, human accommodation. As he had come from Beaune, which is an ancient town surrounded by walls and battlements, he was not aware of this rural attitude to livestock.

Monsieur Tichet was informed that I was within my 'rights' to have livestock and poultry on my property.

He then complained about my boat on the river.

This is a little fibreglass dinghy that acts as a sort of photographic focal point. I moor it on the river and it adds a little animation to an otherwise blank screen. I had to point out to everybody that, under the regulations, I have every right to moor a boat on the river, and that it adds interest to the view.

Monsieur Tichet makes a point of checking my cars, when they are parked outside my property, to see if the insurance and roadworthy certificates are up to date. One day he strikes gold, when we are waiting for the car scrap-yard company to collect my son's car. We had de-registered it and we were waiting for it to be scrapped. It had an expired 'Control Technique'.

He called the Gendarmerie.

They come to see me, very apologetically, to explain that we have to move the car. They are right, so we move it. They don't like to get involved with such a minor infraction, but they have to do something because they have received a complaint. They use us for doing English translations and for dealing with English speaking people who have problems in the area. As a result we have a good relationship with them.

They tell me that there are several other such abandoned cars in the village, but they explain to me that they do not pursue such low level indiscretions, because they do not want to live in a Police State, any more than we do.

Monsieur Tichet then complains that I am renovating my garden wall. I do this without the necessary filing of forms with the Mairie, because there is a fine line between repair and rebuilding. Almost all walls in France, when they are rebuilt, are made perfectly straight and even. This is line with French garden design, which abhors curves, mixed plants and natural shapes. I therefore deliberately build the wall with handmade old bricks of differing sizes, to give it a rustic look. I build a flowerbed along the top so that hanging geraniums can tumble down, which is in steep contrast and in contradiction to the accepted norm, that a garden wall should have a 'roof' of tiles.

The council decision is that the wall was decorative, in an area of the village that is better off now, as a place where villagers can walk and enjoy the scenery. The clincher is that the wall borders on the river, and so is outside the jurisdiction of the village, as the riverside is controlled by the Voie de Navigation Fluvial, and not by town councils.

Monsieur Tichet's next complaint is that my ocean going boat is a hazard and is parked on public space. I had contracted with a crane operator to come, with his hundred ton crane, to haul my boat out of the river, so that I could start a slow overhaul of the hull. This operation was perfectly executed by the crane operator, who lowered my twenty two ton yacht onto a prepared concrete slab that I had laid in a niche of my garden wall. The niche was built, over a hundred years ago, around some trees, which have long since disappeared. So the boat is on my property, but outside the wall.

Again Monsieur Tichet's complaint is squashed, and he is advised of the facts, and retires hurt.

He does not give up.

Perhaps he associates me with the foreign Allies who had come to liberate France, which had led to the death of his theatrical aunt and the isolation of his mother. This is partly true, as Marlene's father had fought his way across North Africa, and then up Italy and France with the South African Air Force.

Perhaps he is perturbed by knowledge that Marlene's maiden name is de la Fontaine, which is a noble name from before the French Revolution. Her French Huguenot ancestors were forced to flee from France in those anarchistic days to South Africa, when they lost their estates and were hounded by executioners.

Perhaps it is because everybody not born in the village is considered to be a foreigner for life, and as we are not French as well makes us doubly damned in his eyes. Although he wasn't born here either, he has been associated with the village all his life.

He complains that our trees overhang the public road but again he is overruled by the Mayor, who decides that they are picturesque, and are not a hazard to traffic, as long as we keep them trimmed. We resist any interference to our trees, because they are the home of our red squirrels.

Of course, we are mad.

"They will fall, one day, and damage the house!" explain passing contractors, who want to charge us to pollard the trees.

"In that case, I will repair the house, and replant the trees!' I retort.

Monsieur Tichet complains about our Gîte. He tries to get his contacts in the Tax Department to investigate us.

We had started our Gîte to protect ourselves from being exploited, because of a lawyer in Brighton.

We had met him once fifteen years before when we were still in Brighton, West Sussex. He contacted us to say that his son would like to come and visit us for a couple of weeks, to brush up on his French. We hardly knew him, and had never met his son. I wrote to him to explain that we were now operating a Gîte, and that his son was most welcome to stay. The cost would be £350 per week, including the French lessons.

We did not hear from him again.

We have many friends from the past who come to stay with us, and they enrich our appreciation of France, because they are the reason that we tour and discover new places. They give us the excuse to stop renovation projects and take time off to appreciate our surroundings. However we have also been approached by people who are 'friends of a friend', who have taken advantage of us.

Now, by operating a gîte, we are able to fend off these 'chancers'. These are people who wouldn't bother to walk down the road to see us in the past, but now have a great desire to stop by for a few days or a week, because we are on their route to their holiday destination.

The Gîte saves us more in untoward expenses than we could ever make, but these savings in expense are not taxable, nor need they be declared on a tax form.

So Monsieur Tichet's Tax Investigation of us yields no return 10% dividend for him. The tax department, by applying Monsieur Tichet's own formulae, decide that we are not worthy of deep investigation, because our income is in line with our fifteen year old Chrysler Voyager, that no proud Frenchman would be seen driving, far less owning. They also see that we have been very meticulous in recording these small incomes.

Still Monsieur Tichet persists.

Then he thinks he has me.

Our access road also gives a route to the river for the fishermen and walkers. It is the least important road of the village, and so has minimum maintenance.

Rainwater runs and gouges the gravel surface.

Potholes are formed in the surface of the road which does not concern us, as we are used to African roads. However, whenever I have a left over bit of concrete from one of my renovation projects, I take it out onto the road and use it to fill and fix the potholes with stones. Slowly the road is improving.

Monsieur Tichet comes past with his dog. By this stage of his retirement he seldom walks with his wife. It seems as though they have become bored with each other's company.

He sees where I have recently laid some cement in a hole in the road. I am still tidying up after plastering a wall.

He storms into my garden, furious.

"You can't throw rubbish in the street!" he declares.

"What rubbish?"

"This... This residue from building. It is prohibited. It is against the Law. You have no Right."

"Monsieur Tichet," I try to explain, "I am putting the remains of cement and sand from my concrete mixer onto the road to repair the holes."

"This you can not do. If I see you doing this again, I will report you to the Mayor. I will make a written complaint against you. I have had enough!"

And with this, he turns and stomps off my property with his dog. I am amused and bemused by this attack. I know that he is deeply unhappy, but that is not my problem.

I wanted to defuse the situation by wishing him 'Bonjour Monsieur' in the middle of his tirade, but there wasn't a chance.

My friend Jacques had taught me how effective a 'Bonjour Monsieur' is, to stop a temper tantrum in France.

When somebody is waving their arms and getting emotional, if you proffer a hand and smile and say 'Bonjour Monsieur', it seems to act a brake on their tirade. It seems to stop most people, and makes them remember their manners, but Monsieur Tichet had not paused long enough for me to inject it into the exchange.

I carry on tidying up, while I consider what to do.

Monsieur Tichet has become a village bully.

He has had a fight with one neighbour because this person's dog barks at him, whenever he walks past with his own dog. The situation was exacerbated by the fact that Monsieur Tichet's dog has become as aggressive as his master, and growls at everyone, and all other dogs that he meets. These two neighbors had finished up having a fight which ended in court. Monsieur Tichet had to pay a fine, because he refused to attend the hearing. This outcome seems to have made him more vindictive than before.

Clearly I have to do something, because I feel that if he thinks he has the upper hand, then he will not let up searching for some way to continue to interfere with my life.

So I write a letter to the Mayor.

This is a standard way of making a complaint in France, in the first instance.

It is one of the reasons why the position of Mayor has become so important, because it is the Mayor who is the first person to try to find reconciliation between warring factions, before the situation aggravates itself to the level of legal proceedings.

I complain in my letter that Monsieur Tichet saw fit to come onto my property to confront me in an aggressive fashion. I point out that he is the one leaving rubbish in the road, from the rear end of his dog. I add photographs of ‘merde’ (dog-shit) outside my gate to emphasize the point.

“This is not what I understand to be ‘Liberty, Egalité et Fraternité’.” I add. “I will greet him and be polite when I see him, but I ask that he stops interfering in my life!”

He does, by adopting another route to ‘walk his dog’.

This new route takes him past Marie Peron’s bakery shop window. He starts to study her display of PP’s patisseries in the window. Although he and his wife have remained faithful to the tradition of baguette and croissants for breakfast, one day he decides to buy a ‘pain de campagne’.

This is the equivalent of a whole wheat loaf that is prepared without a mould on a baking tray, so that it resembles a slightly flattened cannonball.

The result is that these ‘pains de campagne’ are all variable in weight and size. Monsieur Tichet starts to keep a record of the weight of each loaf that he buys, which is supposed to be 400 grams. He finds that the weights vary from 310 to 425 grams, and that the average weight is below 400 grams.

"Madame Peron," he says after a month, "this is a list of all the 'pains' that I have bought from you over the last month. They are below that weight which is required by law. If there is not an improvement, I will be forced to report you to the authorities!"

Marie Peron, characteristically, says nothing. She wipes her counter top, places a Pain de Campagne on it, takes the money for it and turns her back to put it in the till.

"I mean it," warns Monsieur Tichet, as he pulls open the door to leave the shop.

He is used to people pleading innocence, arguing or trying to twist the facts, so he is not sure how to counter this buffer of silence.

He leads his dog home, muttering to himself. He decides that he will carry his kitchen scale to the bakery the following morning, so that he can weigh the bread before he pays for it.

'That will make her pay attention,' he thinks.

The following day at 10am he arrives at the bakery, armed with his kitchen scale inside a supermarket carrier bag. Before he can place it on the counter, in order to confront Marie Peron, she smiles at him.

What a shock!

"Bonjour Monsieur Tichet! I have thought about what you said and I have spoken to PP about it. He says that sometimes the weight of the bread varies because of the humidity. He is very sorry and he has asked me to give you this special nut bread as a gift, for your generous support over the years."

She smiles again.

This is too much.

Monsieur Tichet is completely unprepared for this tactic.

"Bonjour Madame Peron," he mumbles, "yes, thank you, I appreciate this."

He doesn't know that this is the longest conversation that Marie Peron has participated in, with a customer, for the entire year. He enjoys the nut bread, which now becomes his staple food.

His wife elects to stay with eating baguette, because she is worried about her weight and she is trying to keep it under control by reducing her intake of carbohydrates.

Monsieur Tichet finds that this new nut bread isn't fattening at all.

In fact, although he starts feeling a bit nauseous from time to time, he believes it is good for him.

He starts to lose weight.

It is when he starts vomiting for no reason that he goes to see his doctor in Seurre.

Doctor Melun does tests, which consist of blood analyses, stool samples and x-rays of Monsieur Tichet's abdomen.

He receives the results with a sense of foreboding.

They show the same inexplicable deterioration of health that he has seen before. His patient is a man who has displayed nothing untoward regarding his health in the past, but is now is losing the will, and the ability, to live.

Monsieur Tichet stops walking with his dog. His wife collects his nut bread for him until he finds that it is too hard to digest. She cancels the nut bread order with Marie Peron.

The next day Marie introduces Madame Tichet to a special light weight croissant.

Marie tells her, 'This is a speciality of PP's. It is very easy to digest. I give this to my special customers, if they are feeling unwell. I am sure your husband will enjoy it."

He does, but his health does not improve.

Doctor Melun calls in to see Monsieur Tichet who is now complaining about having nightmares. The doctor prescribes further tests at the hospital in Beaune. The results show a rapid rate of liver deterioration, but for no apparent reason.

Eventually there is nothing more that can be done for Monsieur Tichet.

When he goes to hospital his condition seems to stabilise, but each time he returns home his condition deteriorates again. He becomes too weak to be considered for a liver transplant operation.

There is not enough time left for him to hope for a donor.

Monsieur Tichet's funeral takes place exactly three months after his initial confrontation with Marie Peron, about the weight of her 'Pain de Campagne'.

She is developing and refining her skills with each target.

Marie Peron's hat, which she uses only for funerals, is getting more and more exposure these days.

Pierre and Francine

Marlene is not only bringing up our three children, but she is living in a half renovated house while I disappear off to work for a week at a time. In spite of this, she wants more involvement with life.

She is a natural giver, which is why, when she left school, she started nursing.

She has worked in South Africa, Rhodesia and England as a qualified nursing sister and midwife, but the French authorities did not want to let her work in France. This was because they thought her French was not good enough. This is understandable in the Côte d'Or because there are not as many immigrants here, as there are in other parts of France. Her fluency in Dutch, German and English would not be of as much use here as perhaps it might have been near the Swiss, German or Belgian borders, or in the areas of France that have been overwhelmed by English speakers.

She still wanted to do something that involved people, so she went to the Hospice in Seurre, to volunteer to work for nothing.

This caused a shock to the system that would have amused us, had it not been so sad.

The Director, when he finally understood what Marlene was proposing had leant back in his chair, crossed his arms and declared, "Madame! Nobody, but nobody, does anything for free in France."

Then she found out about the 'Restos du Coeur', which is an organisation started by a comedian, Col uche, in France. His idea was that out of 'sell by date' food and discardable items from supermarkets should be collected and redistributed to people living on low, or no incomes.

He was the son of immigrant Italians and he was born in Paris during the final phase of the Second World War. He left school at fourteen and joined a theatre group. In a short while he was famous for his 'one man show'. He had very incisive things to say about French Society. In 1980 he announced that he was going to stand for election as President of France. He received death threats and was castigated by the press, partly because high political office is only possible in France if you have attended one of the three top colleges.

It is a system almost as exclusive as royalty.

He withdrew his candidature.

In 1985 he organised an anti racist and anti National Front rally in Place de la Concorde in Paris, which was supported by an estimated 300,000 people. Almost exactly a year later, at the age of 41, he was killed in a motorcycle accident on a small road in the Alpes Marritime.

Conspiracy theories, concerning his death, abound.

His came from poor beginnings, became a controversial political figure, beat the World Motorcycle Speed record in 1985 in Italy, but his legacy to France was the Restos du Coeur, which distributes many millions of meals to underprivileged people in France, in winter.

Villages and towns throughout France have joined in the scheme. Committees are formed to administer the different branches usually consisting of professional people who are prepared to give their time for the cause, voluntarily.

This, happily, contradicts the Hospice Director's statement about people in France doing voluntary work.

This is an ideal way for Marlene to become involved with the community.

The local branch of the 'restos' operates from a building near the railway station in Seurre. Marlene volunteers and starts her involvement with the group. There is a core of assistants in the group which consists of friends who have known each other from childhood, and of course for them, this is a social gathering where they are able to disseminate news and scandal about everybody.

The problem for Marlene is that the 'core' communicates with each other using a slang type of French known as argot. This argot varies from region to region.

This organisation, she finds out, is not the best place for learning 'better French'.

Everyday she asks the children, as she drives them home from school, "What is the meaning of 'putin'?" or some other expression that she had heard.

Each time the children answer, "No Mum, you mustn't use words like that!"

This is a rather interesting parent/child role reversal.

Then somebody hits on the idea that perhaps Marlene could help some of the children at the 'Restos' with their English schoolwork.

This proves to be very popular.

Of course, our children have to learn 'Eengleesh' at school as well. Chamonix describes to me how they need to do a double translation when writing down a dictation. They have to translate the French teacher's Eengleesh into English before they can understand what to write. Many French teachers, who teach English are unable to communicate in English, which makes them very sensitive when our children correct their mistakes.

Marlene's little English class was how we come into contact with Pierre and Francine.

Pierre is the only son of a mother who had been a mistress of an important lawyer in Dijon. His father had never acknowledged that he had a son by this lovely person, so she had raised Pierre by herself. With most people, this would have given the boy every right to become resentful and bitter about life, but in Pierre's case this did not happen. He developed into an optimist with a wicked sense of humour but also with a very real conviction about what constitutes correct behaviour.

He is an ideal salesman.

He has sold magnets to plant under fruit trees that are guaranteed to enhance their growth. He has sold salt crystal lights that ionise the air to improve health. He has sold ceramic knives from the Far East, which never get blunt. His sells specialised insulated boxes designed for the transport of blood, all around the world. Every product that he sells he became totally immersed in, with an enthusiasm that he communicates to his clients. Francine, his beautiful partner, is a professional pharmaceutical sales lady and together they make a great team.

However, they decide that they will do better if they go to the United States, as a country so well adapted to new ideas, consumerism and sales. But they have to learn English rather than 'Eengleesh'.

The grapevine, without which rural France would seize up, brings Marlene, Pierre and Francine together. They propose to Marlene that she could do private lessons for them, once a week, and so they organise a schedule.

For five weeks they meet and Marlene leads them through the intricacies of basic grammar and sets homework for them.

The problem is that Pierre reverts to his schooldays behaviour when he was a bright but undisciplined child. The lessons turn into hilarious fun which Marlene says she is enjoying more than her pupils, so she stops doing formal lessons and we all become friends.

For us, these two people become a vital contact into our understanding about the complexity of life in France. They are the conduit by which we learn more than we could ever discover by mere observation and experience. They explain to us the intricacies of life in France, which has parallels to, and also differences from, our lives in other countries.

Both of our friends have had difficult childhoods which has converted them into people who are eager to sample life, perhaps in order to make up for their deprivation as children.

They surround themselves with animals, possibly because they find that the friendship and feedback that they get from animals is more reliable than from people.

The two largest of their friends are Filou and Caramel. These are a matched pair of 'trait comtois' horses. They are sturdy animals, similar in build to the Shire, and coloured with a dark honey coat with a blond mane and tail

Francine had saved them both from the butcher's knife.

They now live in a field behind their house and twice a week Francine harnesses them to a four wheeled cart for exercise. It is enlightening to see these great beasts standing patiently while Francine fastens their straps and bridles into position, like a seamstress adjusting corsets for a Duchess, in preparation for the Ball.

Working horses have such a wonderful patience for humans and their complications. With only the occasional 'stamp' of a hoof to frighten a tickling fly, they wait until all the preparations are complete.

Historically these horses were treated as venison, until the eras of Louis XIV and Napoleon when they were used to pull wagons and artillery. Knights used them for jousting, because they were large stable platforms on which to ride with armour, feathers, plumes and lances.

The losses sustained by these horses in warfare up to the Great War put their survival at risk. Now they have a dedicated following of breeders who, for the last hundred years have refined and perpetuated the species.

It is wonderful that they have no genetical memory of the way man has treated them in the past.

The consumption of horsemeat has declined in France, and most of the meat is exported to Italy. The gastronomes claim that eating horses gives the animals a certain value which enhances their worth for all the owners. The horse lovers declare that this argument is similar to parts of Africa, like Zimbabwe, where safari operators claim that killing animals is what preserves them.

The controversy continues.

I have travelled by most forms of transport that require wheels, from ox wagons to machines that retract their wheels for flight, but one of the most captivating of all of these is the horse drawn carriage.

Perhaps it is because I like old bits of wood, antique wagon wheels and the ambiance that you feel from ancient stone walls that I enjoy this transport from the past.

A motorcycle has power but a horse has soul.

A one horsepower carriage through a forest is all the power you need.

We have time to study the way the branches of trees interlace overhead. The birds detect an animal rather than a car, and so don't flee for cover. Deer are less suspicious and allow us to see them, as we do not resemble the four-wheel drive, all terrain, vehicles of hunters. We can enjoy a pace of life that discards urgency in favour of the quality of perception of nature.

It reminds me of how I felt when cruising at sea, because it was there that I learned that the voyage is more important than the destination. That the daily experience and appreciation of life is more important than the accumulation of assets during decades of normality and conformity.

Pierre and Francine introduce us to a wide variety of people, from Departmental Politicians to Gypsies, from Doctors to house painters.

But perhaps more importantly, they introduce us to their love of France, to its countryside and mountains, to the love of food and wine, to the appreciation of History and modernity and to the knowledge that we are all but milestones along the path to a destination that we contribute to, but will never reach.

They share with us a tour of a chateau, a picnic on a mountain next to a wild waterfall or a stroll through fields of golden sunflowers in twilight.

Each experience they share with us satisfies a hunger and creates a lust for more.

And, in this country of contrasts, there is still so much more to appreciate.

Monsieur Le Duc and Marie Peron

Marie Peron's new door closing mechanism is a source of frustration for Le Duc. He is used to going where he wants, doing what he wants and behaving the way he wants.

It is a trait of his character that, as a cat, he is able to behave in a way that Monsieur Lafarge would not have tolerated, had Le Duc been a child.

Why Monsieur Lafarge puts up with Le Duc's behaviour may be that Le Duc does rub his body against his host's leg occasionally. He does gaze at his host with a direct stare, that Monsieur Lafarge interprets as 'Love', but is more likely a 'cat moment', which is a 'pause in time' when a cat lets its mind slip into neutral.

Le Duc allows himself these 'cat moments' when he is at home. Sometimes, when he 'comes back' from where he 'has been' in his mind, he finds that the 'cat moment' has lasted most of the afternoon. The shadows have moved in his absence, and he feels hungry.

However, Le Duc never permits a cat moment to occur when he is in danger.

And he is addicted to danger.

And adventure.

But clawing at chained up dogs and then leaping out of the way is getting boring for him, these days. Running across the road just in front of a car or a truck is becoming too commonplace. He has watched hedgehogs try to do it, but they are useless. Somehow, they never seem to learn the techniques needed, in the time available.

Just waiting for a suitable car to come along is tedious for him of late. Perhaps he is getting more mature. Not older. Just more mature. And anyway, the cars never stop, so the only feedback that he gets is that sometimes they squeal their brakes or hoot at him.

But the best fun of all is still teasing the baker's wife.

She screams and threatens.

She shakes her broom at him.

It is much more fun than sitting on the lap of his geriatric host, who strokes him until the static in his coat gives him shocks.

There is so much more to life than that.

Le Duc sits pondering his meaning of life on the raised roadside flowerbed, outside the baker's shop. There is not a lot to consider.

It is well before dawn.

He is out of the splash of light that falls from the display window, but he can see inside.

There she is, full of activity again, busy with her early morning pummelling of something on the counter top. And her door is shut. It is shut firmly, with that dreadful automatic device.

It is far too early for customers to arrive.

There will be nobody to come and open the door, so that Le Duc can tease her by dashing around the shop and galloping out of the door before it sighs shut again.

Boring, boring, bor-ring.

Marie finishes kneading her nut bread.

She places a light linen cloth over it, puts it on a wooden board that she uses for letting the dough rise and takes it through to her kitchen. It is warmer in her kitchen.

She walks back into the shop, wipes her counter and picks up the broom, out of habit. She slaps it at a couple of nuts that she has dropped on the floor and then continues to sweep towards the door. She yanks it open and holds it there with her foot while she sweeps the few crumbs and nuts outside.

There is a blur across the threshold.

A black blur.

That dammed cat!

She jabs at it but misses.

It has disappeared under the short legs of the display cabinet. She leaves the door and chases around to the other side of the counter. It has dashed into her kitchen. *Her Kitchen!*

She doesn't hear herself screaming, but PP does.

He has just finished loading one of his warm ovens with sausages of dough that are going to be a part of this morning's supply of baguettes. He closes the oven door gently, treating the contents with respect, the way old man Rufin had taught him.

Marie is screaming something about, "I'll kill you, you satanic cat. Just let me catch you, you evil devil. I'll teach you to pee on my door."

'Why does Marie want to teach the cat to pee on the door?' wonders PP.

He goes to investigate.

Marie is in the kitchen, running around the table waving her broom. She is slapping at the chairs to get them out of the way.

The cat is running between the legs of the table and then it dashes towards the lounge-seating end of the room, where PP has his old leather chair and television set.

The cat takes refuge behind the sofa.

Marie raises the broom with her skinny arms and charges at the sofa.

The broom smashes the overhead light assembly and shatters two of the light bulbs. The room is plunged into twilight.

The cat makes a dash for the bakery. PP jumps to the front door to let it out, in order to get rid of it.

It scrams into the darkness of the dawn.

"What did you do that for?" yells Marie. "I want to kill that bloody cat, for once and for all!"

She scampers past PP, through the door and out onto the pavement. The cat is trotting across the zebra crossing as if it owns the road.

Marie screams at it and charges.

She would have been a credit to her fellow soldiers if she had been doing a bayonet charge at an enemy. She gallops towards the cat with her broom horizontal, handle first, bristles under her arm, prepared to impale the animal.

She is so engrossed with her hatred and pent up frustration that she doesn't hear the electric car.

The only sound from it is the swish of tyres on the road.

The driver of the car thinks that he is low on energy to get home, so he has doused his lights to conserve his battery power. The road is deserted and the street lights are sufficient for him to see where he is going. He is exceeding the speed limit, because he believes that the faster he gets home, the less power he will use.

He sees a streak of black of the cat as it runs onto the road and then it pauses, as if to tempt him to hit it.

He is so engrossed with seeing if he can get past it without applying his brakes, or running over it, that he doesn't see the mad woman until it is too late.

He strikes her with the front of the car. It is a big muscular car with bars across the radiator grill. Of course there is no radiator as the entire front-end of the vehicle is filled with batteries to power the electric motors.

She bounces up over the windscreen, slides across the roof and tumbles onto the road behind him.

Now he ***has*** to apply the brakes and lose energy. Damn!

He can see, in his rear view mirror, a shape lying on the road. Another shape, like a man, runs across to the person on the road.

'Should I go back?' he wonders.

'They can't see my number plate, because my lights are off. No dammit… Go! I'll be in a hell of a lot of trouble if I stop. The Police will give me a blood alcohol test and that will be catastrophic!'

He pushes at the accelerator with his foot and swerves around the bend of the road ahead, and passes out of sight of the man behind him.

PP can't identify the car that has killed his wife.

His eyes are blinded from working with the bright lights inside the bakery. The sodium street lights distort the colour of the car, so he isn't able to describe the make, or any identifying feature.

He thinks that it must have been a quiet car, but he isn't even sure about that, because Marie had been screaming so loudly at the time.

He can't see what has happened to the cat.

In fact Le Duc is well satisfied with his morning. It has been one of his most exciting patrols, and he is looking forward to reminiscing about it at his leisure. He trots up the road, past the little roundabout, back towards home.

He pushes the cat flap open, sniffs the interior of the house and detects the same old familiar scents of garbage, unwashed slippers and unflushed urine in the toilet.

His host, Monsieur Lafarge, is lying on the floor of the lounge. He is dressed in his pyjamas and dressing gown. Why he should be lying on the floor is of no concern to Le Duc.

Le Duc sniffs at the cat biscuits.

Not worth bothering about.

He jumps into his raised basket in the enclosed patio and settles down to sleep. In spite of the sound of emergency sirens coming from the direction of the village, he manages several hours of repose before he is awoken by someone hammering on the front door.

He hears a key being pushed into the lock. He knows it must be that annoying woman who comes each week to do the cleaning. Why she hammers and then opens the door with her key does not strike le Duc as being odd. It is what she always does. He knows that she will chase him out of the house when she starts working with the vacuum cleaner. He sits and glowers to himself anticipating when he will be forced to move.

Now, what is all the fuss about?

She is calling to Monsieur Lafarge.

Calling his name and jabbing at him.

Now she is using that jangling instrument that his host uses from time to time.

Le Duc stays in his basket, watching the agitation of the cleaning woman who, after she has made a telephone call, goes to stand outside, to smoke a cigarette.

She is still there when the ambulance comes.

Le Duc watches as the men from the ambulance come in and examine the body of Monsieur Lafarge. Le Duc doesn't like so many people in his house at the same time.

He hops down from his basket, pushes open his cat flap and leaves the house.

When he returns, later in the day, the house is completely locked up, including his cat flap.

He never does get inside again, but it does not bother him, because he adopts a family near the chateau. They take him in and feed him properly, not with cat biscuits, but with meat and gravy that comes in individual packets.

It is luxury.

After a week they take him for a ride, in a car.

It is the first time he has been in a car. He refuses to meow, even though he finds the sensation of movement disorientating. They take him to a place of strange smells where they hold him down and then apply a mask over his face.

He doesn't remember anything after that, until he wakes up again in his new home. He can smell the same strange smell that he had detected on that female cat, ages ago. That one that got fat.

Also, he is sore under his tail.

He doesn't feel the same urge to roam any more.

Somehow the stress of the world and his need to investigate the sights and smells of the neighbourhood is diminished. The six year old son of his new hosts becomes his best friend. He allows himself to be carried about by this boy. In fact, he misses his new friend when the lad has to go to school. But when the young scholar comes home again, Le Duc makes up for his absence by following him around the house and butting his legs gently with his head.

Life is so much more tranquil now.

Monsieur Lafarge was buried on Tuesday and Marie Peron was buried on Thursday in the village cemetery. Both funerals did not have many mourners.

Monsieur Lafarge was lowered into his final resting place and the priest threw a handful of dirt onto his coffin. There were two elderly men who also tossed a handful of dirt into the grave. They seemed to know each other. Each of them had a medal pinned to the lapel of his jacket. Perhaps the medal was a commemoration from some experience of the past, which each of these two men had shared with Monsieur Lafarge. There was nobody else present at the burial who would know, or care.

There were also three women from the village, who waited for the priest and the two war veterans to leave.

Then they joined hands, looked at each other, and together spat on his coffin.

At Marie Peron's interment there is also only a small gathering. PP is distressed, because he knows he should be, but he is still confused and has not come to terms with what had happened. The whole episode has been so sudden for him. He lives in a world where he has found sanctuary in his schedule and a sense of purpose in his routine.

People depend on him, and he delivers.

He listens to the tales of woe that people bestow on him, but they don't affect his outlook.

He knows that people found Marie difficult to understand, but she had always let him be his creative self. Providing that he produced the quantities of bread and patisseries that she listed for him, she had left him alone.

His friends on his delivery rounds have always given him all the companionship that he needs.

Now, suddenly, everything has changed.

The biggest sense of loss that PP feels is that he has lost the rudder to his ship of life.

He has never experienced love with Marie in the accepted sense of the word, because she had dominated his life and he had accepted the situation. It had not occurred to him that working for her for forty years was more than enough compensation for the gratitude he felt to her parents, for bringing him into the bakery business

He makes a 'rendezvous' at the Notaire's Office in Seurre to consult with Monsieur Fontaine. The elderly man is in semiretirement now, having run his bureau for more decades than he cares to remember. PP wants to talk to Monsieur Fontaine, because that is what Marie had done all those years ago, after her parents had been killed. Somehow it seems the right thing to do.

Monsieur Fontaine is pleased to see PP, because the bakery has brought him occasional business over the years. Although the Notaire had tried to get Marie to make a will she had resisted, perhaps for the common enough reason that she never wanted to think about her own death.

The deaths of other people, perhaps, but not her own.

There is nobody surviving on Marie's side of the family to inherit anything from her estate. There are no children, surviving parents or even any aunts or uncles. As a result all Marie's side of the bakery business comes to PP.

PP is astonished to find that he is a wealthy man.

Marie had been putting the profits of the bakery into a savings account which had grown beyond imagination. There are death duties to pay but the cash on hand is more than enough to settle the demands.

"You can sell the bakery and retire." says Monsieur Fontaine.

"But, what will I do?" asks PP.

"You can do anything. Travel? Buy a new car? Buy an apartment in the South? Go on holiday?"

"No! All I know is here," answers PP. "I don't want to be anywhere else. This place, the bakery, is my life. But I can't do it by myself. I need help. I can't do what Marie did, with the accounts and everything."

"Would you consider an assistant?" asks the Notaire.

"Yes of course, but where do I find such a person?"

"I will find someone. I will place an advertisement in the Bien Public. But better still, I have a niece. She is working for a hotel in Dijon. I know that she would like a change. Perhaps I can call her and see if she can help you, until you find somebody permanent."

"I think that is a fine idea," responds PP. "But I need somebody right away. I have been making emergency bread these last few days, for our clients, and giving it to Monsieur Bulot to sell. He is the new proprietor of the tabac in the village."

"Yes," says Monsieur Fontaine, "I know him of course. But you need someone to run your shop for you. Let me phone my niece right now!"

He picks up the telephone on his desk and asks his secretary to put the call through. The call is unsuccessful as Pierrette Sevenou, his niece, is off duty.

"They say that she is on duty this afternoon," explains Monsieur Fontaine, "So I will call her later and I will let you know. I am sorry but I do not have her mobile phone number. Will that be alright, PP?"

"Yes… certainly. I must be getting back to the shop. I have my deliveries to make. I can't stop. People need me now, more than ever. I must go."

They shake hands and PP leaves to 'putter' back to his bakery over the bridge from Seurre. It occurs to him that he should now get himself a smart new van to make the deliveries.

Gosh, he could buy one for cash!

Immediately he quashes the thought.

'What would everyone say?' he wonders. 'They will complain that the price of my bread is too high, and this new van would be all the proof they need! No, I think I will stick with what I have got. There is no need to change anything.'

PP loads up his van with the bread that he had laid out before he went to the Notaire's Office. He doesn't need a list of who wants what on his rounds. He has all the details in his head, along with the occasional extras that people sometimes order at the last minute. He has to remember to lock up the bakery when he leaves now. He putters off to Montmain, the first village on his rounds.

At each stop he sees his friends who he has known for so long. Some of them have been friends since he first started making deliveries. They have all heard the news, and each one holds his hands and commiserates with him. Of course, none of them knew Marie personally, because they never had any reason to go to the bakery, but they sympathise with PP. Each one shares a little bit of grief with him and the cumulative effect on PP is almost overwhelming.

He had been coping with his change of circumstances as best he could, but each person passing on condolences means another surge of grief. He is driving with his eyes streaming. Fortunately the little van seems to know the way by habit, and the roads that PP uses are rural ones, so his meanderings do not endanger anyone else on the road.

His delivery round normally takes him about an hour and a half, which gives him time to chat briefly to each of his customers.

Today it takes him more than three and a half hours.

He arrives back at the bakery emotionally exhausted.

He parks his van in the alleyway, outside the side doors to the bakery. He has to remember to go into the bakery through the front door now, as he has bolted the swing doors of the oven room from the inside. He walks to the front with his satchel of cash and receipts, wondering how he is going to find time to enter all these transactions in the ledger.

There is a woman standing near the front door. She looks as though she is waiting for the bakery to open. She gives him the most open, generous and genuine smile that he has ever seen.

'She must be a foreigner. People don't do that here!'

She looks to be about thirty with fair shoulder length hair and eyes that sparkle blue light.

PP is lost for words. This is definitely a stranger.

"Bonjour," she says, holding out her hand. "I am Pierrette Sevenou. My uncle is Monsieur Fontaine of Seurre."

"Ah, y-yes," stammers PP. "Good morning; Enchanté ; Welcome; Um… I am pleased to meet you."

She smiles gently at him, as if she knows the devastating effect she has on men.

As PP fumbles for his keys he wonders how she can be nearly thirty and not seem to be afflicted with the disappointments and realities of life.

She seems untouched.

It just doesn't seem possible.

His clients smile at him as he does his rounds, but this woman's smile is quite different.

She seems to squeeze his heart as he looks at her.

This has never happened to him before.

He unlocks the door, pulls the key from the slot and then accidentally drops the bunch of keys on the threshold. He bends to pick them up and nearly bangs his head on the door handle.

'This is ridiculous,' he thinks to himself. 'I am fifty seven. This girl is my daughter's age, if I had one. And I'm a married man for goodness sake! Well, was... Get a grip on yourself PP!"

"Come in, please," he gestures with a little bow.

For the first time in his life PP notices that the shop looks shabby. He is ashamed. For some reason he wants to impress this young lady and it has all gone wrong before he had a chance.

He feels genuine disappointment, which hurts all the more, because it is a sensation that is foreign to him.

'It must be my emotional morning,' he consoles himself.

"Would you like to come through to the back, Mademoiselle?"

"Why, thank you, but please call me Pierrette. Everybody does. All my friends that is."

"Thank you, and please call me PP"

"I will be delighted to, thank you."

PP realises that he is supposed to be interviewing this young lady as a prospective employee, but he has never employed anyone in his life. He hasn't any idea how he should proceed. Should he ask for a curriculum vitae? References? Shouldn't he ask questions? What questions?

Nothing in his life has ever felt so right before.

"When can you start?" he asks.

Pierrette smiles at him, which PP feels is a reward as good as a lollipop is to a small boy.

"Well, soon I think. The tourist season is nearly over, so things are quiet at the hotel and I am due some vacation time. They have people who can stand in for me, in an emergency. Shall I tell them that it is an emergency?"

"Oh, yes please… I mean, yes that would be very good… Umm, but shouldn't we discuss terms, or something?"

"Yes I suppose we should. I don't know what will be fair. Perhaps we should go to see my uncle André in Seurre? He will know what is right, I am sure."

Pierrette smiles at PP and his heart constricts.

Aprés Vie

The first sign of change that I see in the village is a jogger.

I am so surprised when I see him that I call across the garden to Marlene, "You'll never guess what I have just seen!"

"What?"

"I've just seen a jogger!"

"Well, so what?"

"A jogger, for goodness sake. We don't have joggers here!"

"Why not?"

"Well it's just something that I haven't seen before. I see the odd old man on a bicycle perhaps. Sometimes I see shuffling men with sticks or dogs, or unhappy retired fisherman throwing bait to accustom the fish to feed where they want to catch them. Once a week I see the old lady on the corner going down to the abandoned hunting shack by the river to have a liaison with her eighty five year old lover. Everyday I spy the postman, who stops to have a pee against the neighbour's wall, who is nearly the youngest person that we see around here, and he's nearly at retirement age. But a *jogger!* There is something strange going on. Mark my words!"

It is a turning point.

The next day I see a woman pushing a pram.

"Marlene, sweetheart, you've got to see this!"

"What?"

"A pram!"

"Why? I've seen hundreds of prams! I've pushed them, loaded them, unloaded them, and dismantled them. There's not much I need to see or learn about prams."

"But here? In this village?"

"Okay, you've got a point!"

It is the end of the past, and the beginning of the future.

The village is changing.

People are moving into the area.

I see new faces in cars that pass through the village. There are people stopping and buying goods from the 'tabac'.

The new owner of the village shop, Monsieur Bulot, who everybody said would never make it, seems to be doing well.

The empty house on the corner that has been for sale for years, with a business licence, has a new owner who is starting up as a butcher's agent.

There is a young couple who are planning to start a coiffure, as a 'his and hers' hairdressing salon.

Something has altered.

There is a new vitality creeping in to the village as though a spell has been cast off.

People are moving out of Dijon and Beaune to buy houses here in the countryside.

I see new house owners repairing garden walls.

Contractors are stripping roofs and re-battening and re-laying them with smart new tiles. Others are installing a swimming pool. *A swimming pool!*

Old wooden shutters are being removed and new electric ones installed, with remote controls.

There are more cars on the road.

There is traffic.

There are more dogs.

I see a sign announcing that a new house is going to be built on the main road. It is a large placard with details of dimensions and contractors. I see that a row of old labours' cottages have been bought by a syndicate which intends to renovate them and rent them.

I meet the new teacher who has joined the village school because the pupil numbers are rising.

He tells me, "People said to me that this was an unfriendly village. But I don't think so. Everybody I meet here seems to be new to the area. The baker's wife is especially delightful. She is so cheerful, always smiling. I believe that she has only been married to PP the baker for a couple of months."

"Well that's news to me," I answer. "I haven't been into the bakery for ages. I heard that people thought that the bread was as miserable as the baker's wife. That's why I make my own!"

"Oh no," he said, "That is all changed. The new Mrs Peron is lovely. She has changed the bakery completely. She has had it painted out and redecorated with new display cabinets. She has encouraged PP to start a whole new range of patisseries. *And* I heard that PP claims that they are going to have a baby by autumn."

"You're joking! A baby? PP's baby? Are you sure?"

"Oh yes," he said, "there is new life burgeoning everywhere. I think this village is entering a new era. I hope so. That is why I came here!"

There *is* new life coming to the village.

It will make a pleasant change from the despondency that has hung like a pall overhead this small community. When the ceramic factory died, the village died. And recently the people have been dying. One drowned in the river, another was run over by a truck and yet another was killed by a hit and run driver. Several have been struck down by disease. There has been a suicide in the church.

And now there seems to be a glimmer of hope for a new beginning.

But once again I feel that my wandering star is coming to take me by the scruff of the neck.

Once again my yearning for space and Nature instead of civilisation and cities is taking control of me.

Development will come, and with it will come PTA's, clubs, organisations, committees and a plethora of people who will believe that they know better than me how I should run my life.

There will be bureaucrats with rules, laws and clipboards. They will lay concrete slabs to eliminate lawns and they will cut the trees into submission with chainsaws. Neighbours will judge each other by the neatness of their hedges.

The rural France of 'laisser faire' that I have come to love and enjoy is under threat.

For me the time has come to migrate.

And set sail, once again, into the unknown.

THE END

Thank you for your company on this little 'Tour de France'.

Free Flight

I bred some ducks to let them fly, with flocks of Snipe and Tern
This was the crux, to fill the sky, then hope they would return
Give me pleasure I can treasure, if they migrated back
Formation flights and landing sights as they splash down and quack
I get more joy than from some toy to see these birds arrive
Like souls that swoop they dive and stoop and make me feel alive
If you feel trapped with life that's scrapped then listen to my plea
Give freedom to a soul like you, and set a wild bird free

Chris Higginson, Provocative Verse E-book

Other books written or produced by Chris Higginson are listed below. All of these books can be found at amazon.com
Or amazon.co.uk

Appendix

"**Reluctant Assassin 1**" ISBN 1-4196-1975-6 from **amazon.com**

A young man grows up in Rhodesia and is sucked into the 'war and violence' of Central Africa. He returns to take revenge on the despotic President who is the root cause of the anarchy. This book reveals a reality of Africa, within a novel, that will interest those who have an interest in this continent.

"**Reluctant Assassin 2**" ISBN 1-4196-4792-X from **amazon.com**

A sequel which examines subsequent lives of a soul and what may happen when a life is cut short prematurely.
Is there a way that fury, memory, resentment or love from the past can be carried forward to the next life?

"**1st Provocative Verse**" ISBN 1-4196-4792-X from **amazon.com**

A selection of sad, fun, angry and humorous poetry concerning Life, Nature and Africa. Over 200 of these poems are available in the form of an e-book.
E-Mail **provocativeverse@gmail.com** for a free sample.

“Rhodesian Memories” ISBN: 1-4196-4390-8 from **amazon.com** and also from **Digital Print Australia**.

A large compilation, with 100 authors, to record the happy and sad memories of Rhodesians between 1890 and 1980. Personal anecdotes rub shoulders with war stories. Historical fact vies with tribal myths. Historical Time-lines compete with school days memories. This book is available as a printed book and an e-book.

“Rhodesian Memories E-book” for details of how to download and view a free sample, contact **rhodesianmemories@gmail.com**

“At the Going Down of the Sun” ISBN 1-4196-4217-0 from **amazon.com**

A true story of life in the Rhodesian Light Infantry, from 1973 to 1980, as recorded by Sergeant Charlie Warren and produced by Chris Higginson. Close up encounters are recalled exactly as they happened, in the words and the slang of the RLI. This is not a sanitised war story created after the event; this is the reality of a Central African conflict.

“French Bread” is available as an ‘E-book’ from **bread.french@gmail.com** (€3,50)

ISBN: 978-0-9805083-0-7

Printed in the United Kingdom
by Lightning Source UK Ltd.
130198UK00001B/70-87/P